MW00844352

STANDARD PLANT OPERATOR'S QUESTIONS & ANSWERS

RELATED BOOKS OF INTEREST

Standard Basic Math and Applied Plant Calculations (1978)
Stephen M. Elonka

Standard Plant Operators' Manual (3d ed., 1980)
Stephen M. Elonka

Standard Refrigeration and Air Conditioning Questions and Answers (2d ed., 1973; reprint 1980)
Stephen M. Elonka and Quaid W. Minich

Standard Boiler Operators' Questions and Answers (1969; reprint 1978)
Stephen M. Elonka and Anthony L. Kohan

Standard Industrial Hydraulics Questions and Answers (1967; reprint 1979)
Stephen M. Elonka and Orville H. Johnson

Standard Electronics Questions and Answers (1964)
Stephen M. Elonka and Julian L. Bernstein

Standard Instrumentation Questions and Answers (1962; reprint 1979)
Stephen M. Elonka and Alonzo R. Parsons

Standard Boiler Room Questions & Answers (3d ed., 1982)
Stephen M. Elonka and Alex Higgins

Electrical Systems and Equipment for Industry (1978)
Arthur H. Moore and Stephen M. Elonka

Marmaduke Surfaceblow's Salty Technical Romances (1979)
Stephen M. Elonka

Plant Energy Systems: Energy Systems Engineering (1967)
The Editors of Power

Mechanical Packing Handbook (1960)
Stephen M. Elonka and Fred H. Luhrs

STANDARD PLANT OPERATOR'S QUESTIONS & ANSWERS
Second Edition

VOLUME I

Stephen Michael Elonka

Contributing Editor, Power *magazine; Licensed Chief Marine Steam Engineer, Oceans, Unlimited Horsepower; Licensed as Regular Instructor of Vocational High School, New York State; Member, National Association of Power Engineers (life, honorary); National Institute for the Uniform Licensing of Power Engineers, Inc., Honorary Chief Engineer*

Joseph Frederick Robinson

Retired Borough Supervisor of Custodian Engineers, Bureau of Plant Operation and Maintenance, Board of Education, City of New York; Licensed Chief Marine Steam Engineer, Oceans, Unlimited Horsepower; Stationary Engineer, New York City; Commissioned Inspector of Boiler and Pressure Vessels, National Board (New York, Pennsylvania, Maryland, and Washington, D.C.); Lieutenant Commander (Engineering Duties), U.S. Naval Reserve, Retired

McGraw-Hill Book Company

New York   St. Louis   San Francisco   Auckland
Bogotá   Hamburg   Johannesburg   London   Madrid
Mexico   Montreal   New Delhi   Panama   Paris
São Paulo   Singapore   Sydney   Tokyo   Toronto

Library of Congress Cataloging in Publication Data

Elonka, Stephen Michael.
  Standard plant operator's questions & answers.

  Includes index.
  1. Power-plants. I. Robinson, Joseph Frederick,
joint author. II. Title.
TJ164.E42 1981   621.4   80–29066

1234567890   MUMU   8987654321

ISBN 0-07-019315-0 {V.1}

The editors for this book were Robert L. Davidson, Frank J. Cerra,
and Olive Collen, the designer was Mark E. Safran, and the production supervisor was Teresa F. Leaden. It was set in Baskerville
by The Kingsport Press.

Printed and bound by The Murray Printing Company.

Dedicated to the plant operator of today,
who is so vital in conserving
our precious lifeline of finite fuels

CONTENTS

PREFACE

This second, revised edition has the latest on EPA pollution and OSHA safety information, solar heating, examination questions and answers, firing information for efficient combustion, and today's license requirements in the United States and Canada.

Few occupations offer such an opportunity for youngsters to rise rapidly as does that of an operator of energy systems. Anyone who can read and write and absorb the technical study material written in simple, clear English in these two volumes may, while gaining experience on the job, advance from boiler operator all the way up to chief engineer, on land or sea.

Today, over a quarter of a million of the books in the *Standard* series are in use around the world in various languages. Since the first edition, in 1956, they have become the "bible" for:

1. Plant and building operators and other practical persons who study to pass examinations and improve their basic knowledge.

2. Industrial and utility firms that have a training program for upgrading employees.

3. License examining boards (stationary engineers; refrigeration, diesel, building operators, etc.), as a source of answers in one reliable, up-to-date work.

4. Schools, especially short-course cram schools, and trade schools and technical institutes that seek a practical textbook. It is also intended

as a text for preliminary courses on the many power services covered.

5. Executives and personnel managers, to use as a guide when interviewing candidates for employment or upgrading.

6. Sales and service personnel, to gain a better background on plant equipment.

7. Professional and consulting engineers, for reference in many practical areas not usually found in handbooks.

8. Boiler operators, oilers, water tenders, plant operators, and engineers, as a study for upgrading or for obtaining an original license.

The titles in this *Standard* series provide probably the most complete information published today, from calculations to operation and maintenance, on energy equipment.

In acknowledgment, we are deeply grateful, for illustrations, technical data, and even books for reference, to the many manufacturers of energy systems, *Power* magazine, Babcock & Wilcox, Combustion Engineering, and too many others to mention here in detail. Our thanks go, too, to the many license examiners for sample questions and answers. In addition, material from some of the other books in this *Standard* series has been used here where appropriate.

As we mentioned above, the opportunities for operators of energy systems are excellent nowadays. We do not wish to suggest, when we use the pronouns "he" or "his" to refer to the plant operator, that these opportunities exist only for one gender; in fact, women are increasingly entering the field. Our purpose in using these pronouns, and terms such as "fireman," was for ease of communication and to avoid stilted language.

Stephen Michael Elonka, 1980
Charleston, South Carolina

Joseph Frederick Robinson, 1980
Williamsburg, Virginia

STANDARD PLANT
OPERATOR'S
QUESTIONS & ANSWERS

1

EPA POLLUTION CONTROL

Pollution is anything that adversely affects our environment. Today, pollution is strictly controlled with heavy fines by the Environmental Protection Agency (EPA). Under such laws as the Clean Air Act and Clean Water Act, *you* are held mainly responsible for (1) air, (2) water, (3) solid waste, (4) heat, (5) noise, (6) radiation, and (7) objectionable odors from your plant.

Engineers in industrial and utility plants, commercial buildings, mines, etc., must not only be energy-conscious, they must also be fully aware of the pollution their operation generates as a by-product. While most chapters in these two revised volumes have some specific information on pollution control, here we touch on the most recent information for you to pursue. To avoid lawsuits, damages, and fines, you, the plant operator, must have at least this basic knowledge.

AIR

Q What is the plant operator's prime concern about air pollution?
A Stack gases (flue emissions), which contain sulfur oxides, carbon monoxide, nitrogen oxides, particulates, stenches, and contaminants such as vanadium.

Q How is the Ringelmann chart used?
A See Fig. 1-1, also Chap. 12, "Fuels and Firing."

Q Discuss sulfur in fuel.

1

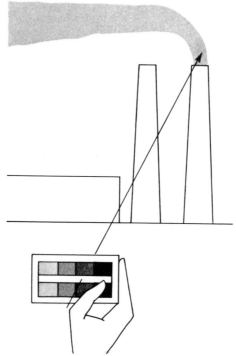

FIG. 1-1.   Ringelmann chart is used for visual comparison of stack emission.

A Burning sulfur produces sulfur dioxide (SO_2), which combines with water to form sulfurous acid (H_2SO_3), an irritating and corrosive substance. It may also form sulfuric acid (H_2SO_4), which is the familiar strong battery acid. Sulfur gases can combine with other atmospheric pollutants to form extremely objectionable substances.

Q Can sulfur emissions be controlled?
A Yes, either by using a low-sulfur fuel (different codes vary, but approximately less than 3 percent sulfur by weight) or else by chemical treatment of the gases either in the furnace or beyond. Some codes forbid all fuels except liquefied petroleum (LP) gas, which naturally contains very little sulfur.

Q Name difficulties experienced in changing from high-sulfur to low-sulfur oils.
A The lower viscosity of low-sulfur oils causes worn pumps to slip, resulting in transfer and atomization difficulties. Unexpected or old leaks become

apparent. Fuel consumption increases because lighter oils contain less heating value. Instrumentation, especially some automated controls, will need to be recalibrated. New-sized sprayer plates may be needed. Because the changed lighter "blended" oils burn at lower temperatures, the "low-temperature" oil control may trip out, preventing start-up.

Compatibility and solvent action: The new oil may loosen up old sludge and carbon deposits in the piping and heaters, making problems in dead ends such as gages. For some reason there seem to be "water-in-the-oil" problems at first.

Storage and delivery: Some vendors occasionally concoct a legal low-sulfur oil by blending a light low-sulfur oil with a heavy above-legal sulfur oil in the distributor's tanks. These oils tend to stratify, with light oils in the uppermost and tar the lowermost layer. Careless delivery or poor storage may result in either an oil that is too light to burn, besides having low heating value per gallon, or else a heavy oil that causes all sorts of problems, usually when the storage tanks are cold. Be sure to recirculate even when the storage is idle if you suspect this problem. Simply expressed, operators in older plants should be prepared for new problems during the early change to various low-sulfur oils.

Q What are the disadvantages and advantages in using no. 4 oil instead of no. 6?

A More gallons will be burned if the lighter no. 4 oil is used. The dollar costs must be considered. Other factors are: little or no heat is used for pumping and burning; the lighter oil may be easier on the entire system; perhaps less soot is generated; and fewer worker-hours may be required overall.

Q What about sulfur in coal?

A Some coals, particularly western coals, are naturally lower in sulfur. They may have less heating value. Careful selection may control sulfur emissions.

Q Describe two basic schemes for SO_2 treatment during combustion of high-sulfur fuels.

A Two basic ideas are (1) blowing pulverized limestone into the furnace or (2) washing the flue gases with water-curtain sprays or baths, both using limestone solutions (Fig. 1-2). The idea is to combine the acid sulfur gases with the alkaline limestone. More expensive alkaline materials are also used, such as ammonia compounds, in an effort to produce salable by-products such as agricultural ammonium sulfate. Aluminum hydroxides and some other alkalies are also reported to be producers of salable by-products. These sales may offset some of the costs of treatment. If coal is to replace oil, sulfur and other obnoxious emissions must be controlled.

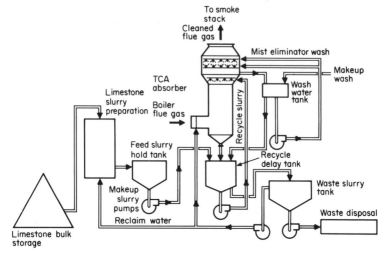

FIG. 1-2. System for SO_2 removal is complex but needs many operations to comply with EPA standards.

Q What is the relationship of sulfur to fuel oil grade number?
A Grade 6 is the heaviest residue of the refining process and thus has the most impurities. As the numbers decrease, the sulfur decreases; 3, 2, and 1 are relatively sulfur-free.

Q Nitrogen oxides are pollutants. If nitrogen comprises 78 percent of the air supplied for combustion, how can this inert gas make problems?
A Nitrogen is not as chemically inactive as many people believe; it is the source of many of our most irritating pollutants. It may well become the largest challenge of all. In many areas of our country the internal-combustion engines in automobiles are the largest source of nitrogen oxides, followed by high-temperature boilers. Sunlight causes further photochemical action, with other chemicals from industry combining to generate the most complex irritating pollutants of all. The nitrogen oxides are designated as NO_x, the x indicating unknown combinations. A brown haze over your stack means that more air is needed. And maybe when excess air is used, the NO_x will be greater. Only a chemical test will show the best procedure for a given plant. Visible NO_x is called "brown gas."

Q What is particulate matter?
A Any solid or liquid that is airborne. Uncombined water vapor is excluded.

Q What are soot, fly ash, and odor?
A Soot is unburned carbon that damages everything it falls upon. It is

also a particulate (see Chap. 12, "Fuels and Firing"). Fly ash is a noncombustible particulate. Odor is stench, or any obnoxious smell.

Q Why are some stenches difficult to identify and trace to their source?
A Think of the atmosphere as a polluted river with all sorts of chemicals dumped into it. Photochemical action of the sun and other atmospheric chemical actions combine to produce stenches beyond description. Individual materials are almost impossible to identify.

Q Are the various state codes uniform?
A No. Each state and its subdivisions may formulate codes and procedures acceptable to the EPA. In addition, neighboring states and regions may form compacts, since winds and water currents have no political boundaries. In addition, official scientific bodies advise controls that almost have the effects of laws. Finally, if you create a nuisance, some institution will seek relief in either law suits or administrative action by the EPA, Coast Guard, Fish and Wildlife Agency, local health agencies, and so on.

CODE REQUIREMENTS

Q Is the plant operator responsible for monitoring emissions?
A Yes, along with the owner. Larger plants are required to have instruments that both indicate and record emissions. These are usually based on millions of Btus consumed (Fig. 1-3).

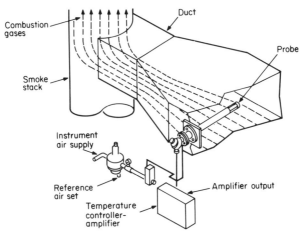

FIG. 1-3. Oxygen-analyzer system monitors the stack gases, remotely indicates gas quality in power plant.

Q Who services these sophisticated instruments?

A Highly qualified specialists are best; the average operator has neither the necessary test instruments nor the skills. He should be able to read and act upon whatever information the monitors display.

Q What is the code definition of *control apparatus*?

A Any device which prevents or controls the emission of any air contaminant.

Q Explain two important code certificates.

A One of the certificates has to do with design, construction, and alteration approval, and with the operation of the installation. It is similar to a building permit and certificate of occupancy, issued upon approval by various local bureaus. The other certificate concerns us operating engineers. It empowers operators to take action to prevent pollution: to operate for sewage treatment, to operate incinerators, to institute air-pollution-alert procedures, and to do whatever the authorities deem is a license need.

Q Briefly define each of the following code terms: dose, soiling index, RUD, RUD hours, ppm/hr.

A Dose: the measure of exposure of a person to contaminated air; calculated on time and degree of contamination. Soiling index: a measure of soiling by suspended particles. A measured volume of sample air is drawn through a known area of Whatman no. 4 filter paper for a measured period of time (expressed as RUD/1000 lin ft). RUD: the negative logarithm of the percent of light reflected from the soiled area divided by number of thousands of linear feet passed times 100. RUD hours: the soiling index dose. ppm/hr: the parts per million dose per hour.

AIR POLLUTION STATUS

Q What does the term *air pollution status* mean?

A The degree of impending air pollution forecast by the U.S. Weather Bureau.

Q How is "air pollution status" proclaimed in a typical code?

A Based on the U.S. Weather Bureau forecast, local authorities commence a watch. They proclaim three stages: alert, warning, and emergency. Each stage is based upon information regarding the preceding 24 hr and the forecast for the next 12 hr.

Q What are the limits for each stage?

A Alert: If in the last 6 hr of the preceding 12, the SO_2 dose equals or exceeds 2.0 ppm/million hr, the soiling index equals or exceeds 25 RUD hr/1000 lin ft, the CO (carbon monoxide) dose equals or exceeds 180 ppm/million hr; or if SO_2 for the preceding 24 hr equals 6 ppm and the dose is increasing and if the RUD soiling index equals 100 RUD hr/lin ft and there is a continued adverse U.S. Weather Bureau forecast for the next 12 hr, alert status is proclaimed.

Warning: If for any consecutive 24-hr period SO_2 equals 15 ppm/million hr, soiling index equals 200 RUD hr, or continued adverse report are forecast for the next 12 hr, warning status is proclaimed.

Emergency: If during the warning period in any consecutive 24 hr the U.S. Weather Bureau predicts adverse conditions for an additional 12 hr, an emergency is proclaimed.

Termination: The U.S. Weather Bureau advisory determines an end to the air pollution potential. Local authorities may continue the emergency to meet some hazardous condition in their area.

Q How does this affect plant operators?
A Each plant is required to submit a procedure for abatement and control of emissions during each stage.

Q How does this concern operators?
A Each plant must receive approval of standby procedures for each of the three stages. Each plant has a category based on several different criteria for need, pollutants, and process.

EXAMPLES: Central electric power plants and hospitals are necessary, refineries and chemical plants cannot be immediately shut down without damage, retail stores and mercantile offices can be shut down together with schools, the use of automobiles may be stopped, and so on. There is appeal from these rulings by having reviews and hearings.

Q What is generally planned?
A How emissions of contaminants will be reduced or eliminated in accordance with the type of plant. The source and the amount of contaminants and the manner in which reduction is to be achieved for alert, warning, and emergency. These plans must be available to the authorities when they visit the premises.

Q Are plant operators responsible?
A Yes, the same as with smoke violations. These codes are rapidly coming into being and are also rapidly being revised. Some local codes, which require using soot blowers during daylight hours only or using certain fuels during daylight, are typical.

Q Isn't this matter of testing far beyond the average operator's knowledge?

A Yes, but modern instruments (see (Fig. 1-3) perform all these tests, and they warn about and control many of the problems. But you should have basic understanding and be able to run the plant properly. Some of this testing is performed by college-trained persons; you should know what they report and recommend.

PARTICULATES

Q What are the basic schemes for controlling particulates?
A The basic ideas are separating by (1) centrifugal force, (2) impingement, (3) trapping in a bag, (4) electrostatic precipitation, and (5) spraying and bathing. See Fig. 1-4. All these ideas and devices will recur in various chapters of these two volumes.

Q Explain how each of these basic ideas work.
A Whirling creates centrifugal force. Impingement results from abrupt change of direction. Sprays scrub, and baths trap. Meshes and filters trap.

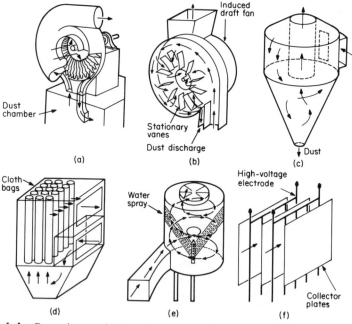

FIG. 1-4. Removing particulates from boiler exhaust is done by one or all of these methods, depending on installation and fuel used.

Electrostatic precipitators charge the particles, and then in turn catch particles with unlike charges.

Q How does a scrubber work?

A Dirty gas is centrifugally whirled, the heavier particles being thrown outward to leave the stream and fall into the bath. The resulting dirty gas and water are mixed in a venturi tube, which imparts both whirling and upward motion. The entry causes an abrupt change of direction, again forcing heavy particles out. The bath both traps falling particles and provides entrained water, which may be supplemented by sprays. The rapidly ascending gas-water stream strikes an impactor plate, which again drops the heavy particles out into the upper shell and into the contaminated water, which drains down into the bath. The cleaned gas discharges into the atmosphere.

> BEWARE: Disposing of contaminated water in a sewer is controlled by local water pollution codes. Be sure to check.

Q Are there many different forms of scrubbers?

A Yes, both packaged and specially designed types are commercially available for every size and problem. Megawatt steam generating plants, chemical processes, public incinerators, and metal refineries all have their own special problems. Some scrubbers and baths use chemicals for neutralizing harmful substances.

Q Are water-spray curtains and baths alone used without the other equipment to perform as scrubbers?

A No, most codes require more than sprays and baths.

Q Why is quench water used?

A Two purposes: spray water is introduced to cool the gas stream to flow at a desired temperature, or in emergencies to protect the equipment. This may be both automatically and manually controlled.

Q Why are float control valves used in the bath, and where does the water go?

A Float control valves provide makeup water for a constant level. The water goes to the atmosphere, because of evaporation and entrainment, and to waste by designed runoff and systemic leaks.

Q What is a diverter damper?

A One or more diverter dampers may be used to provide proper velocities in normal operation, or as an emergency bypass to the atmosphere.

Q What is the advantage of induced-draft fans?

A They lower temperatures, which make the equipment easier to handle.

Q What is a settling chamber?

A A binlike compartment which traps and contains dropped-out particles in a slow-moving gas stream.

Q What is the meaning of *operator?*

A The person actually in charge of the equipment. Watch engineer, shift engineer, fireman, or whatever may be the equivalent local name, but do not confuse these with the plant owner.

Q Describe the bag filters in Fig. 1-4.

A Bag filters of coated-fiberglass, Teflon, or felt-fluorocarbon-fiber tubes open on one end and closed on the other. Dirty gas is fed upward into the bags, which are supported on a frame. The particles (fly ash, etc.) cannot pass through the mesh, but clean gas passes on. Periodic automatic shakers dislodge the particles, which fall into the collector below. These devices are also useful for metal reclamation and grain-handling industries.

Q Describe an electrostatic precipitator (Fig. 1-4).

A An electrostatic precipitator consists of a series of plates or wires having opposite high-voltage electric charges. The incoming dirty gas stream flows into the first zone, which imparts a static charge on the entrained particles. The second zone has an opposite charge which attracts the charged particles out of the stream. Automatic periodic shaking drops the charged particles during interrupted current flow.

Q What is the "tall stack" idea illustrated in Fig. 1-5?

A Dispersing pollutants to higher levels to decrease local pollution by spreading and thus diluting the contaminants. One way to lessen the possi-

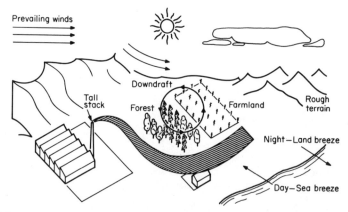

FIG 1-5. Tall stack spreads pollution thinly, over larger area, which may be acceptable in your area; check your code.

bility of lawsuits from neighbors, but probably not a good long-term solution because resulting acid rain may be detrimental to vegetation.

WATER POLLUTION

Q Water and air pollution are threats to our survival, since good health requires both to be as pure as possible. What are the principal types of pollutants produced by human beings and what are their sources?
A Sewage from any source. Chemicals, such as agricultural fertilizers and pesticides runoff, which permeate the ground waters. Chemical waste, both illegally and legally dumped, finds a way to water. Landfill dumps receive whatever comes and leaches into earth and waters. Petroleum from any source.

BEWARE: Under no circumstances allow oil to be dumped in sewers, ground, or water. Figure 1-6 shows a liquid-waste burner.

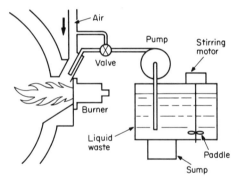

FIG. 1-6. Liquid waste, if it can be burned, is disposed of in several ways.

Mine wastes, upon exposure to air, break down to pollute water. Flue emissions travel hundreds of miles to contaminate the remotest lakes and streams.

Q What are the principal control methods?
A First and foremost is prevention against contamination from any source. This is usually enforced by stringent regulations and large fines coupled with massive money settlements. If it is within your responsibilities, never allow pollutants to leave your plant to escape to water.

Q Describe basic treatment schemes.
A Chemical treatments either neutralize harmful substances or else make

them insoluble so that they can precipitate or filter out. Some processes cause flotation to allow skimming out. Centrifuging is another process to separate different densities (see Chap. 2, "Water Conditioning"). All kinds of equipment have been used by plant operators for many years, and the larger-sized equipment is different only in size and automatic controls.

Sewage treatment is different because bacteria is involved and the methane gas produced is either used as a fuel for the plant or discharged as waste. Methane is hazardous, being the same as methane fuel, which is often an LP commercial fuel. Special training and often special licenses are required to operate sewage-treatment plants. Unlike the process, all the equipment is familiar.

The sludge that remains after treatment presents problems of disposal because it is often contaminated by chemical wastes discharged to sewers by local industries. If uncontaminated, it is sometimes used as fertilizer. Otherwise it is further treated and incinerated.

Q   What other contaminants go to sewage?
A   Phosphate in laundry detergents, which is now regulated. Other chemicals are under scrutiny. Nitrogen and certain other contaminants may soon be controlled.

Q   What are the essential differences between domestic water and industrial water?
A   Domestic water must be healthful to drink and pleasant to taste, smell, and see. Industrial water need not be any of these, but it must be suitable for both the equipment and the process.

> EXAMPLE: Most tap water is good to drink but is not suited for either storage batteries or high-pressure boilers.

Q   How are water resources used and recycled?
A   About 80 to 90 percent is first taken by industry and agriculture. Industry returns most of this to earth supplies. Treatment is required before release if there has been contamination from industry. Industry is relatively simple to control, but agriculture is different, natural evaporation leaving the solids behind to leach down or run off to water supplies to be absorbed elsewhere.

The use of dangerous pesticides and chemical fertilizers is cause for concern. The current approach is to ban such chemicals entirely near water-supply systems, to limit certain chemicals elsewhere, and finally to ban the manufacture, sale, and use of some toxic materials. Agricultural chemical use is not a simple subject because some difficult choices must be made.

Q What are the problems of domestic water?

A Most of this water is returned as sewage with a high organic content. The harmful bacteria can be destroyed by chlorine, and in fact this primary treatment has been and still is the only treatment used in many areas. Organic materials putrefy and, upon discharge into water, soon use all the dissolved oxygen, which causes most life to be destroyed. Stench always accompanies putrefaction. Thus all life is destroyed, foul smells are created, recreation is destroyed, and the water is unsafe to drink and unfit for industry.

Chemicals sent to sewers further complicate a bad situation. The United States is now engaged in constructing massive sewer systems to treat sewage and to recycle water. Regulation of such substances as detergents and industrial wastes is increasing. Ideally, two systems are used—one to receive waste to be treated and the other to provide surface and storm-water conduits into drainage.

Q Is this a new career field for operators?

A It certainly is rapidly expanding opportunities for us.

SOLID WASTE

Q Since time began, we have disposed of solid waste by either dumping it "out back" or else burning it. Most of us do not want to see a dump, nor do we enjoy smelling it in any form, including burning. This almost tells how little progress has been made despite technology. What is solid waste?

A All the waste collected to be discarded, usually the following: garbage and rubbish of every description, industrial wastes, and in fact everything that is to be "thrown out."

Q Name seven major problems.

A 1. Limited landfill areas near urban areas with no further expansion permitted.

2. Stench due to putrefaction as well as dump fires.

3. Leaching and runoff of chemicals that find their way to contaminate water supplies.

4. Rat and other rodent harborage.

5. Health problems related to bacterial hazards.

6. Blighted landscape.

7. Dumped dangerous chemical substances, which become menaces to the future well-being of an unsuspecting population.

Q What is meant by *the geography cure,* and is it a viable solution?
A It means moving the dump farther out of town. It is certainly the most popular way of handling any unpleasant problem, including waste disposal. Extensions of this idea include filling in old mines, stripped earth areas, and barren places, all of which are away from urban areas. Apologists state that this will prevent old mines from collapsing and that the organic waste will restore fertile earth and maybe help restore the use of the now ailing railroads. They may well be right in their thinking.

Q What does compacting do?
A The volume of the waste is reduced, but all the problems remain.

Q Is burning a good solution to the solid-waste problem?
A Properly designed incinerators are perhaps the best solution of all (Fig. 1-7). It is not a simple matter, and there are many different forms of incinerators, ranging from mortuary crematoriums to municipal inciner-ators and almost everything in between for special industrial applications.

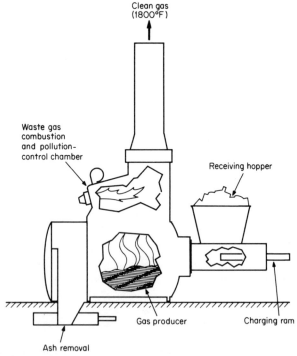

FIG. 1-7. Solid waste may be burned in incinerators and clean gas utilized as heat.

Q What about economical recovery from waste by recycling materials and fuel use?

A Deriving fuel from refuse is a growing process with various reports of success. Recycling materials is not a new idea—there have always been rag and scrap pickers. Salvage by segregating and processing methods is required: Iron is handled with magnets, electronic sensors handle other metals, flotation beds select various materials, shakers throw out glass, and acid and chemical baths recover selected materials. Pressure-cooking processes recover oils and other substances. The oldest method of all is hand picking.

All or some of these processes are part of recycling and fuel processing. Water-wall incinerators are, in fact, water-tube boilers, and all the equipment is familiar enough in tanks, conveyers, blowers, and pumps. Here again is the operating engineer's same familiar equipment, but in new surroundings.

Q The use of plastic materials is ever increasing. Has this aggravated disposal problems?

A Very much. Most plastics are chlorinated substances, and the gases that result when they are burned contain acids which attack ordinary metals. If heat is not recovered, most refractories will be satisfactory. If heat is recovered, corrosion will be a problem inside and outside the furnace. Then there is concern about the hazard of flue emissions being both toxic and carcinogenic.

Q What is an incinerator?

A Any device, apparatus, equipment, or structure used for destroying, reducing, or salvaging by fire substances including, but not limited to, refuse, rubbish, garbage, trade waste, debris, or scrap; also a facility for cremating human or animal remains. Figure 1-8 is a large municipal incinerator for disposing of a city's garbage and also for generating steam as a by-product.

Q Are wastes classified by type?

A Yes, all wastes are categorized into mixes and types. Types are based on the primary source, broadly considered as rubbish, garbage, incombustible solids, Btu content, treated paper, rubber, plastics, moisture, hospital human remains (organs, tissues, limbs, etc.), animal matter, by-product wastes (tar, paint, solvents, sludge, etc.) from industrial sources, foul gases (often seen burning on refinery towers), and other industrial wastes such as wood and plastics. The source materials are usually broken into allowable mixes considering the various materials.

Q State some incinerator problems.

A Stack emissions contain both particulates and odors. Local stench arises

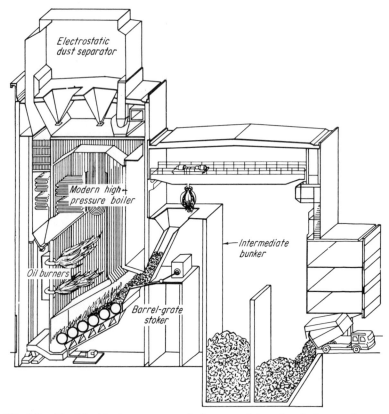

FIG. 1-8.   Municipal incinerator not only burns trash but absorbs heat and superheats steam for power generation.

from collections and storage. Disposal of incinerator residue and contaminated spray and wash waters is complicated. Rodents and bacteria are
attracted. The facility may be an eyesore and may lower real estate values.
Noise of trucks and associated equipment is also a problem.

Q   What is "caking?"
A   Industrial wastes and sewage sludges are compressed into cakes for
disposal as into incinerators or fuels.

Q   Besides "picking" segregation, are there other economic salvage possibilities?
A   Yes. Methane is successfully collected from large landfill dumps and
sewage plants. Incinerator ash is compressed with a binder to provide

building blocks and certain chemicals, and mineral recovery is meeting with limited success.

Q What about bacterial processes?

A Putrefaction is a natural process which can be controlled to break down many substances. Much progress is reported, including biodegrading petroleum products.

Q What about license requirements?

A Steam generators require boiler licenses, and various air pollution control operators licenses are coming, even if they are not yet required in your locality. See License Requirements in Chap. 21.

NOISE POLLUTION

Q Noise pollution (Fig. 1-9) is a nuisance to neighbors and a health hazard that impairs hearing by cumulative and permanent loss of sensitivity to upper speech ranges and ultimately may cause substantial deafness.

FIG. 1-9. Mechanical noises are hard on nerves and may indicate that equipment is failing.

Workers are further affected by fatigue and other health disorders. The Occupation Safety and Health Commission (OSHA) is primarily the code requirement, and increasingly stringent standards are expected. When is noise considered to be pollution?

A See Table 1-1 for decibel levels. Acceptable levels range from 40 to 80 dB.

Q Do personal protection devices such as earmuffs and earplugs help?

A At best an expedient in permanent places, a necessity for flight-line personnel, and helpful while shooting firearms, such devices are never a substitute for proper controls in situations regulated by required OSHA industrial code.

Q What is considered quiet operation?

A Quiet operation is a relative condition. Figure 1-10 indicates the arbi-

TABLE 1-1   Decibel Scale Indicating Sound Power, Intensity, and Pressure

Sound source	Power range, W	Decibel range re 10^{-13} W
Ram jet	100,000.0	180
Turbojet with 7000-lb thrust	10,000.0	170
	1000.0	160
4-propeller airliner	100.0	150
75-piece orchestra, pipe organ	10.0	140
Small aircraft engine		
Chipping hammer	1.0	130
Piano, blaring radio	0.1	120
Centrifugal ventilating fan		
at 13,000 ft³/min	0.01	110
Automobile on roadway	0.001	100
Vane-axial ventilating fan		
Subway car, air drill	0.0001	90
Conversational voice	0.00001	80*
Traffic on street corner		
Street noise, average radio	0.000001	70
	0.0000001	60
Typical office	0.00000001	50
Very soft whisper	0.000000001	40*

* Limits of range of acceptable levels.

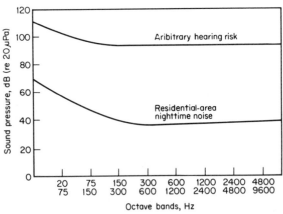

FIG. 1-10.   Quiet operation is between the two curves shown here.

trary hearing risk. Satisfactory noise level in one plant may be entirely objectionable in another. Under relatively quiet conditions, as in an office, low-level noises such as the sound of an air-conditioning unit can take on annoying prominence. In a manufacturing area with a higher noise level, this same unit may be the quietest machine around.

Various levels of noise have been proposed as maximum safe levels at which people may work for extended periods without danger of permanent hearing loss. Nighttime noise level in a residential area is plotted on the same graph as daytime levels for comparison. Acceptable noise level for most plants lies between the curves.

Q Briefly list some permanent control methods.
A Start with a three-step program: (1) reduce noise at source, (2) control noise along the transmission path, and (3) take protective measures at the receiving end. Figure 1-11 shows how noise can be reduced by seven methods in an air-conditioning system. Use noise barriers, acoustical materials (some materials reflect noise; others absorb it), mufflers, etc. The subject of noise is complex. Consultant specialists are often required.

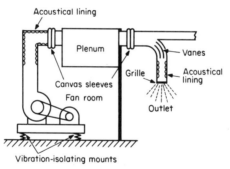

FIG. 1-11. Air-conditioning noise can be reduced by vibration-isolation mounts, flexible connectors, duct lining, guide vanes, etc.

Q State some considerations in soundproofing.
A Whatever new machines or redesigns are used, they must be no less efficient than the old. Fire is a hazard, and the new materials should not readily burn nor should toxic fumes result in a fire. There should be no interference with operation or maintenance of equipment and process.

Q Are thick masonary walls effective sound barriers?
A No, thin acoustical walls that absorb sound are far more effective than thicker masonary walls, off of which sound bounces.

Q If an unusual noise change occurs, what is needed?

A An investigation. A sudden quiet may be a hot bearing. Increased noise or pounding is sure to be mechanical trouble. You should be familiar with the normal sound of speed and load changes. The same is true for unusual changes of vibration.

RADIATION POLLUTION

Q There is a growing awareness of three entirely different sources of pollution, radiation, heat, and appearance. Operators are exposed to all three, and some familiarity is necessary, however limited the individual exposures. What is radiation pollution? Describe some familiar sources.
A Few of us have escaped x-ray examination of teeth and lungs. At work we make use of metallurgical x-rays for welds and inspections (Fig. 1-12). X-rays are hazardous and have lifetime cumulative effects. Nuclear power and weaponry produce hazardous, if not fully understood, effects of radioactive elements such as uranium, plutonium, and radium.

The debatable effects of electromagnetic devices are being investigated. We are bathed in radar, television, CB, and other communications transmissions and high-voltage aboveground electric power transmission systems. A whole new industry is proliferating around industrial processes

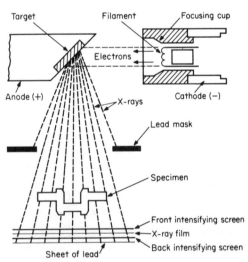

FIG. 1-12. X-rays pass through the component to be radiographed, but radiation is harmful to operators unless they are protected.

and home microwave ovens utilizing electromagnetic radiation. The list is growing and the exposure is growing, and many answers are developing.

Q Are there regulations?

A The FCC, EPA, U.S. Public Health Service, OSHA, various scientific bodies, academicians, and medical bodies all have their share. The present U.S. standard for exposure to electromagnetic radiation is 10 mW/cm², set in 1957. It is based on heat effects rather than biological damage effects. The FCC has standards for emanations from microwave ovens, radios, and televisions. Such devices must have approval seals displayed.

Q Are we unduly alarmed?

A· There is some growing evidence that electromagnetic radiation does have adverse effects on some biological processes, but again not much is conclusive. Certainly, operators of such equipment would be the most likely to suffer. About microwave heaters, be sure to maintain safety shielding because we do know they can be hazardous. Studies of the incidence of cataracts in World War II radar operators are in progress.

Q What precautions are needed for operators exposed to nuclear radiation and x-rays?

A These people receive special training and monitoring, the methods of which are beyond this book.

HEAT POLLUTION

Q Heat or thermal pollution is the nuisance effect of heat that has been "dumped" into water or the atmosphere. What are the long-term effects of a gradual rise in water temperature?

A Gradual elevation of water temperature will alter life forms to favor warm-water forms and to discourage cold-seeking forms. If temperatures are high enough, the dissolved oxygen will decrease, which discourages most life.

Q What are the effects of rapid temperature changes caused by your cooling water discharging into streams?

A If fish kill results, severe penalties will be levied.

Q What procedures must be followed with well-water replenishment?

A Even for contaminated well-water sources, cooling and process water must be returned in a cool, purified state to maintain proper water-table height. Among other things, the dissolved gases in the water are affected by heating. There are local codes for well-water replenishment, and in some instances licenses are required.

Q Describe some atmospheric effects of heat pollution.

A Temperature seemingly increases in large urban areas because of energy consumption in all forms. This is gradual and is tolerable in most instances. Occasionally some localized condition such as a large fire will cause rapid changes.

Q What is the responsibility of the plant operator?

A Careful operation of condenser discharge and boiler blowdown has always been ours. Cooling towers must be properly operated, but beyond careful operation, keeping equipment in good repair depends on high-quality design.

Q Is it true that some fisheries depend on rejected heat?

A Yes, fisheries raising various edible species have developed in areas where industries have caused increases in water temperature.

APPEARANCE POLLUTION

Q Call it what you will, eyesore is a local term to describe a nuisance that offends the viewer for whatever reason. How can operators possibly be affected?

A Untidy or unsightly storage invites trouble. Billboards are banned along federal highways, fences above certain heights or of certain construction are often banned locally, art commissions oversee and control monuments and building facades, Washington, D.C., regulates the height of buildings to prevent obscuring the Capitol dome, etc. The list is endless and ancient. Some of us, sooner or later, may find ourselves in trouble for marring a view.

SUGGESTED READING

For additional reading of the various codes pertaining to your operation, see Stephen M. Elonka, *Standard Plant Operators' Manual,* 3d ed., McGraw-Hill Book Company, New York, 1980.

2

BOILERS AND AUXILIARIES

Here are the most important answers to questions asked today for *boiler operator* and *stationary engineer licenses.* This information is also important in becoming a safe, efficient operator. Our answers are generally correct, should enable you to pass exams as well as become a good operator of energy systems equipment, and should help you "do the right thing" when an emergency occurs.

Follow our safe practices outlined here, heed the manufacturer's advice about equipment, *trace* out all systems in your plant, and sketch them on paper, so you know them thoroughly. If equipment is old, study early technical editions of books and literature for exact information.

EXAMPLE: Boilers today are welded and not riveted. But our survey of all examiners in the United States and Canada (see Chap. 21) revealed that questions on riveted boilers are still asked by some examiners. In this new edition, some old questions asked in previous years have been deleted and new questions and answers have been added on today's stricter pollution requirements.

FIRE-TUBE BOILERS

Q What is a boiler?
A A boiler is a steam generator. Steam is generated by burning fuel; that is, heat from the fuel causes the water inside the boiler to evaporate and produce steam.

Q How are boilers classified?
A Boilers fall into two broad groups: (1) fire-tube boilers and (2) water-tube boilers. Fire-tube types can be divided into *(a)* horizontal tube and *(b)* vertical tube. Water-tube boilers can be divided into *(a)* straight tube and *(b)* bent tube.

Q What is meant by the terms *fire tube* and *water tube?*
A Combustion gas passes through the fire tube; water passes through the water tube.

Q Are there other ways to classify boilers?
A Yes, there are many ways. The most common are:

1. Mobility: *(a)* stationary power or heating, *(b)* marine, *(c)* portable, *(d)* locomotive (railroad) or stationary with locomotive firebox.
2. Furnaces: *(a)* externally fired, *(b)* internally fired.
3. Position of tubes: *(a)* horizontal, *(b)* bent tube.
4. Shape of tube: *(a)* straight tube, *(b)* bent tube.
5. Position of drums: *(a)* longitudinal, *(b)* cross.
6. Number of drums: *(a)* single drum, *(b)* multidrum.
7. Header construction: *(a)* header, *(b)* box.
8. Gas passage: *(a)* single pass, *(b)* return pass, *(c)* multipass.
9. Water circulation: *(a)* natural, *(b)* accelerated, *(c)* forced.
10. Fire tube, known by common names: *(a)* horizontal return tubular (hrt), *(b)* locomotive firebox (lfb), *(c)* scotch marine (sm), *(d)* vertical tubular (vt).
11. Water tube, known by older names: *(a)* straight tubes, as Babcock & Wilcox (B & W) or Heine box header, usually having straight tubes that connect headers to headers; *(b)* bent tubes, as Stirling and other multidrum types, usually having bent tubes that connect drums to drums, or drums to headers; and *(c)* cast-iron header type, comes under water tube type.
12. Special: *(a)* once through, *(b)* coil type, *(c)* electric.

Q Sketch and label an hrt boiler.
A See Fig. 2-1.

Q Describe an hrt boiler.
A The shell (cylinder) of an hrt boiler is horizontal, made of rolled steel plate, and closed at each end with flat tube sheets. The tubes are inserted into reamed holes that have been drilled into the tube sheets. Then the tubes are expanded into the sheets, and the extended ends of the tube are bent or beaded back to the tube sheet with a beading tool. Beading helps to (1) prevent the tube ends from burning and (2) stay or support the flat tube sheet. The tube sheets are also supported by short diagonal stay rods, flat gusset stays, or long head-to-head stays. Most shells have

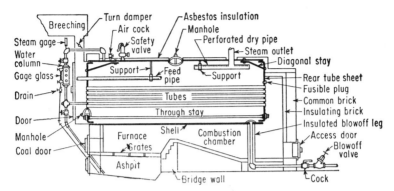

FIG. 2-1. Horizontal-return tubular boilers are externally fired; gases pass under the shell to the rear, then back through the tubes and up through the breeching to the stack.

openings for access and maintenance, a manhole in the top, and an opening in the lowest part of the front tube sheet. Other shells may have a second manhole, handhole, or pipe plug opening.

Hrt boilers have supporting lugs on the sides of the shell. The drum is supported by rods hanging from an external steel structure or from lugs resting on rollers on a steel-reinforced brick setting. In both cases the settings are made of common red building bricks and lined with refractory brick to resist furnace heat. The shell is pitched about 1 in. toward the back to help drain water and sludge through the blowoff piping.

Insulation and brick protect the leg of the blowoff piping where it goes through the furnace. This shields the leg, which is filled with stagnant water and sludge, from the hot, erosive furnace gases. The blowoff line goes to a quick-closing or cock valve, then through a slow-closing valve to the blowoff tank. A steel door, protected by loose firebrick in the rear of the setting, gives access to the back of the furnace and to the rear tube sheet for cleaning, repairing, etc.

No less than two nozzles (opening connections) are fitted to the top of the shell; one is for the safety valve, the other for the steam line. These two openings are separated from each other so as not to weaken the shell. Pads or bushings are often used to strengthen the lines that lead through the shell or tube sheets. The lines that pierce the shell are for the water column, pressure gage, blowoff valve, and feed-water inlet.

Coal-fired boilers have bridge walls to direct the gases against the shell and to support the rear end of the grate bars. An hrt boiler is externally fired. Gases pass under the shell to the rear tube sheet, through the tubes to the front tube sheet, up to the breeching, and to the chimney flue.

Steam-generating tubes are seldom less than 3 in. in diameter, and pressures rarely exceed 125 psig.

NOTE: Some examiners expect you to know the hrt boiler thoroughly. Be able to sketch it and name the parts.

Q Describe an lfb boiler.

A See Fig 2-2. An lfb boiler is internally fired. Most stationary units are of the return type, with both long and short fire tubes (Fig. 2-3). The short tubes lead the gases from the firebox to the rear tube sheet. Gases pass through the long tubes to the front, where they are led up to the breechings. The flat surfaces, forming the sides and top of the

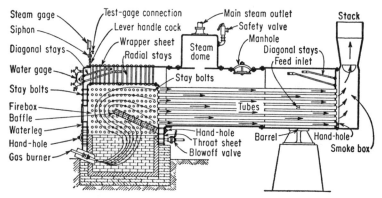

FIG. 2-2. Lfb boilers of single-pass design are internally fired by gas, coal, or oil.

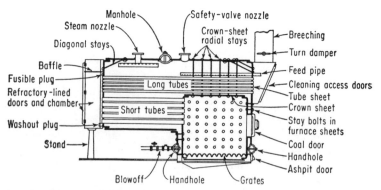

FIG. 2-3. Return-tube lfb boilers have two passes, used mostly for stationary work.

firebox, are relatively weak and must be supported. Numerous stay bolts support the sides and front. The top, or crown sheet, is supported by crown stays and sometimes by crown bars. The outer sheet over the furnace is called the wrapper sheet. There is one manhole in the top of the shell, and handholes or washout plugs in the legs and rear tube sheet. The short tubes usually have a larger diameter than the long tubes. Four-inch diameters are common for short tubes and three-inch diameters for long tubes. There are different forms of the lfb boiler for low-pressure heating: oil-, gas-, or coal-fired. Lfb boilers are used in smaller designs, seldom exceeding 150 psi.

Q Describe a vt boiler.
A See Fig. 2-4. A vt boiler is an internally fired fire-tube boiler. The dry-top and the wet-top are two types. A cylindrical steel shell is mounted vertically on a base ring that is set on either a cast-iron or a concrete pedestal. The tubes are vertical, and the bottom tube sheet is the top of the cylindrical furnace.

Because the furnace is comparatively weak, it must be supported with

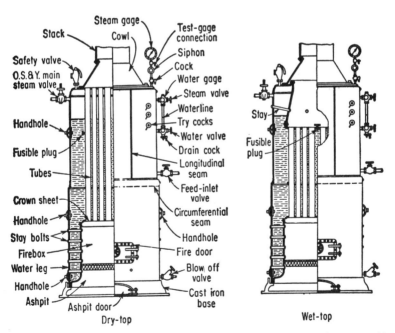

FIG. 2-4. Vt boilers are either dry- or wet-top and are used mostly on portable jobs.

stay bolts. The shell is pierced by the coaling door which goes through to the firebox. Handholes are provided for the inspection and cleaning of the internal water areas, especially over and around the furnace. In most vt boilers, the upper tube areas and the top tube sheet are dry.

In the wet-top design, the top tube sheet and the tubes are below the water level. Some dry-top designs have a return gas passage, but these are not common.

The common dry-top unit is surprisingly efficient and may produce a slightly superheated steam. But, uneven or too rapid heating of the furnace will cause trouble. The vertical furnace seam or the fire-door frame seams will leak. Stay-bolt breakage is a frequent complaint.

The vt boiler is used in small plants where floor space and steam demand are limited. It is commonly used for (1) portable hoisting rigs, (2) steam shovels, (3) steam rollers, (4) pile drivers, and (5) other mobile applications. However, the vt boiler is rapidly being replaced by the internal-combustion engine.

Q Sketch and describe an sm boiler.

A See Fig. 2-5. An sm boiler is a horizontal tubular boiler having from

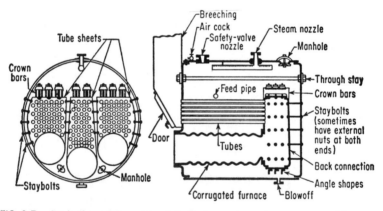

FIG. 2-5. Sm boilers of the wet-back design have one to three corrugated furnaces; combustion gases are completely surrounded by water and have stays and stay bolts.

one to three cylindrical furnaces. The furnaces connect with the tubes in a back connection of the wet-back type, or in a chamber of the dry-back type (Fig. 2-6). The furnaces may be smooth cylinders but are usually corrugated to better resist collapsing from outside pressure. These corrugations also make the furnace more flexible during heat expansion and contraction. A metal ring or horsecollar is often built in on the inside

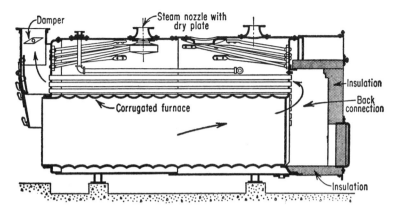

FIG. 2-6. Sm boilers of the dry-back design have an insulated back connection and are common for packaged-type stationary use in heating and industrial plants.

end of the steel furnace itself, or one can be made separately of refractory materials. The ring slows down the hot gases that pass to the rear of the wet-back types. Sm boilers need a foundation but no brick setting, because fuel is burned entirely inside the internal furnaces. Dry-back types have a heavy refractory lining for back connection. This eliminates the expensive and weak area of the wet-back type. The dry back is used in stationary plants. Wet-back boilers have a separate back-connection chamber for each furnace. Besides the pressure that tends to collapse the furnace, the flat back-connection surfaces are also subject to collapse. An elaborate system of stay bolts, crown stays, girders, braces, and stays is needed in all wet-back designs. Wet-back types are usually used for greater fuel economy or to conserve space and weight because they have a larger heat-transfer area for a given size. Sm boilers may have one, two, or three furnaces, each separately fired. Stay tubes are often used to support head-to-head in place of horizontal stay rods. The stay tubes are very heavy. They are threaded at each end, screwed, then rolled into the tube sheets.

Take great care when lighting off an sm boiler. Raise the steam slowly. Heating must be gradual and even, because forces of heat expansion are great enough to fracture the bolted areas during this period.

The basic disadvantage of these boilers is poor water circulation. Cool water settles to the bottom under the furnaces and remains there undisturbed. Various schemes are used to increase water circulation. Some boilers have a steam nozzle working on the feed-injector principle. Others have internal ducts and baffles to direct hot water under the furnace and thus to move the mass of cold water through the boiler. To gain further economy, provide for an air preheater. This is a tube-lined duct in the breechings that preheats the incoming combustion air with hot flue gases.

Sm boilers are commonly used in seagoing plants and stationary units. At times, the uppermost rows of tubes are as large as 5 in. in diameter, with superheater tubes fitted inside. Thus, a little superheat is raised for turbines or for high-speed reciprocating engines. Sm boilers are usually limited to less than 200 psi. The reason for this is that at higher pressures the shell becomes too thick. The problem of building the furnace strong enough to resist collapse is also a difficult one. See ASME code.

Q What is meant by the term *packaged boiler?*
A See Fig. 2-7. A packaged boiler is a complete steam-generating unit.

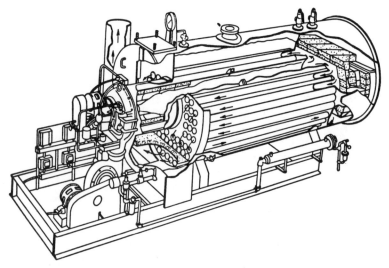

FIG. 2-7. Packaged steam generators are mounted on skids and come complete with auxiliaries like this sm dry-back type, which needs only piping and electrical connections.

Most packaged boilers are completely self-contained, with boiler, firing equipment, draft fans, feed pump, and automatic controls mounted on a single base. Such a unit may be shipped completely assembled and installed with a minimum of erection and construction. Since the packaged steam generator is designed as a unit, various elements are coordinated to produce the desired results and the entire job is a single responsibility. These packages are modified versions of the dry-back sm boiler, but each manufacturer has individual variations. The common features of most packaged units are (1) a single furnace, usually without corrugations, (2) a dry back, and (3) a multipass baffling system to chase the gases back and forth through the boiler. Packaged boilers are finding an ever greater acceptance in small plants and may be fire tube or water tube.

WATER-TUBE BOILERS

Q Describe an older type of straight-tube water-tube boiler.

A See Fig. 2-8. This boiler consists of a series of inclined tubes that

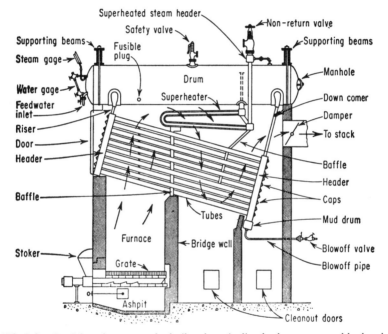

FIG. 2-8. Straight-tube water-tube boilers have inclined tubes connected by headers.

connect two headers. The headers are erected at each end of a brick-set furnace. One header, at the low end of the tubes, is a downcomer that distributes water to the tubes. The higher header is a riser that collects steam and water mixture for the steam drum. Steam separates from the water in the steam drum. The position of the drum identifies this type of boiler. Drums that are parallel to the tubes are long-drum (longitudinal) types and drums positioned across the tubes are cross-drum types. The trend for some time has been toward cross-drum boilers.

The straight-tube water-tube boiler is usually designed for medium-sized plants of around 200 psi, for both stationary and marine use. Some designs, however, have exceeded 1000 psi. Many straight-tube water-tube boilers have refinements such as economizers, superheaters, and extended water-walls.

Q What is a header in a straight-tube water-tube boiler?
A Headers are hollow steel manifolds into which boiler tubes are expanded. The tops of the vertical headers pass to the steam drum. The headers are equipped with handholes and caps to permit inspection, cleaning, and repairs to each tube.

Q How are straight-tube water-tube boilers supported?
A They are supported by a structural steel framework, never by a brick furnace setting. Steel rods are bent around the drum or fitted into suspension lugs to support the drum. See Fig. 2-8.

Q What is a sectional header?
A See Fig. 2-9. A sectional header is a vertical hollow steel manifold

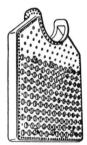

| Riveted drum and crossbox | Front box header | Vertical sectional sinuous header |

FIG. 2-9.   Three types of headers used in riveted water-tube boilers of older design.

with a sinuous design that permits staggering of the tubes. When assembled, the headers connect the boiler tubes and pass water and steam vertically through nipples to the steam drum. Handholes give access for tube maintenance.

Q What is a box header?
A See Fig. 2-9. A box header is fabricated of flat steel plates. One side of the box is a tube sheet into which the boiler tubes are expanded. The outside plating has handholes for access to the tubes. Hollow stay bolts are needed to support the large flat surfaces. If the bolt is fractured, steam and water will leak through the hollow bolt end, thus warning the operator of danger.

Q Examination questions often refer to a B & W boiler. What is it?

A A B & W boiler is a straight-tube water-tube boiler of a sectional header design. B & W stands for the Babcock & Wilcox Company. However, this firm produces many types and sizes of boilers besides the straight-tube water-tube type. This is an old question still asked.

Q Describe the bent-tube multidrum water-tube boiler shown in Fig. 2-10.

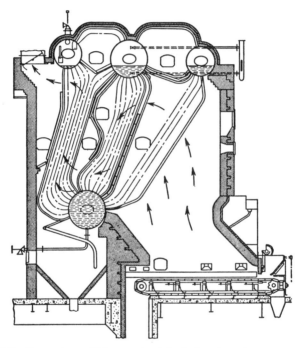

FIG. 2-10. Bent-tube multidrum water-tube boilers have two or more drums.

A The boiler in Fig. 2-10 consists of two or more drums. The uppermost is the steam drum, and the lowest the mud drum. Additional drums have various names. Those below steaming water level are called "drowned drums." Besides the manufacturers' names or types, the boilers are known by the number of drums they have, such as two-drum, three-drum, and four-drum boilers. The top drums are supported by structural steel framework, the bottom drums by the generating tubes connected to the upper drums. When bricking the furnace, be sure to allow free movement to the swinging drums. Some smaller types of stationary boilers and large marine boilers have the bottom drums fitted with a sliding shoe or saddle to support the boiler. In these types, the steam drum is supported by generating tubes and is allowed to move. Sliding supports, which are grease-lubricated, allow for heat expansion of the bottom drums.

Modern high-pressure bent-tube boilers are usually designed with water-walls, superheaters, economizers, and at times with air preheaters.

Q   Are boilers classifed by water circulation?

A   Yes. There are four such classifications: (1) natural circulation, (2) accelerated circulation, (3) forced recirculation, and (4) forced circulation.

Q   Discuss natural circulation.

A   Boilers, such as the fire-tube and older straight-tube water-tube types, are heated at the bottom. A mixture of steam bubbles and hot water rises to the surface where steam is released. Such circulation is due to heavier, cooler water displacing the lighter hot-water steam mixture.

In a simple water-tube circuit (Fig. 2-11) steam bubbles form on the

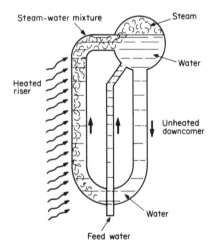

FIG. 2-11.   Natural circulation in simple water-tube circuit results because cold water is heavier than hot.

heated side shown. The resulting steam-water mixture weighs less than the cooler water on the unheated side and is accordingly displaced. In the drum, steam bubbles rise to the water's surface and steam is released for energy uses.

Q   Discuss accelerated circulation.

A   In water-tube boilers, the water circulation is down through some tubes and up through others. In general, the cooler tubes are downflow while the hotter tubes closest to the fire are upflow. This is satisfactory up to a point, but in high-heat-release, high-pressure installations there are other factors. For example, a bent-tube boiler under an increasing load will have a pressure drop. All tubes tend to become risers as more steam is formed. Boiler tubes then overheat and are damaged from water-circulation starvation. To overcome this problem, heavily insulated, large-sized tubes are installed outside the furnace. These tubes, called external downcomers, provide water to the lower drums under any condition. Most new marine designs and many high-pressure bent-tube stationary boilers are of this accelerated design.

Q What is a forced-circulation boiler?

A It is a boiler, known as a "once-through type" (see Fig. 2-12), that

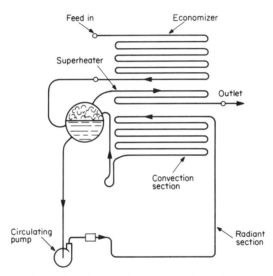

FIG. 2-12. Pump in this forced-circulation generator is used to overcome resistance in long tubes.

uses a feed pump to force water into the circuit. Here, the weight of the steam emerging at one end of the tube circuit is equal to the weight of the water pumped in at the other end. Briefly, the feed pump forces water into a tube circuit as superheated steam issues at the other end. Water and steam drums aren't needed, although some designs (Fig. 2-12) use a drum. The advantage of this boiler is that it will carry extremely high pressures since it needs no heavy steam drum. In this circuit, the weight of water and steam tend to merge as the pressure increases. If the steam weighs as much as the water, there is no gravity head to produce circulation, and a pump is needed.

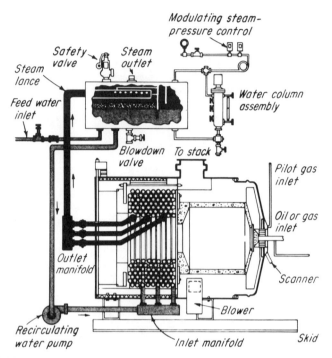

FIG 2-13. Forced-circulation (coil-type water-tube boiler has drum for water-steam separation.

Q Describe the coil-type controlled-circulation boiler shown in Fig. 2-13.

A Here, the boiler has a pump that forces water through a flow circuit. The water is pumped from a steam drum that may be mounted externally to the boiler. The water is divided into various circuits. An orifice plate at each inlet provides several times as much water as the circuit will generate into steam at the maximum firing rate. An important feature is the recirculation of the water, which can be done with educators as well as with pumps.

Intense heat is released from a gas or oil burner. With automatic operation, some designs come to full capacity and pressure within only 5 min from cold start-up. This makes them ideal for quick-steaming service for emergency use. Being light and compact, they are portable and can be mounted on a truck and transported to wherever steam is needed.

These quick steamers are ideal as low-capacity output or for standby service from 1500 up to 15,000 lb/hr at pressures as high as 900 psi.

Some designs take the hot exhaust gases from a gas turbine or internal-combustion engine, and thus are ideal as a waste-heat boiler for saving money in these years of energy crunch.

Q Name three modern classifications of medium-sized water-tube boilers shown in Fig. 2-14.

A (a) A type has two small lower drums or headers. The upper drum is larger to permit separation of water and steam. Most steam production occurs in the center furnace-wall tubes entering the drum. (b) D type

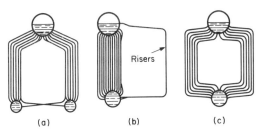

(a)　　　　　　(b)　　　　　　(c)

FIG. 2-14   Three basic designs of industrial boilers today are the (a) A-type, (b) D-type, and (c) O-type.

FIG. 2-15.   Packaged water-tube boiler is skid-mounted at the factory, will generate over 100,000 lb/hr of superheated steam. (*Combustion Engineering, Inc., Windsor, Conn.*)

allows much flexibility. Here the more active steaming risers enter the drum near the waterline. Burners may be located in the end walls or between the tubes in the buckle of the D, at right angles to the drum. (c) O type is also a compact steamer. Because transportation limits the height of the furnace, a longer boiler is often required for capacity. Floors of D and O types are generally tile-covered.

Q Describe the compact O-type unit in Fig. 2-15.

A This general design is skid-mounted at the factory, comes as a packaged unit, and may generate over 100,000 lb of superheated steam per hour at a maximum of 775 psi and 750°F. A conventional superheater is located at the point where the flow of gases, directed by finned-tube waterwalls, splits into two parts. Each turning point of 180° directs flow toward a flue-gas exit located on either side of the upper drum.

A forced-draft fan (not shown) may be located at any convenient place. The furnace is pressurized, and no induced-draft fan is required. Soot blowers serve to keep convection banks clean. Tubes are arranged in rows with alternate wide and narrow spacing.

Q Describe briefly the modern industrial boiler in Fig. 2-16.

A This is a versatile design needed today to burn a variety of fuels, auxiliary gas, coal, oil, and/or waste liquid, for which burners are high over the grate to prevent overheating. The front wall has spouts to handle solid industrial wastes. This spreader-stoker water-tube unit comes in sizes of 250,000 lb/hr of steaming capacity and is popular today because of high energy costs and EPA Clean Air Act requirements.

ASME BOILER CODE

Q What is the ASME boiler code?

A Most stationary boilers in the United States are designed according the ASME code. The ASME code is the American Society of Mechanical Engineers' code for boiler construction. This is the basic code for most states and cities. Since there are local rules that modify some sections of the code, be sure to obtain a copy of your state's code, if one is in force.

The code, while not written specifically for repair work, does require that all materials and constructions used in repair work also meet code requirements. Repairs to pressure parts are made under the guidance of the National Board Inspection Code, published by the National Board of Boiler and Pressure Vessel Inspectors, Columbus, Ohio. This code covers problems of inspection and repairs to boilers and auxiliary equipment that are not otherwise covered by the ASME code. It suggests laws

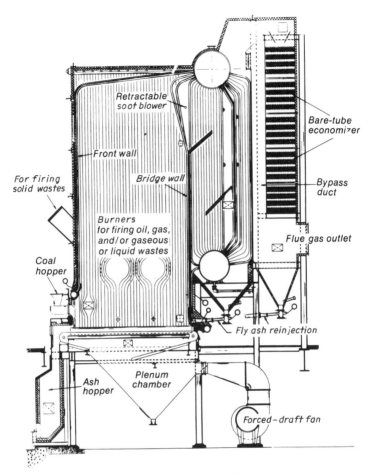

FIG. 2-16. Field-erected spreader-stoker-fired unit can burn a variety of fuels, as well as waste products.

and regulations for inspection of pressure vessels, and rules for repairs by fusion welding. These rules are acceptable in most states.

CODE DETAILS AND CALCULATIONS

Q How does one recognize boilers and components built according to the ASME code

FIG. 2-17. Official symbol for stamps to denote ASME Standard Heating Boilers, Section IV.

FIG. 2-18. The ASME standard symbol must be stamped on your safety valve.

A Figure 2-17 is an example of the official symbol for stamps to denote ASME Standard Heating Boilers. This stamp must be noted first; other required stamping indicates allowable pressures and capacities.

Q Does the phrase *an officially rated ASME pressure-relief valve* have any specific meaning?

A Yes, an officially rated ASME pressure-relief valve is specifically for hot-water boilers. And most important, it must be stamped for its pressure setting and its Btu per hour relieving capacity. Also, it must be equipped with a hand test lever, must be spring-loaded, and must not be of the adjustable screw-down type. A typical safety relief valve approved by the ASME is stamped with the symbol shown in Fig. 2-18.

Q What other specifics does the code define?

A The code defines materials used in the construction of boilers and outlines the limitations of these materials.

> EXAMPLE: Cast iron and copper are severely limited as to pressure, temperature, and specific parts. Steel, to be used for forgings, welding, and exposure to fire, is specified by chemical composition as well as by physical strength. Each plate is marked at the mill with a steel stamp, and a record is made of each plate. The method of calculating the strength of specific boiler parts is given in the code. The code also provides standards for boiler inspectors to follow,

The code defines construction methods and gives the strength and method of calculating safe pressure. We suggest that you buy a copy of the ASME code and/or your state code. Illustrations in the code are good and clear, and examples are worked out for you. They will help you pass your examinations with more assurance.

Q State the formula for safe working pressure (SWP) of a boiler shell.

A $SWP = \dfrac{TS \times t \times E}{FS \times R}$

where SWP = safe working pressure
TS = tensile strength of metal
t = thickness of metal
E = efficiency of longitudinal seam
R = radius of shell
FS = factor of safety

Q How do you find safe working pressure?

A GIVEN: Diameter of a shell is 48 in., plate thickness is $\frac{5}{16}$ in., tensile strength is 55,000 psi, efficiency of longitudinal seam is 85 percent, factor of safety is 5.

SOLUTION:

$$SWP = \dfrac{TS \times t \times E}{FS \times R}$$

$$= \dfrac{55,000 \times 0.3125 \times 0.85}{5 \times 24}$$

$$= 121.7 \text{ psi} \qquad Ans.$$

Q What is meant by efficiency of a joint?
A Efficiency is the ratio of the strength of a joint in relation to the solid plate of the shell or drum.

NOTE: The appendix in the ASME code is well illustrated to show you various ways a joint may fail.

Q Sketch the following joints: (1) lap-riveted, (2) butt and double strap, (3) circumferential (girth seam) riveted, (4) welded longitudinal.
A See Fig. 2-19 and the ASME sketches.

Q What is a lap-seam crack, and how are lap-seam cracks repaired?
A A lap-seam crack runs parallel to the seam and is in the shell plate. There is no way to repair it. When so damaged, the shell is condemned.

Q What is meant by strength of rivets in shear?
A There are two types of shear: (1) single shear, the condition in a lap joint, and (2) double shear, the condition in a butt and double-strap joint.

NOTE: See ASME code.

Q For what three reasons do riveted joints fail?

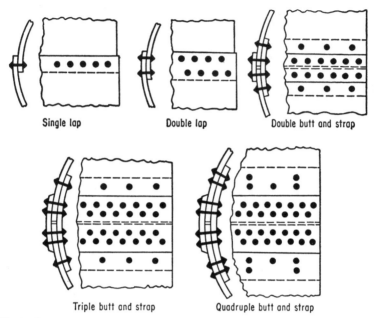

Single lap   Double lap   Double butt and strap

Triple butt and strap   Quadruple butt and strap

FIG. 2-19.   Riveted joints are used in older boilers, but some license examiners still use them in tests.

A   Riveted joints fail because of (1) shearing of the rivets, (2) plate crushing before the rivets, and (3) failure of the plate between rivet holes.

Q   Why are examiners interested in riveted joints?
A   Because old boilers are often repaired, and the operators are involved.

Q   What is the minimum thickness allowed for boiler plates?
A   The minimum thickness for unstayed plates is $\frac{1}{4}$ in.; for stayed surfaces, $\frac{5}{16}$ in.; for heads of fire-tube boilers (tube sheet), $\frac{3}{8}$ in. See ASME code.

Q   What is the maximum allowance on properly welded joints?
A   All properly fusion-welded joints are calculated at 100 percent efficiency. See ASME code.

Q   What is a ligament and how is the ligament's strength calculated?
A   A ligament is the metal remaining between the tube holes in a tube sheet. It is calculated with the aid of graphical charts in the ASME code.

Q   Calculate the efficiency of ligaments of evenly spaced tube holes.

GIVEN: Pitch of the tube holes is $5\frac{1}{4}$ in., diameter of tube is $3\frac{1}{4}$ in., and clearance of holes is $\frac{1}{32}$ in.

A The formula for evenly spaced holes is

$$\text{Efficiency of ligament} = \frac{\text{pitch} - \text{diameter of hole}}{\text{pitch}}$$

$$E = \frac{5.25 - (3.25 + 0.031)}{5.25}$$

$$= \frac{5.25 - 3.281}{5.25}$$

$$= 0.375 \text{ efficient} \qquad Ans.$$

Q Sketch the following: (1) a common stay bolt with (a) two threads extended before riveting, (b) a telltale hole, and (c) two necked-down cross sections; (2) a hollow stay bolt used for a box header; (3) a flat stay (Huston); (4) a round stay with (a) palms and (b) a crowfoot; (5) a gusset stay; (6) a head-to-head with (a) copper washers and (b) supports every 6 ft; (7) a crow-bar girder; and (8) a structural shape.
A See Fig. 2-20.

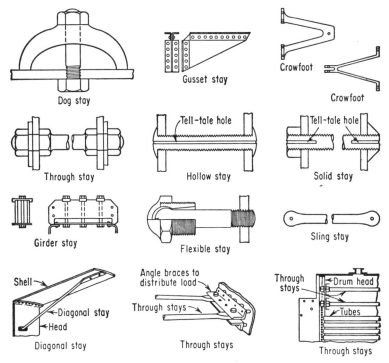

FIG. 2-20. Stays are used to prevent the flat surfaces of a boiler from rupturing.

Q What is a boiler stay?

A A boiler stay is any shaped piece of metal that is stressed in tension. It prevents flat surfaces that are under pressure from tearing apart.

Q Name and describe various forms of stays.

A See Fig. 2-20.

Through stays usually run head to head and use nuts and washers.

Stay bolts are usually used in firebox-type boilers. Their length must be less than 20 times the bolt's diameter. They may be hollow or drilled, and after being screwed between the plates, their ends are riveted over.

Diagonal stays may be the round (Scully) or the rectangular (Huston) type. When inserted at an angle between two members, this stay forms the long side of the triangle.

Gusset stays are triangular pieces of metal that are right-angled to serve the same purpose as diagonal stays.

Crown bars or girder stays are used in the top of combustion chambers or back connections. They consist of two plates of the same thickness that are cut exactly alike. These plates are spaced apart with thimbles or short pieces of tubing. Countersunk rivets pass through the tubing and bind the plates together. Crown bars rest and bear down on the curved parts of the chamber, and thimbles take up the space between the bottom of the girder and the top of the furnace. Flanged-lip washers are placed on top of the girder. Bolts pass through these washers, the bottom thimbles, and the crown sheet. Nuts and washers are used to draw the assembly rigid. The bottom thimbles prevent the top of the crown sheets or the bottom of the girders from buckling, and the flanged washers prevent the top of the girder from spreading. Several crown bars may be equally spaced in the back connection of an sm boiler.

Stay tubes are very heavy tubes with threading on each end. The threads on one end are larger in diameter than those on the other end. This permits the smaller end to pass through the front tube sheet. The small diameter has a longer thread to permit engaging and screwing before the greater diameter engages. The minimum wall thickness under the threads is $\frac{3}{16}$ in. To screw or unscrew the tube, a square-shanked sharp-edged inserter is driven into it. After the tube is screwed into place, it is expanded, calked, flared, and beaded back. Nuts are sometimes used. This is an older, less desirable method that is occasionally used on old boilers.

Structural shapes may be used to stay the upper segments of boilers that are 36 in. or less in diameter and do not exceed 100 psi. The usual practice is to rivet two angle irons back to back and to rivet the short flanges to the head. The edge of the bottom flange must be more than 2 in. over the top of the tubes. See ASME code for details.

Q Do boiler tubes stay the tube sheets?

A Yes. Stays are not required in areas supported by tubes or in areas that are less than the maximum pitch of the stays. See ASME code.

Q What are telltale holes in solid stay bolts?

A Telltale holes are $\frac{3}{16}$ in. or more in diameter and extended to $\frac{1}{2}$ in. beyond the least diameter of the bolt. The holes always extend $\frac{1}{2}$ in. beyond the inside of the supported plate. If the bolt cracks or corrodes, steam and water will flow out of the tiny hole to warn the operator of danger. See ASME code for the additional information you will be expected to know.

Q In calculating the strength of stay bolts, are the telltale holes included in the calculation?

A Yes. In determining the net cross-sectional area of drilled or hollow bolts, the cross-sectional area of the hole is deducted.

NOTE: Always use the least area, such as the bottom of the threads, or the necked-down portion of the bolt.

Q What is the stress allowed on screwed-and-riveted bolts?

A For SA 31 grade, 11,300 psi, depending on metal temperature. Consult the ASME code for stress allowances on the different grades of metal.

Q What load is placed on a stay bolt that supports a stayed area 5 × 5 in. at 60 psi?

A $P \times P$ = area to be supported
5 × 5 = 25 in.²
25 × 60 = 1500 lb   *Ans.*

Q Calculate the safe working pressure of a furnace that is symmetrically stayed with $\frac{3}{4}$-in. screwed-and-riveted solid stay bolts that are pitched 6 in. apart and have 12 threads per inch. Allowable stress is 11,300 psi (SA 31 grade).

A SOLUTION: The smallest diameter at the bottom of the 12-pitch threads is 0.6057. See ASME code.

Area of bolt = $(0.6057)^2 \times 0.7854 = 0.288$ in.²

NOTE:

Area = $(\text{diameter})^2 \times 0.7854$

$$\text{SWP} = \frac{\text{allowable stress} \times \text{area of bolt}}{\text{area supported}}$$

$$= \frac{11,300 \times 0.288}{6 \times 6} = \frac{3254.4}{36}$$

$$= 90.4 \text{ psi} \qquad Ans.$$

Q Calculate symmetrical pitch of stay bolts with smallest diameter of 0.7932 in., allowable stress of 11,300 psi, and safe working pressure of 125 psi.

A $SWP = \dfrac{AS \times \text{area of bolt}}{\text{pitch}^2}$

$p^2 = \dfrac{AS \times a}{SWP}$

$a = (0.7932)^2 \times 0.7854 = 0.494$

$p^2 = \dfrac{11,300 \times 0.494}{125}$

$= \dfrac{5582.2}{125}$

$= 44.6576$

$p = \sqrt{44.6576}$

$= 6.68$ in.   *Ans.*

NOTE: The area of the bolt may be deducted from the pitch area.

NOTE: The nearest commercial bolt size, larger if necessary, is to be selected.

Q Sketch a diagonal stay.

A See Fig. 2-21 and ASME code.

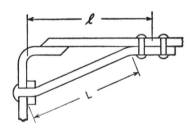

FIG. 2-21.   Diagonal stay for fire-tube boiler.

Q How are diagonal stays calculated?

A First calculate the net area of a direct stay required to support the surface. Then use this formula to obtain the size of diagonal stay:

$A = \dfrac{a \times L}{l}$

where $A =$ sectional area of diagonal stay, in.^{2}

$a =$ sectional area of direct stay, in.^{2}

$L =$ length of diagonal stay from inside of head sheet to center of palm between rivets

$l =$ length from inside of head sheet to center of palm between rivets

EXAMPLE: Given diameter of direct stay is 1 in.

$a = 0.7854$ in.²
$L = 60$ in.
$l = 48$ in.

$$A = \frac{0.7854 \times 60}{48} = 0.981 \text{ in.}^2$$

To solve for diameter:

$$d^2 = \frac{A}{0.7854}$$

$$= \frac{0.981}{0.7854} = 1.2490$$

$$d^2 = 1.2490$$

$$d = \sqrt{1.2490}$$

$$= 1.117, \text{ or } 1\tfrac{1}{8}\text{-in.-diameter diagonal stay} \qquad Ans.$$

NOTE: See ASME code.

Another, and simpler, way to determine the diameter is to examine the two lengths. If the ratio is 1.15 or less, use 90 percent of the allowable load for the straight rod.

EXAMPLE: Given a 1-in.-diameter straight rod that is 48 in. long, calculate as a diagonal stay 55 in. long. What commercial size rod is necessary?

SOLUTION:

$$\frac{L}{l} = 1.15 \text{ or less}$$

$$\frac{55}{48} = 1.14 \text{ (use 90 percent rule)}$$

Area of 1-in. rod $= 0.7854$ in.²

$$\frac{0.7854}{0.90} = 0.8726 \text{ area of the new rod}$$

To solve for diameter:

$$d^2 = \frac{A}{0.7854}$$

$$= \frac{0.8726}{0.7854} = 1.111$$

$d = \sqrt{1.111} = 1.05$, or $1\frac{1}{16}$-in.-diameter diagonal stay   *Ans.*

Q What is the difference between a drum and a shell?
A A drum is usually associated with water-tube boilers, a shell with fire-tube boilers.

Q What are the minimum sizes for elliptical and round manholes?
A Elliptical manholes are either 10 × 16 in. or 11 × 15 in. Round holes are 15 in. See ASME code.

Q What is the minimum width of the gasket-bearing surface of a manhole opening?
A The gasket-bearing surface has a minimum width of $1\frac{1}{16}$ in. See ASME code.

Q How many washout openings are needed in a locomotive-type boiler?
A Six handhole or washout plugs are located in a locomotive-type boiler—one in the rear head below the tubes; one at the front head, at or near the crown-sheet line; and four in the lower part of the water leg. When possible, a seventh is located near the throat sheet. See ASME code.

Q State the formula for calculating a concave (bumped-plus) drumhead.

A For the usual segment of a sphere-type head use:

$$t = \frac{5\,PL}{4.8\,SE}$$

where t = thickness of head, in.
　　　　P = maximum allowable working pressure, psi
　　　　L = radius to which the head is dished, measured on the concave side, in.
　　　　S = maximum allowable stress per ASME code
　　　　E = weld efficiency if welding is done on the head ($E = 1$ for seamless head)
　　See ASME code.

Q What does bumped plus or bumped minus mean in regard to drum-heads?
A Bumped plus means a dished head with pressure on the concave side. Bumped minus has pressure on the convex side.

Q Which is stronger, bumped plus or bumped minus?
A A bumped-plus head is stronger, since it has pressure on the concave side. The ASME code allows only 60 percent for a bumped-minus head of the same construction.

Q What is the maximum radius of a dished head?

A The radius of a dished head should not be greater than the diameter of the drum to which the head is attached.

Q How are boiler tubes measured?

A Boiler tubes are measured by (1) outside diameter of the tube, (2) wall thickness, expressed as Birmingham wire gage (BWG) or more simply as "gage," and (3) length of the tube.

Q How is heating surface calculated?

A Heating surface is calculated by the number of square feet of the furnace and the tubes exposed to the hot gases. Unless a table is furnished, tubes are figured on the external side in fire-tube boilers.

Q How many square feet of heating surface was considered to equal 1 boiler hp in older boilers?

A Ten square feet was considered to equal 1 boiler hp. Although this does not mean anything today, questions are still asked based on this area.

Q How does the ASME calculate boiler horsepower?

A One boiler horsepower is equal to the evaporation of 34.5 lb of water per hour from and at 212°F. Expressed in heat units, this is 970.3 Btu × 34.5 = 33,475 Btu. Boilers usually don't evaporate at 212°F; therefore, you must consider the factor of evaporation in calculating boiler horsepower. The factor of evaporation is the total heat in 1 lb of steam as it leaves the boiler, less the heat in 1 lb of feed water, divided by 970.3.

Q Calculate the horsepower of a boiler marked "1250 HS."

A Since HS means square feet of heating surface, 10 ft² HS = 1 hp and 1250/10 = 125 boiler hp.   *Ans.*

Q Calculate the heating surface of forty-eight 4-in. tubes that are 14 ft long.

A SOLUTION: First, find the circumference of one tube:

$\pi \times d = c$

$3.1416 \times 4 = 12.5664$ in.

Convert inches to feet.

$$\frac{12.5664}{12} = 1.0472 \text{ ft}$$

Next, find the surface area of one tube.

Circumference × length = surface area of a cylinder, or 1.0472 × 14 = 14.6608 ft²

Then, find the total heating surface of all tubes.

14.6608 × 48 = 703.71 ft²   *Ans.*

Q An hrt boiler has thirty-six 8-gage 3-in.-diameter tubes. The boiler shell is 48 in. in diameter. What is the horsepower of the boiler? Consider three-eighths of the shell as heating surface. Wall thickness of the 8-gage tubing is 0.165 in. Length of shell is 14 ft.

A First, determine the heating surface (HS) of the shell.

$$\frac{48}{12} = 4 \text{ ft diameter}$$

$\pi \times d = C$
$3.1416 \times 4 = 12.5664$ ft
$C \times L = \text{area}$
$12.5664 \times 14 = 175.9296$ ft²
$175.9296 \times 0.375 = 65.97$ HS of the shell

To find the inside circumference of the tube,

3 in. = OD (outside diameter)
0.330 = twice the wall thickness of 0.165

Then:
$3.000 - 0.330 = 2.670$ ID (inside diameter)
$\pi \times d = c$
$3.1416 \times 2.67 = 8.3881$ in.

$$\frac{8.3881}{12} = 0.6990 \text{ ft}$$

$0.6990 \times 14 = 9.7860$ ft² per tube
$9.7860 \times 36 = 352.296$ HS in the tubes
$352.296 = $ HS in the tubes
$65.97 = $ HS in the shell

Then:
$352.2960 + 65.9736 = 418.266$ total HS

$$\frac{418.27}{10} = 41.8 \text{ hp} \qquad Ans.$$

Q The major axis of elliptical manholes should be circumferential or longitudinal on a shell. Why?

A The least amount of unit strain comes when the long axis is circumferential. There is twice the amount of unit stress on a longitudinal seam as there is on a girth seam.

Q Prove by calculation that a girth seam has one-half as much stress as a longitudinal seam. Assume that the shell has a 6-ft diameter and a pressure of 100 psi.

A SOLUTION:

6 ft = 72-in. diameter

$A = d^2 \times 0.7854$

Area of head = $72 \times 72 \times 0.7854 = 4071.5136$

Stress = area $\times$ pressure

Stress = 4071.5136 in. $\times$ 100 psi = 407,151.36 lb

Length of girth seam = $\pi \times$ diameter

Length = $3.1416 \times 72 = 226.195$

$$\text{Stress per inch of girth seam} = \frac{\text{total stress}}{\text{length of seam}}$$

$$\frac{407,151.36}{226.195} = 1800 \text{ psi} \qquad Ans.$$

To calculate stress per inch of longitudinal seam:

Stress = pressure $\times$ radius

Stress = 100 psi $\times$ 36 in. = 3600 psi

$$\frac{1800 \text{ psi stress girth seam}}{3600 \text{ psi stress longitudinal seam}} = \frac{1}{2} \qquad Ans.$$

Q How do you prepare a boiler for a hydrostatic test?
A Clean the boiler thoroughly and open all access doors in the settings. Hold the safety-valve disks on their seat with test clamps (gags), or remove the valves and insert a blank flange in place of the safety valve. Be sure to replace all gaskets that were disturbed when the boiler was opened.

Q What pressures are used to test boilers?
A The official test pressure is 150 percent (1½ times) maximum allowable working pressure. The pressure must be kept under proper control. Never let the required test pressure exceed 2 percent. For a simple and unofficial test of a gasket or minor part, 90 percent is enough. You need not over-stress the boiler in such cases. Be careful not to raise the safety valves with water, as this may cause damage. See ASME code for new boilers.

Q Describe a fusible plug.
A A fusible plug is a fire-actuated device that melts away a tin core at 400 to 500°F. See ASME code. There is much to read on this subject.

Q What is the ASME factor of safety?
A The specified ASME factor of safety is generally 4 for welded boilers and 5 for riveted boilers, or those boilers that do not meet code welding requirements. Check the latest ASME code and your jurisdiction for requirements.

Q What is a hydrostatic test for boilers and how is it applied?
A The pressure parts of a boiler are subjected to water pressure. The boiler is completely filled and pressure is applied with a hand pump. As the pressure climbs, a calibrated test gage attached to the boiler is watched during the official tests. Some states also require 70°F minimum water temperature, with water temperature above room air temperature.

Q Are fusible plugs required for all boilers?
A No. They are not advisable above 225 psi.

Q Can fusion welding be used to build up a corroded stayed area?
A Yes, provided that 60 percent of the original metal remains.

Q What limits are placed on longitudinal lap seams in boiler shells?
A (1) No course should exceed 12 ft and (2) no lap-seam crack should be repaired, nor should the cracked boiler shell be used.

Q Can a riveted joint be as strong as the metal it joins?
A No. The plate is weakened by the holes drilled for the rivets.

Q What determines the location of a fusible plug?
A The location of a fusible plug is determined by the lowest permissible water level.

Q What does the term *soft patch* mean?
A A *soft patch* is fastened with bolts instead of being riveted or welded.

Q Should a patch be placed on the outside or the inside of a shell?
A Whether the patch should be placed on the inside or outside of the shell depends on the use and location of the patch. If the patch is on the inside, pressure tends to keep it tight and prevents scale pockets from forming. At times, however, an external patch is more practical, as, for example, on a tube sheet.

Q What is the difference between *beading* and *flaring*?
A In *beading*, a tube end is bent back 180° to the tube sheet with a beading tool. In *flaring*, the ends of water tubes are flared to prevent them from pulling out of the tube sheets. The flaring tool is part of the tube expander. See ASME code.

Q What can be done if the hole in a tube sheet is oversized from overexpanding a tube during past repairs?
A This can be corrected by placing a ferrule in the tube sheet to fill out the excess space between the tube and the tube sheet.

Q Name some common causes of boiler explosions.
A Many boiler explosions are cuased by (1) low water, (2) scale deposits, (3) oil in the boiler water, (4) corroded or thinned parts, (5) cracks, (6)

improper repairs, (7) inoperative safety valves, and (8) human failure, the greatest cause of all.

Q What are the requirements for a properly functioning safety valve?

A A properly operating safety valve must (1) lift to full opening at a definite pressure without excessive preliminary simmering (popping pressure), (2) remain open until pressure has dropped to a definite amount (blowback), (3) close tightly without chattering (reseating pressure), and (4) remain tight when closed (no leakage).

Q A boiler operating at 250 psi has a 3-in. safety valve. What force is exerted on the valve disk?

A The area of the valve is $0.7854 \times 3 \times 3 = 7.0686$ in.^{2} Force on the valve is then $250 \times 7.0686 = 1767.15$ lb.   *Ans.*

Q What are the requirements for setting the popping pressure of safety valves when there is more than one valve?

A The ASME code says: "One or more safety valves on the boiler proper shall be set to or below the maximum allowable working pressure. Remaining valves may be set within a range of 3 percent above the maximum allowable working pressure, but the range of setting of all the valves on a boiler shall not exceed 10 percent of the highest pressure to which any valve is set."

Q What care must you give to safety valves?

A (1) Prevent leakage in your safety valves. (2) Correct lifting and blowback pressure reseating without chattering or sizzling. (3) Make periodic trials to determine whether your safety valves will function properly. (4) Examine your valves visually to see that there has been no tampering or visual distress.

Q How many safety valves are required for each boiler?

A Each boiler should have at least one safety valve, and if it has more than 500 ft^2 of water-heating surface or the generating capacity exceeds 4000 lb/hr, it should have two or more safety valves. See ASME code.

Q Two boilers evaporate the same amount of water per hour. One operates at 300 psi, the other at 30 psi. Can both boilers have the same-size safety valve?

A Both boilers may have the same-capacity valves, but they must be of different sizes. See ASME code.

Q Should the safety valve on a superheater be set at a higher or a lower pressure than the steam-drum safety valve? Why?

A The superheater valve must be set for lower pressure. The reason for this is that the superheater must have steam flow to prevent burning out.

Q Upon checking the boiler you notice that the steam gage registers higher than the safety-valve popping pressure. What should you do?
A Try the hand release or the lifting lever to see if the valve will open. If it does and resets properly, check the steam gage with a calibrated or test gage. If the second gage indicates that the first gage is correct, the valve must be reset. If the first gage is in error and the valve lifts and resets properly, the gage should be recalibrated. Never operate a boiler having faulty safety valves or gages.

Q How can you tell if the safety valve is really large enough for your boiler? Quote the ASME code on this as closely as you can.
A The ASME code says: "Safety-valve capacity for each boiler shall be such that the safety valve or valves will discharge all of the steam that can be generated by the boiler without allowing the pressure to rise more than 6 percent above the maximum allowable working pressure.

"If the highest pressure at which any valve is set is less than the maximum allowable working pressure, the safety-valve capacity shall be such that the pressure cannot increase more than 6 percent above the maximum allowable working pressure. If the highest pressure at which any valve is set is less than the maximum allowable working pressure, the safety-valve capacity shall be such that the pressure cannot increase more than 6 percent above this highest set pressure."

All this means that if the steam stop valves are closed and the boiler is fired at the maximum rate, the pressure will not exceed 106 percent of the least-set valve or maximum safe working pressure of the boiler (whichever is least).

NOTE: Protect the superheater and the economizers because this is a no-flow condition. See ASME code for more information.

Q How is the discharge capacity—i.e., the diameter and the lift of spring-loaded safety valves—computed?
A The computation is made by multiplying the discharge area of the circumference by the lift of the valve:

$D \times 3.1416 \times L$

Discharge capacity is based on the formula for weight of steam as follows:

For 45° bevel seats, $W = 110 \times P \times D \times L$
For flat seats, $W = 155 \times P \times D \times L$
For seats of any angle, the sine of the seat angle is used.
$A = 3.1416 \times D \times L \times$ sine
$W = P \times A \times 50$

$$D = \frac{W}{3.1416 \times L \times P \times 50}$$

where W = weight of steam, lb/hr
P = absolute pressure gage + 14.7 atmosphere
A = area of valve opening, in.^{2}
D = diameter of valve, in.
L = lift of valve, in.

See ASME code, Appendix.

Q Give the formula for finding the capacity of a safety valve based on the maximum amount of fuel that can be burned.

A $W = \dfrac{C \times H \times 0.75}{1100}$

where W = weight of steam, lb/hr
C = total amount of fuel burned at maximum load
H = heat (Btu content) in unit of fuel, Btu/lb, or Btu/ft^3

Q A boiler at times of maximum forcing uses 2150 lb of coal per hr or 12,100 Btu/lb. Boiler pressure is 225 psi. Are two 3½-in. 45° bevel-seat safety valves with 0.11-in. lift sufficient? Use formula for safety-valve capacity.

A $W = \dfrac{C \times H \times 0.75}{1100}$

where W = weight of steam, lb/hr
$C = 2150$
$H = 12,100$
$C \times H = 2150 \times 12,100 = 26,015,000$
$26,015,000 \times 0.75 = 19,511,250$
$19,511,250 \div 1100 = 17,737.5$ lb/hr

The discharge of a 3½-in. valve with 0.11-in. lift with 45° seat is calculated as follows:

$W = 110 \times P \times D \times L$
$P = 225 + 14.7 = 239.7$ abs
$D = 3½$ in.
$L = 0.11$
$W = 110 \times 239.7 \times 3.5 \times 0.12 = 11,074.14$ lb/hr   *Ans.*

This is more than required.

Q Two 4-in. flat-seat safety valves have the same geometrical shape. One is for 250-psi service, the other for 50-psi service. Lift is 0.250 in. What is the capacity in pounds per hour of each?
A For the 250-psi valve (250 psi + 14.7 = 264.7 abs):

$W = 155 \times P \times D \times L$
$\quad = 155 \times 264.7 \times 4 \times 0.250$
$\quad = 41,028 \text{ lb/hr}$

For the 50-psi valve (50 + 14.7 = 64.7 abs):

$W = 155 \times 64.7 \times 4 \times 0.250$
$\quad = 10,028.5 \text{ lb/hr} \qquad Ans.$

Q What is a thermal-actuated safety valve?
A It is a pressure-actuated safety valve that combines with a thermostatic spindle which can trigger the valve. These valves are used on some heating boilers and also on some hot-water heaters for protection against low-water explosion.

Q Why do some engineers remove the safety valves and use blank flanges for 150 percent hydrostatic tests?
A This practice is common because gagging a valve is apt to bend the spindle. Common causes are (1)setting up too hard on the clamp and (2) loading the entire length of the stem, instead of only the bottom half from the spring stepdown.

When a hydrostatic test is applied, a further load is placed on the stem, so it may bend permanently.

Q What would happen to a safety valve if it didn't have enough body and atmospheric pipe drainage?
A See Fig. 2-22. The valve would load up with water and sediment if

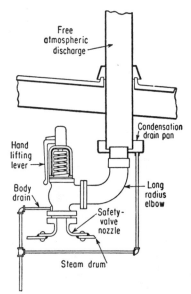

FIG. 2-22.   Correct drainage is most important for a safety valve.

the body drain were plugged. Upon opening, an explosive-like slug of water would be fired out of the valve. Sediment would interfere with the opening or the reseating of the valve.

Atmospheric pipe drainage prevents a column of water from building up over the valve disk and thus increasing the popping pressure. Again, a slug effect would occur if the pipe filled with water.

CAST-IRON BOILERS

Q Describe the cast-iron (ci) sectional boiler.

A Figure 2-23 shows a ci boiler, which is akin to the water-tube type,

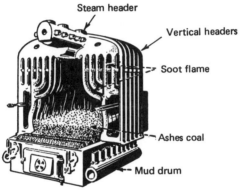

FIG. 2-23. Cast-iron sectional boiler has water inside of vertical cast-iron sections, which are connected to cast-iron header.

because water is inside the vertical cast sections. But pressure is limited to 15 psi. Sections are assembled to each other with tapered push nipples and are held secure with tie rods. Cast iron is highly corrosion-resistant, and three basic types of ci boilers are built today: (1) sectional (horizontal), (2) sectional (vertical), and (3) round, where a firepot (furnace) section has a base and crown sheet and a top, known as the dome. The round ci boiler is often fired with wall-flame rotary oil burners or gas, while the sectional units are suitable for all fuels. The ASME code requires a low-water fuel cutoff on a ci boiler, which must be located so that it automatically cuts off the fuel supply when the water level drops to the lowest safe waterline.

Q What are the most frequent failures occurring in a ci boiler?

A Usually cracks develop in a section or sections, and steam and water escape. Like all boilers under pressure, ci boilers also explode, but in these designs, the cast-iron fragments into small pieces, while a steel boiler rips and tears. All boiler explosions are dangerous to life and property; so the operator must always be alert and know the boiler and how to prevent failures.

ELECTRIC BOILERS

Q What is an electric boiler?
A Electric boilers can be divided into two basic types: (1) In one type the horizontal heating elements (electrodes) remain constantly submerged in water, as in Fig. 2-24a. These elements do not depend on conductivity

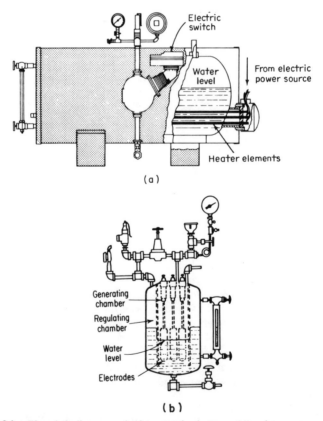

FIG. 2-24.   Electric boilers come in these two basic types: (a) resistance-type electric steam generator, and (b) electrode-type electric steam generator. In b, if water uncovers electrodes, unit stops steaming.

or resistance of water for heating and steam generation. (2) In the other type water is heated and converted into steam by a set of electrodes located vertically in a central generating chamber (Fig. 2-24b). The water level recedes as the demand for steam decreases, so that at "no load," the electrodes are entirely uncovered, and thus there is no consumption of electricity.

Q Are low-water controls required in electric boilers?

A Low-water level and pressure controls are required for boilers designed as in Fig. 2-24a, but not for the second type, as in Fig. 2-24b.

REASON: Because the boiler is inoperable when the water is low or no steam is required. In the type with electrodes, to ensure that the boiler carries the proper salinity, a conductivity control is usually supplied. Salts are added (salt water is more conductive than fresh water) or blowdown is practiced, according to the condition of the water.

Basically, all electric boilers have the same efficiency, nearly 98 percent. They are popular in small plastics processing plants, in laundries, in chemical industries, in hospitals, and in cities where smoke pollution laws are strict. Capacity ranges from 60 bhp (about 2000 lb steam per/hr) to small portable units as low as 1 bhp, while steam pressures go as high as 600 psi, although 100 to 150 psi is average.

SPECIAL TYPES OF BOILERS

Q What is a once-through steam generator?

A As the name implies, feed water is pumped into one end of a continuous tube and discharged steam emerges at the other. There is no steam drum, because there is no recirculation of water. The entire process of heating, forming steam, and superheating is carried out in a single tube. Large modern boilers consist of many tubes of once-through circuits discharging into a common outlet and handle pressures either below or above the critical pressure of 3206.2 psia.

Water-steam flow is through the furnace walls, the primary horizontal superheater, and finally the first and second sections of the secondary superheater.

Q What is a supercritical-pressure steam generator?

A At the critical pressure of 3206.2 psia, steam and water coexist at the same density, being neither water nor steam. Steam is produced by heating this high-pressure mixture above its 705.4°F saturation temperature, thus producing dry superheated steam. Supercritical-pressure steam generators are of the once-through design, having no steam drum.

NOTE: In supercritical units, some of our largest utilities generate up to 5000 psi steam at the rate of 2 million lb/hr at temperatures as high as 1200°F.

Q What is a waste-heat boiler?

A These steam generators take used heat, such as the hot exhaust of gas turbines or diesel engines, to generate steam. Present-day high fuel costs make these generators popular. Many types of waste-heat boilers are used today in various installations.

SUPERHEATERS

Q What is a superheater? Name the two basic types.

A A superheater is a series of tubes that receives steam from the boiler drum, or if a reheater, from a turbine. The steam is heated above the temperature of saturated steam at boiler pressure. The two basic types are: (1) the radiant type, heated by radiant flame, and (2) the convection type, heated by hot gases.

Q Classify superheaters by arrangement within the boiler.

A (1) Overdeck superheaters are located above all the generating tubes. (2) Interdeck or interbank superheaters are placed between the tubes. (3) Intertube superheaters are fitted between the tube rows. See Fig. 2-25.

Q Describe the pendent superheater in Fig. 2-25.

A It is a nondrainable superheater; the superheater tubes are suspended below the superheater header. A pendent superheater may be a radiant, convection, or combination type.

Q What happens if feed-water temperature is increased at a steady firing rate?

A Since the boiler will generate more steam for the same fuel consumption, the superheat temperature decreases.

Q Explain why a radiant superheater has a drooping characteristic.

A As load is increased, more steam flows through the superheater. Since the superheater is in the hottest zone to begin with, there is little additional radiation effect, and steam temperature decreases.

Q Explain why a convection-type superheater has a rising characteristic.

A As load is increased, the firing rate is increased and more hot gases flow through the boiler. The zones closest to the furnace take on more heat. Even though more steam flows through the superheater, there are more hot gases to heat this steam. This causes the temperature to rise.

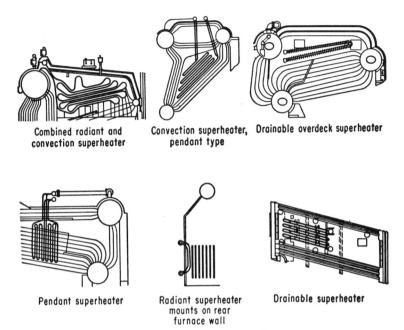

Combined radiant and convection superheater

Convection superheater, pendant type

Drainable overdeck superheater

Pendant superheater

Radiant superheater mounts on rear furnace wall

Drainable superheater

FIG. 2-25.   Some of the more common superheaters used in modern boilers.

Q   What is a combined superheater?
A   Both radiant and convection principles are used in a combined super-heater. It is usually installed behind two or three rows of screening tubes. By combining, a nearly flat curve characteristic of temperature can be achieved over a wide range of load and firing rates.

Q   Are superheaters made of ordinary boiler-tube steel?
A   Sometimes, but not always. At high temperature the metal must be of special alloys to withstand the severe service. Extra rolling of alloy-steel tubes is needed because of the toughness of the steel. Welding is often used to seal the alloy tubes to the header.

Q   Why does superheat temperature increase on combined-type super-heaters when there is excess air?
A   Less steam is generated (see CO_2 flue-gas analysis); therefore, the superheater has comparatively more heat available for each pound of steam generated. Sometimes white smoke is formed between the tubes, reflecting the radiation to the back of the superheater and increasing the steam temperature.

Q   Under what conditions might steam be generated in a superheater?

A This depends on the quality of the steam at the superheater inlet. All the moisture is evaporated to steam if there is superheat. It can be inferred that some evaporation does take place. Flooding the superheaters also causes evaporation to take place on lighting off.

Q Why were some older superheaters flooded?
A Some older designs deliberately had water added to the superheater on starting up a cold boiler. The evaporation kept the superheater tubes cool. But the added scale did great harm to the tubes. Flooding frequently caused far more trouble than it prevented.

Q What is superheater protection steam?
A Steam from another boiler is bled into a superheater to protect it when the boiler is lighted off. Superheated steam is sent to the exhaust system, or to feed heaters, until the boiler generates enough steam to establish its own flow.

Q What causes scale to form in superheaters?
A Since there is some moisture in steam from carry-over, each particle of water carries the same proportion of solids as does the boiler water. These solids encrust the superheater with scale. The scale must be removed by either mechanical or chemical cleaning.

Q Does a superheater outlet have the same pressure as the boiler drum?
A No. The many bends of the superheater have considerable friction, causing a big drop in pressure. As load increases, the pressure drop becomes greater.

Q How are superheater tubes supported?
A Pendent-type superheater tubes are suspended from the inlet and outlet headers and need a minimum of support. Horizontal types need support by means of lugs, support sheets or baffles, clevis rods, etc. Weight is carried by the generating tubes or by the boiler structure. The big problem, since superheaters are often in high-temperature zones, is the selection of alloys that can withstand heat. The supports act as spacers as well as supports. The system must be flexible enough to allow for heat expansion.

Q What is an attemperator or a desuperheater?
A Any device or scheme that lowers the superheat temperature of a gas or steam that passes through it is a desuperheater.

  EXAMPLE: In the indirect type, a series of tubes are submerged in a steam drum to desuperheat some of the superheated steam for auxiliary plant use. With this there is no mixing of mediums. In the direct type, also called a spray-type desuperheater, cooling water is sprayed into a chamber and mixes with the flowing superheated steam.

Q Why are pilot-operated safety valves used on superheaters?
A The superheater safety valve must be the first safety valve to open and the last to close so that flow through the superheater is not interrupted. If flow is stopped, the metal will overheat. Because a 10 percent pressure drop in the superheater is not unusual, an ordinary safety valve at the superheater outlet cannot be used. A small, conventional spring-loaded valve is mounted on the steam drum. When this valve lifts, it actuates a pressure-control system that triggers off the superheater valve. There are several systems of pilot operation, but all work by the same principle. When the drum valve (pilot valve) closes, a pressure equilibrium is set up, reseating the superheater outlet valve. Drum pressure, not superheater pressure, controls the superheater safety valve.

ECONOMIZERS

Q What is an economizer and why is it used?
A An economizer (Fig. 2-26) is a waste-heat recovery device that heats incoming feed water by exit flue gas. Remember that for each 10 to 11°F of heat recovery, there is about a 1 percent gain in plant efficiency. Most boilers are designed to have the exit gas 100°F above saturated-steam temperature at the last row of tubes. As the pressure increases, the designed exit-gas temperature also increases. This heat would be wasted if the economizer didn't recover much of it.

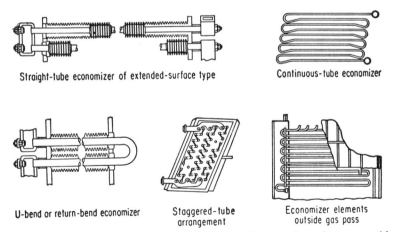

Straight-tube economizer of extended-surface type   Continuous-tube economizer

U-bend or return-bend economizer   Staggered-tube arrangement   Economizer elements outside gas pass

FIG. 2-26. Economizers come in many designs; they heat incoming water with flue gases.

Q What will be the savings in percentage if the feed water is raised from 140 to 190°F in a boiler operating at 75 psi?
A This savings would be worked out in the following way: 75 + 14.7 = 89.7 psia (use 90). The total heat of steam at 90 psi is 1185.3 (use steam table). The formula for the percent of saving is:

$$P = \frac{t_2 - t_1}{H - q} \times 100$$

Where P = percent savings due to feed heating
  t_2 = highest feed-water heating temperature
  t_1 = lowest feed-water heating tempeature
  H = total heat of steam, Btu
  q = heat of lowest feed temperature, Btu

then $t_2 = 190°F$
  $t_1 = 140°F$
  $H = 1185.3$
  $q = 140 - 32 = 108$

Working out the formula, we get

$$P = \frac{190 - 140}{1185.3 - 108} \times 100 = 4.64 \text{ percent} \qquad Ans.$$

Q What happens to economizers if the feed temperature is too low? Explain.
A Corrosion will result from too low a feed temperature. The temperature should be high enough to prevent condensation and acid attack on the gas side of the tubes. Dew-point temperature and acidity are in direct proportion to the sulfur content of the fuel and the method of firing.

Q Is steam generated in economizers?
A Yes. In some designs using little makeup feed water it is practical to design the economizer to furnish steam.

Q What are the corrosion problems of economizers?
A Cold water causes condensation on the gas side. Condensation, in turn, causes acid attack and soot deposits. Scale forms at increased heat and tends to deposit in economizers. Oxygen attack is also great unless thoroughly deaerated water is used, and pH of 8 or more is necessary to prevent such attack. It is therefore important to use a scale-free, hot, deaerated feed water.

Q What is the counterflow principle as used in an economizer?
A Flue-gas flow and feed-water flow are in opposite directions. This allows the hottest gases to heat the hottest water.

Q Why are economizer tubes often fitted with gill rings, fingers, fins, etc.?

A Economizer tubes have extended surfaces to gain efficient heat transfer. Since gas carries little heat as compared with water, the solution is to extend the gas-heating surface in proportion to the water-heating surface.

Q How are economizer tubes cleaned?

A Economizer tubes are cleaned internally by mechanical or chemical cleaners, or externally by water washing or mechanical cleaning, including soot blowers.

Q Are safety valves required on economizers?

A If there is a shutoff valve between the generating section of the boiler and the economizer, a safety valve is required. The reason for this is that water will be trapped between the feed check-and-stop valve and the shutoff valve. When the boiler is being fired, this water will expand and cause a rupture.

AIR PREHEATERS

Q What is an preheater?

A An air preheater heats combustion air. It generally utilizes flue-gas heat, but some types get their heat from the steam coils or other waste heat in the plant.

Q What are the two basic types of air preheaters?

A See Fig. 2-27. The two basic types are (1) the recuperative, and (2) the regenerative type.

Q How does a recuperative air preheater work?

A It transfers heat through a metal wall, from one medium to another. As a shell-and-tube device, hot gas passes through one side and incoming combustion air passes on the other side. These units are called "plate-and-tube" or "plate" types.

Q How does a regenerative air preheater work?

A It works by an indirect process of heating an intermediate material and then heating the air from this material. The Ljungstrom rotary type is an example of a regenerative design. Here, a steel cage revolves, the exit gas heats the inside of the cage, and the cage rotates and brings the heated metal plates into the path of the inlet air.

Q What efficiency gain can air preheaters give?

A Since there is a gain of 1 percent in boiler efficiency for each 35 to

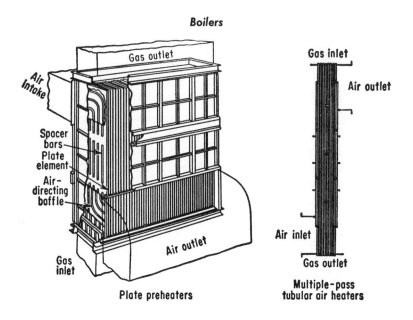

Plate preheaters

Multiple-pass
tubular air heaters

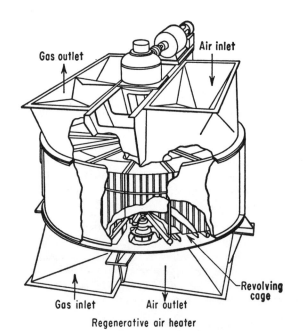

Regenerative air heater

FIG. 2-27. Air preheaters heat incoming air for combustion with used stack gases.

40°F drop in flue gas, there is a considerable gain. High-combustion-air heat is also used to dry the fuel in coal-pulverizing units.

Q What temperature consideration is there in designing air preheaters?
A The consideration here is that the stack gases are not cooled to the dew point, which would cause excessive corrosion. See the section Economizers (above).

SAFETY VALVES

Q What fittings and trim are needed for the safe operation of a boiler?
A Figure 2-28 lists names and functions.

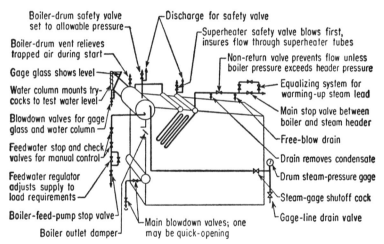

FIG. 2-28. Most fired boilers, regardless of type, should have fittings shown here for safe operation.

Q Name the basic safety valves.
A The three basic designs are called (1) dead-weight, (2) ball-and-lever, (3) spring-loaded, and (4) thermal.

Q What are the three most common types of blowback adjustments for modern safety valves (blowdown)?
A Three common types of blowback adjustments are (1) the huddling-chamber, (2) the nozzle-reaction, and (3) the jet-flow.

Q What are the limitations on safety valve blowdown?

A To close without chattering, blowdown should not be (1) more than 4 percent of the set pressure or (2) less than 2 psi in any case. For valves up to and including 300 psi, the blowdown should not be less than 2 percent of the set pressure.

Q How many adjustments are provided for safety valves?

A Two. The first is for the release of pressure, which is a function of compressing the spring. The second is for the adjustment of the blowback, which causes the valve to close at a lower pressure than when it opened.

Q Explain how the huddling-chamber safety valve works.

A See Fig. 2-29. In this valve, the static pressure acting on the disk area

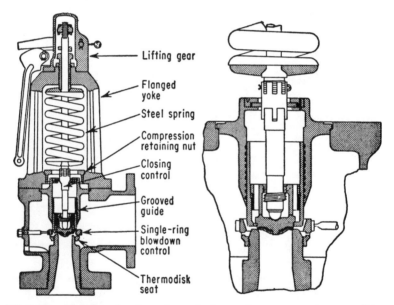

Lifting gear

Flanged yoke

Steel spring

Compression retaining nut

Closing control

Grooved guide

Single-ring blowdown control

Thermodisk seat

FIG. 2-29. Huddling-chamber safety valve has static pressure acting on a disk to cause initial opening.

causes the initial opening. As the valve pops, steam space within the huddling chamber, between the seat and the blowdown ring, fills with steam and builds up more pressure on the roof of the disk holder. This temporary pressure increases the upward thrust against the spring, causing the disk and its holder to lift to full pop opening. After a predetermined pressure drop (blowdown), the valve closes with a positive action by trapping steam on the top of the disk holder.

Blowdown is adjusted by either raising or lowering the blowdown adjusting ring. Raising this ring increases blowdown and lowering it decreases blowdown. The capacity figure, which is stamped on the nameplate and required by the ASME code for steam, is 90 percent of the valve's actual capacity when flowing at 3 percent overpressure.

The huddling-chamber safety valve is intended primarily for steam service but will work with gases. However, it is rarely used for the latter service, as it doesn't have a closed bonnet. It is never used for liquid service.

For precision-closing control, the valve is placed in the open position and discharging steam is bled into a chamber through three bleed holes in the roof of the disk holder. Likewise, the spindle overlap rises to a predetermined position above the floating washer. The area between the floating washer and the spindle is thereby increased by the difference in the two spindle diameters.

Under this condition, steam in the chamber escapes to the atmosphere through the secondary area formed by the floating washer and the spindle. At the instant of closing, the spindle overlap is adjusted to move down into the floating washer, thereby effectively reducing the escape of steam from the chamber.

The resulting momentary pressure buildup in the chamber produces a downward thrust in the direction of the spring loading. The combined thrust of pressure and spring loading results in a tight, positive precision closing without wire drawing or dragging of the seat surfaces.

Q Explain how the nozzle-reaction safety valve works.
A See Fig. 2-30. In the opening phase of any safety valve, the spring force that keeps the valve closed must be counteracted by a greater force on the pressure side. But, as the disk rises, the spring load increases from compression. Therefore, the total force needed to obtain a high lift must also increase. In the nozzle-reaction valve, energy is produced by a conical baffle skirting the disk. This baffle causes lifting energy to be greatest at or near the end of the lift, thus giving full-bore lifts, or greater at low accumulations.

Opening. As the valve opens, steam escaping across the seats impinges upon the conical baffle and acts against the additional in-between areas. This large increase in the head-pressure area produces a sudden upward force, creating "pop" action. The initial force is increased by a dynamic jet force from the nozzle that impinges against the face of the disk. This force increases rapidly with the flow.

The disk rises quickly from these forces, which constantly gain momentum with increased velocity and the help of the enlarging baffle area. Thus, the port (orifice) closes almost instantly.

Boilers

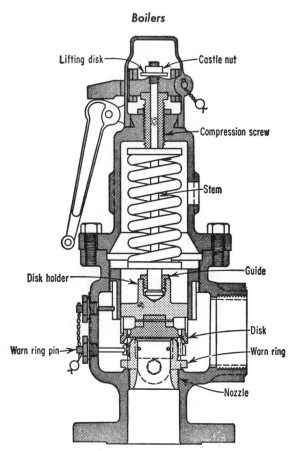

FIG. 2-30. Nozzle-reaction safety valve has opening energy produced by conical baffle skirting the disk.

At the same time, another lifting energy source comes into play. A conical baffle turns the fluid jet downward, giving a thrust effect, as in the case of steam-turbine blades. This reactive force takes up the rising compression load of the spring. At common overpressures of 3 percent for steam, 5 percent for gases, and 25 percent for liquids, the reactive force quickly lifts the disk to the full-open position.

Closing. The pressure drop in the system is usually gradual, with the disk falling slowly at first. The jet action tends to hold the disk open much longer than is needed. In this valve a new control principle comes into play. As the disk falls in response to the system's pressure drop to about 75 percent of the full-open position, the ports begin to vent the pressure under the baffle. This cancels part of the reactive force that holds the valve open. At the same time, by decreasing the pressure under the baffle, the baffle area is constantly reduced. Finally, total upstream forces become less than the spring force, and the disk closes sharply from about 50 percent of its rated lift.

Q Explain how a jet-flow safety valve works.

A See Fig. 2-31. The jet-flow safety valve makes use of both reaction

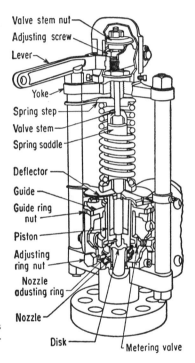

FIG. 2-31. Jet-flow safety valve makes use of both the reaction and the velocity of the escaping steam.

Labels (top to bottom, left side):
Valve stem nut
Adjusting screw
Lever
Yoke
Spring step
Valve stem
Spring saddle
Deflector
Guide
Guide ring nut
Piston
Adjusting ring nut
Nozzle adusting ring
Nozzle
Disk
Metering valve

and velocity of the escaping steam. Static pressure on the disk overcomes the spring tension and causes steam to flow. The escaping steam strikes against the piston, is deflected downward against the nozzle ring, and discharges into the body. This reactive force lifts the disk higher, increases the area of flow, and therefore increases the velocity.

As the velocity increases, a partial steam discharge takes place through the controlled orifices in the guide assembly. Because of its confined velocity, the steam creates an upward force and lifts the valve still higher. The position of the disk at the "pop" lift is such that the area of discharge is greater than the nozzle area. The excess accumulation of pressure needed for full lift in the huddling-chamber and nozzle-reaction types is unnecessary for full capacity in the jet-flow valve.

As pressure in the boiler falls, velocity through the orifices is reduced and the disk drops momentarily to intermediate lift. After this, the diminishing reactive force controls further reseating, as in a reactive valve.

Blowdown adjustment in a jet-flow valve is made by an entirely different method from that in other valves. The blowdown is controlled by the location of the exhaust-belt reaction lip, which is varied by adjusting the guide vertically.

Adjusting. If the valve opens cleanly but does not seat sharply, the nozzle ring is too high. Lower it by removing the adjusting ring pin and turning the nozzle-adjusting ring to the left one notch at a time between trials until the valve seats sharply with a metallic thud. Adjust the ring with a screwdriver.

If blowdown is too long, the nozzle-adjusting ring is again too high and must be lowered. If the valve sounds a warning before popping, the nozzle-adjusting ring is too low and must be raised. To raise it, turn the ring to the right one notch at a time until the warning stops completely.

CAUTION: When raising the nozzle-adjusting ring, keep the boiler pressure well below the popping pressure, or gag the valve while making adjustments. To protect personnel, all safety valves should be gagged while the ring is being adjusted.

Q Explain how a superheater actuator valve and superheater safety valve work.

A See Fig. 2-32. A superheater actuator valve is built into the same body casting as the boiler steam-drum pilot valve. When this valve opens, the superheater safety valve lifts. The rocker arm, working from the valve stem of the drum pilot valve, rests against a ball that contacts with the valve stem of the actuator valve. When the steam-drum pilot valve lifts, this rocker arm causes the actuator valve to open. The outlet side of the actuator valve is connected to the atmosphere through an open drain, and the inlet side is connected to the superheater safety valve.

The superheater safety valve consists of a piston-type disk with no stem. It is held in line by its cylinder. The bottom of the valve disk is connected to the atmosphere through escape piping. Steam enters from the superheater outlet elbow and gathers around the valve disk, above the seat. A feathering ring is also machined into this disk. The only pressure working above the valve disk is the superheater pressure against the feathering ring.

Small ports are provided for the steam from the superheater safety-valve disk. This space is connected to the inlet side of the actuator valve

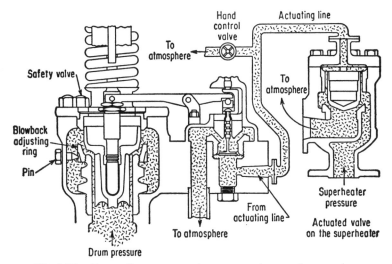

FIG. 2-32.   Drum pilot actuator valve protects the superheater tubes.

by a pipe. The system is closed by shutting off the actuator valve. Steam bleeding through the ports causes pressure to build up in the system until it equals that in the superheater outlet elbow. This pressure on the top of the valve disk holds the valve closed. Then, if the superheater actuator valve is opened by allowing the drum safety valve to lift, the enclosed space is opened to the atmosphere and the pressure bleeds off.

When the pressure has been bled off, the only remaining force on the superheater valve disk is that working against the feathering ring. This is enough (with no pressure above the superheater disk) to force the super-heater valve to open and to allow the steam pressure to be relieved from the superheater.

When the actuator valve closes, because of the reseating of the drum pilot valve, the pressure bleeds rapidly into the space above the superheater valve disk. This builds up pressure on the top of the disk and thereby closes the valve. When the drum pilot valve lifts from excessive pressure in the steam drum, the superheater safety valve must also lift; when the drum pilot valve reseats, the superheater safety valve must also reseat.

Operation. The superheater outlet safety valve doesn't lift from excessive pressure in the superheater. It lifts only when excessive pressure is reached in the steam drum; so the outlet valve is needed to protect the superheater. Should a drum safety valve lift without the superheater safety valve also lifting, pressure in the steam drum might blow down without blowing down the pressure in the superheater. This would destroy the pressure drop through the superheater. Steam flow through the superheater would then cease.

In extreme cases, the steam might even flow backward from the super-heater into the drum. In any case, the superheater would overheat, since there would be insufficient flow of steam through it to carry away the heat transmitted from the fire. The blowback ring is kept from vibrating out of position by a pin that pierces the body of the valve. The tip of the pin extends between the notches of the blowback ring and prevents it from turning. Make sure that the tip doesn't press against a raised edge. When the pin enters fairly deeply into a notch, it can be screwed home by hand.

Levers, attached to the yokes of three-drum valves, are sometimes connected by wires to a single handwheel. By turning this handwheel, you can lift successively the three levers and thus open the three safety valves by hand. When the drum safety valve is lifted, the superheater safety valve will also be lifted by the actuator valve. This should always be done in lighting off a boiler when the drum pressure is close to operating pressure.

A hand-operated valve that connects with the atmosphere leads from the actuating line between the actuator valve and superheater safety valve. By opening this valve, you can bleed the pressure from the actuating line and cause the superheater valve to lift without lifting the drum safety valve. Don't use this hand valve for testing the superheater valve. Operate it only when you must increase the steam flow through the superheater, while still maintaining operating pressure in the steam drum. This condition might occur when you must raise superheat on the boiler before placing it on the line in an emergency.

FEED-WATER REGULATORS

Q What is (1) a single-element feed-water regulator, (2) a double-element regulator, and (3) a three-element regulator?
A (1) A single-element feed-water regulator corrects from water level only. It senses that the water level is rising or falling and controls the feed accordingly. (2) A double-element regulator corrects from (a) the boiler-water level and (b) the steam flow. It senses that the steam load is changing and positions the feed valve accordingly. It is finally corrected by the water level. (3) Three or more elements may be used in a three-element regulator. For example, blowdown, or some special process that will change the boiler load radically, may be accounted for.

Q What happens to the water level in a boiler when the firing rate is increased rapidly or decreased rapidly?

A When the firing rate is increased rapidly, the boiler-water level swells because more steam bubbles form in the water as more steam is generated. When the firing rate is decreased rapidly, boiler-water level shrinks, since there are fewer bubbles of steam.

Q What happens to a single-element feed-water regulator during rapid changes of steam rates?

A During rapid changes of steam rates, the single-element feed-water regulator does the wrong thing. An increased firing rate causes swell, and the regulator shuts off the feed. Since more steam is generated, there ought to be more feed, but a single-element regulator responds to level. This is wrong. The same trouble occurs when the firing rate is decreased. The level drops, and the regulator feeds more water. Since there is less demand for steam, there ought to be less feed.

Q Describe the action of a Copes-type control valve.

A Figure 2-33 shows that the Copes-type control valve is weight-loaded;

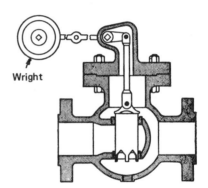

Wright

FIG. 2-33. Feed-water-regulator valve is weight-loaded.

the weight opens the valve and contraction of the element closes it. Linkage within the valve bonnet raises the piston valve, which has a ported skirt to give proportionate flow for the amount of the valve opening. In an emergency, the weighted lever can be used to open or close the valve by hand.

Q Explain how the Copes-type thermostatic feed-water regulator shown in Fig. 2-34 works.

A A long, inclined thermostatic tube, mounted rigidly in a steel frame outside the boiler drum, is connected in the same way as is a water column. The upper end is connected to the steam space and the lower end to the water space in the drum. The water level moves up and down with the drum water level. Expansion and contraction of the thermostatic tube

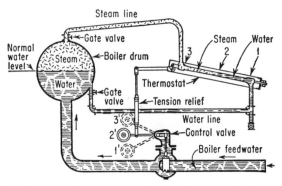

FIG. 2-34. Automatic feed-water regulator is thermostatically controlled.

depends on the proportion of steam to water in the tube. The difference between temperature of the steam and the water causes the tube to expand and contract. As the water level lowers, more steam enters the tube, causing it to expand. This movement is powerful and is magnified by a pivoted link. The enlarged movement controls the opening of the control valve. If the water level rises in the boiler and thus in the tube, the tube contracts and throttles the feed down to shutoff if necessary. Tension relief is necessary to shutoff because the force is great when the tube is cool. There is a spring-loaded device in the actuating rod that controls the valve. The thermostatic tube is always in tension, and the threaded stud at the end of the tube pulls the tube to the desired tension.

Q Sketch and describe a feed-water regulator operated by changes in vapor pressure, such as the Bailey or the Swarthout types.
A See Fig. 2-35. An inclined tube is centered with the water-gage glass on the steam drum. The water level in the drum rises and falls within the heavy middle tube. The generator consists of an internal tube, which is connected to the boiler in the same way as is a water column, and a finned tube which is connected to the control-valve bellows (diaphragm) by a copper tube.

The copper tube and the outer tube are filled with water. There is no communication between the inner space of the finned tube and the boiler water. The external system is filled completely while cold and has atmospheric pressure while cold. When steaming, the inner tube has a proportionate amount of steam and water. The steam heat is transferred to the water in the external system of the generator. (The more steam, the more heat transferred.) As steam forms in the external generator, pressure exerts a force on the bellows and opens the feed valve. This is in proportion to the water level in the inner tube. When boiler-water level rises, there

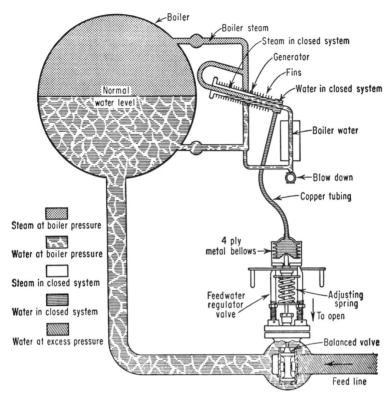

FIG. 2-35. Automatic feed-water regulator is operated by vapor pressure.

is less heat transferred, as the cool leg of water enters the inner tube of the generator.

Copper fins dissipate heat to the atmosphere and the pressure drops in the external circuit. A spring in the control valve closes the valve. The pressure in the generating system is counter to the force of the spring at the high-to-low level in the boiler. The spring will close the valve if the generator leaks or if the bellows rupture. An emergency control is furnished to jack the valve open quickly by hand.

Q Show a scheme for two-element feed-water regulation.

A See Fig. 2-36. A Copes Flowmatic regulator is shown, but the same principle is used for control by steam flow in other manufacturers' regulators. The actuating element is a neoprene diaphragm which measures the rate of steam flow by taking the pressure drop through the superheater.

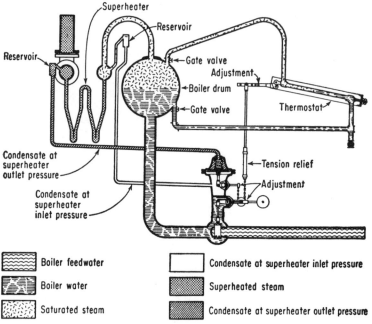

Boiler feedwater

Boiler water

Saturated steam

Condensate at superheater inlet pressure

Superheated steam

Condensate at superheater outlet pressure

FIG. 2-36.   Two-element feed-water regulator has a direct-operated valve.

High pressure is applied to one side of the diaphragm and is counteracted by the lower pressure, plus a compression spring on the opposite side. A constant-level reservoir fills up with condensate so that steam cannot enter the piping to the diaphragm. Changes in the pressure drop through the superheater causes the diaphragm to move. This movement is transmitted by levers and by a rotating shaft to an external lever. As steam flow increases, pressure drop is greater and the lever moves down. As load decreases, steam flow is less, pressure drop is less, and the lever moves up. A thermostat operates in response to changes in the water level, as was previously explained. The movement of the levers is coordinated between the two control units—flow and thermostatic—to transmit the opening of the valve. Usually, the valve is adjusted to respond to steam-flow change as the more sensitive element, in order to control the swell and the shrink fault of the single-element control. The water-level element is less sensitive and acts to correct the water level as a follow-up on the steam flow. These devices are furnished in relay-operated versions by Copes and other manufacturers for remote operation, or to incorporate some other operating feature.

COMMON VALVES

Q Describe the swing-check valve shown in Fig. 2-37.

A A swing-check valve has a flap that is swung into the line of flow to permit flow in one direction only. The flow overcomes gravity; but when it ceases, the flap drops and the reverse flow shuts the valve.

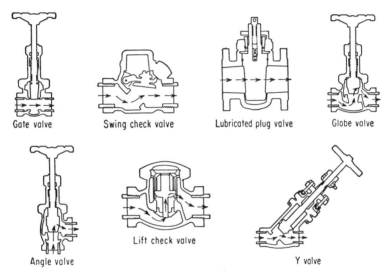

Gate valve   Swing check valve   Lubricated plug valve   Globe valve

Angle valve   Lift check valve   Y valve

FIG. 2-37.   Common valves used in power plants are important; each has its place.

Q Describe a lift-check valve.

A See Fig. 2-37. A lift-check valve has a body and seat similar to a globe valve. A vertical valve with guides is lifted by flow through the valve. Gravity drops the valve when there is no flow and stops the reverse flow.

Q Describe a Y valve.

A See Fig. 2-37. A Y valve is similar to a globe valve except that the seat is at an angle to allow a more direct flow pattern. Flow is almost straight, making the valve well suited for blowdown service.

Q Describe a gate valve.

A See Fig. 2-37. A gate valve has a wedge-shaped gate which closes against two faces on either side. These valves provide straight-through flow with little pressure drop. Gate valves are not suited for throttling service.

Q Should steam pass over or under the disk of a globe valve?

A Steam should pass under the disk for uninterrupted flow and over the disk for interrupted flow. However, there are exceptions to this rule.

Q What is an O S & Y valve?

A An outside-screw-and-yoke (O S & Y) valve has a threaded spindle that rises beyond the yoke or wheel to show whether the valve is open or closed (Fig. 2-38).

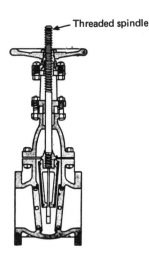

Threaded spindle

FIG. 2-38. Raised spindle of outside screw and yoke (O S & Y) type indicates valve is open.

Q What is a nonreturn valve? Explain the ASME code regulation that governs its use.

A A nonreturn valve is a form of a check valve and is used on steam outlets. The ASME code prefers that a nonreturn valve be used as one of the two valves that connects with a steam main which is common to another boiler. Two O S & Y valves can be used for this purpose, but the preferred setup uses one O S & Y valve with a nonreturn valve placed closest to the boiler. A drain with a visible discharge must be installed so that the operator manipulating the valves can see the discharge.

AUTOMATIC REGULATING VALVES

Q How does a constant-pressure regulating valve work?

A See Fig. 2-39. To control discharge pressure of steam pumps, a constant-pressure pump governor is placed in the steam line of the pump. A change in the pump's capacity requirement is reflected by a momentary change in discharge pressure. This change in discharge pressure adjusts

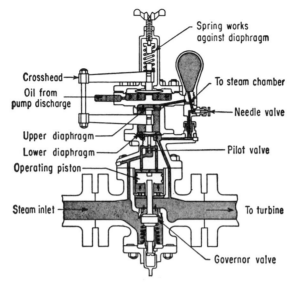

FIG. 2-39.   Constant-pressure regulating valve is used for oil-pump turbines.

a pilot valve in the governor and makes a corresponding change in the opening of the governor valve to restore the pressure to normal.

Discharge pressure in the governor is led through an actuating line to the space below a single diaphragm in the top of the unit. Pump discharge pressure exerts an upward force on the diaphragm. To balance this force, a spring above the diaphragm exerts its force on the diaphragm through a crosshead and mushroom (Fig. 2-39). It is the balance of these two forces that controls the operation of the governor. When the spring force is greater than the upward force, the diaphragm displaces downward. This makes the upper crosshead move downward, carrying the connecting rod and lower crosshead with it. This movement also causes the lower crosshead to press against the lower diaphragm through the mushroom, moving it downward.

Since the lower diaphragm is in contact with the pilot-valve stem, this causes the pilot valve to open. The pilot valve is always supplied with steam from the inlet side of the governor valve. When the valve is opened, steam passes through two ports to the top of the operating piston. Steam pressure on the top of the operating piston forces it downward, opening the governor valve, which in turn admits steam to increase the speed of the pump. This speed increase is reflected by an increased discharge pressure from the pump. When the pressure increases enough to make the upward force on the upper diaphragm greater than the spring force, the diaphragm displaces upward. This reduces the pilot-valve opening and allows the spring to close the governor valve against the reduced pressure on the operating piston.

Oscillations are so rapid that they produce a constant discharge pressure, if all elements are properly adjusted. An increasing spring tension takes a higher discharge pressure to restore the balance on the diaphragm; lowering the tension lowers the discharge pressure.

To reduce the hunt, an intermediate diaphragm bears against the top of the lower yoke through another mushroom. Steam is led from the governor-valve outlet to the bottom of the lower diaphragm and through a needle valve to the top of the intermediate diaphragm. Thus, movement of the lower yoke, either up or down, is opposed by a force of steam pressure on the intermediate or lower diaphragm. This reduces the amplitude of the pilot-valve oscillations, thus reducing the governor hunt. The needle valve regulates the amount of steam going to the intermediate diaphragm.

If the governor is not properly adjusted, it will have excessive hunt and regulation. Experience shows that good operation is obtained by opening the needle valve from one-half to three-fourths of one turn. But you should experiment in order to come up with the best adjustment for your particular governor. The steam chamber continuously provides proper pressure to the intermediate diaphragm, although the space above it may be filled with water from condensation.

Q Describe the constant-pressure pump governor on a turbine-driven boiler-feed pump.

A See Fig. 2-40. The purpose of a governor is to vary the steam pressure to the turbine. This varies the speed of the turbine and the pump, and holds the pressure on the pump constant under varying capacity needs. Changes in capacity cause corresponding changes in the opening of the governor valve. With the pump operating at a specified speed, an increase in capacity causes a decrease in discharge pressure; a decrease in capacity causes an increase in discharge pressure. These changes in discharge pressure actuate the governor valve.

Figure 2-40 shows the water inlet at the upper left. This inlet leads into the space between the two diaphragms and is connected with the actuating line to the pump discharge. Therefore, it carries the discharge pressure of the pump. The two diaphragms are connected as shown. The area of the upper diaphragm is greater than the area of the lower diaphragm. Water discharge pressure of the pump exerts against both diaphragms. But, since the area of the upper diaphragm is greater, the total force exerted is in the upward direction. Opposing this upward force is the spring pressing down on the upper diaphragm. The balance between

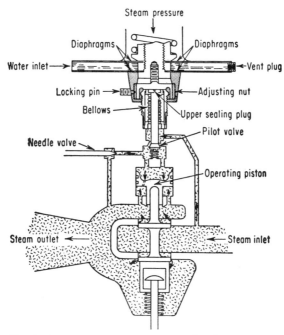

FIG. 2-40.   Constant-pressure pump governor varies the steam pressure to the turbine.

this spring force and the upward force on the diaphragms causes the governor valve to operate.

When the spring force is greater than the upward force, the diaphragms are forced downward. An adjusting nut, threaded to the diaphragm assembly, transmits the downward movement to an upper sealing plug which is in contact with the pilot-valve stem. This action pushes the pilot valve open. The sketch shows a port leading from the inlet of the steam governor valve to the pilot valve. When the pilot valve is opened, steam passes to the top of the opening piston, forces the operating piston downward, and opens the governor valve. This admits more steam to the pump turbine, causing it to speed up and increase the discharge pressure.

An increase in discharge pressure causes the upward force on the diaphragms to become greater than the spring force, moving the diaphragms upward. This raises the adjusting nut, releases pressure on the upper sealing plug, and allows the pilot valve to close. A reduction in the steam flow to the operating piston reduces the pressure in the piston as steam passes through a hole in the piston. See Fig. 2-40.

This reduction in pressure allows the governor valve to be closed by the base of the spring valve. These changes in the position of the valve occur so fast that the valve maintains an apparently fixed opening. Thus, it delivers an apparently constant steam pressure to the turbine, which is reflected in what appears to be a constant discharge pressure. A change in the discharge pressure causes a change in capacity. An increase in capacity (with its consequent decrease in pressure) causes the governor valve to adjust to a wider opening. A decrease in capacity reduces the opening. Changes in the volume of steam flowing to the turbine speed up or slow down the pump to restore pressure to normal at the new capacity.

The major governor adjustment is to the spring, which works in opposition to the force of water pressure on the diaphragms. Increasing the tension of the spring, which requires an increase in water pressure to balance it, causes the discharge pressure of the pump to increase. Conversely, reducing the spring tension causes a reduction in discharge pressure. Adjustment is made with an adjusting screw at the top of the valve. Turning this nut raises or lowers the diaphragm assembly to its most favorable position. You can adjust either diaphragm with the adjusting spring backed off fully or with the unit at full operating pressure.

The needle valve shown is for the third governor adjustment. This valve allows steam to bleed from the outlet side of the pilot valve into the governor-valve discharge. Bleeding away this small amount of steam minimizes the steam-pressure changes on the operating piston. It also reduces the amplitude of the governor-valve oscillations, preventing the governor from hunting or delivering a varying pressure. Needle-valve adjustment is usually from one-half to three-quarters of a turn open. But again, you should experiment to determine the best adjustment for your needs.

A stem at the base of the governor valve, working in a yoke on the governor valve, can be used to pull the valve open manually. By so doing, you can bypass the governor and control the pump speed with the throttle valve. Always warm up the pump with the governor bypassed and put the governor into operation when the pump is ready to go on the line.

BOILER BLOWDOWN VALVES AND TANKS

Q   Name five types of boiler blowdown valves and give their recommended pressures.
A   See Fig. 2-41.
1. An angle blowdown valve is used for services up to 200 psi. Its seating surface is on the outside of the seating ring to protect the seat from the cutting effect of the water, scale, and sediment that pass through.
2. A plug cock accommodates pressures up to 200 psi. The plug is

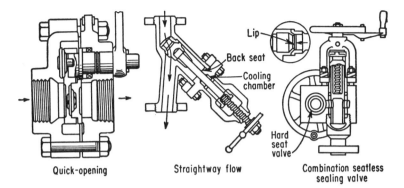

FIG. 2-41.   Boiler blowdown valves come in various designs.

pressure grease-lubricated through the stem so that the tapered cock turns easily. Since the valve opens and closes by turning, the seating surfaces stay clean.

3. A quick-opening valve is usually used for pressures up to 600 psi. A spring, actuated by a lever for quick opening, holds the disk against the sealing surface of the valve. The disk rotates, keeping the joints tight.

4. A straightway flow valve is used for the highest pressures. It has backseating, which allows you to pack the stuffing box under full pressure with the valve open. Straight passage through the valve prevents scale from clogging or eroding the seat or disk.

5. A combination seatless valve is mounted in the same steel block with a hardseat valve. A seatless valve is used for pressures up to 2500 psi. A lip protects the seat from wire drawing. This ported valve needs no seat.

Q   What does the ASME code say about blowoff valves?

A   See Fig. 2-42. The ASME code for power boilers requires all boilers

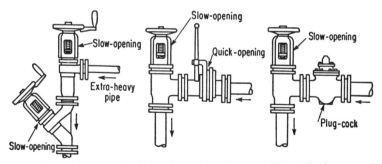

FIG. 2-42.   ASME boiler code requires the use of blowoff valves.

carrying over 100 psi working pressure, except traction or portable boilers, to have two blowoff valves on each blowoff pipe. These may be two slow-opening valves, one slow-opening and one quick-opening valve, or one slow-opening valve and one plug clock. Traction and portable boilers must have one slow- or one quick-opening blowoff valve. On all types of boilers use only extra-heavy pipe to connect the blowoff valves.

Q How would you blow down a boiler?
A See Fig. 2-43. First, have enough water in the gage glass so that you

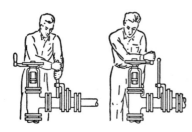

FIG. 2-43. Blowdown is accomplished by opening first the quick-opening and then the slow-opening valve.

can blow down at least a few inches without the water getting out of sight. Then, open the quick-opening valve slowly. Next, open the slow-opening valve slowly enough to prevent shock, but fast enough so that the seat won't wiredraw. To stop blowing, close the slow-opening valve quickly and then the fast-opening valve. Never jam the valve if it won't close. Take a few fast turns to open and clear the valve; then close it again slowly. Jamming the seat against scale wiredraws the seat.

CAUTION: When blowing down, try not to take your hands off an open blowdown valve, or your eyes off the gage glass.

Q What is the difference between a pressure-reducing and a pressure-regulating valve?
A There is very little difference between these two valves. A pressure-reducing valve reduces pressure by throttling the flow of gas, steam, or liquid. A pressure-regulating valve delivers a constant lower pressure.

Q How are boiler blowdown valves opened and closed?
A Where there is a cock or a quick-closing valve and a slow-opening valve, the inner valve (closest to boiler) is the cock or quick-opening valve. Open the quick-closing valve first and close it last. For tandem steel valves, arranged with the pressure under the seat of the inner valve and over the seat of the outer valve, the inner valve is opened first and closed last.

Q What is meant by the flow characteristic of a valve? Explain a gate and a globe valve used for throttling service.

A See Fig. 2-44. In using a valve for throttling service, a given opening will allow a given flow through the valve. The chart shows the percent of flow as contrasted with the percent of opening of a typical globe valve. A gate valve is not suited to throttling service because severe erosion takes place at the bottom of the gate and at the mating seats. Since the

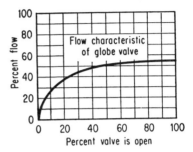

FIG. 2-44. Flow characteristic shows flow through valve at percent of opening.

gate is tapered, it fits loosely and chatters against the seats, damaging the fitted surfaces. But, a gate valve offers little resistance to flow when it is wide open, and it seats tight enough in the closed position.

A globe valve is the best choice for throttling service. Two modifications make it even better: (1) A needle valve is used to meter very small quantities and to give fine regulation. But never use a needle valve to give full flow because the seat is too restrictive. (2) A bell-ported valve is a piston-type valve with a skirt having bell-shaped holes in the cross section. The idea is that the valve throttles a given amount for a given movement of the valve spindle. This makes control by governors, motors, and proportioning linkages possible.

Q Suppose that you find a globe valve in an interrupted flow service with pressure over the disk. Would you remedy this condition by reversing the valve?

A No. It is best to have pressure over the disk where interrupted flow is needed. For uninterrupted flow, as on a boiler-feed line, pressure should be under the disk. See ASME code.

Q What are the minimum- and maximum-size vents for blowdown tanks and what are the purpose and operation of a blowdown tank?

A See Fig. 2-45. Vents must be 1 in. minimum and 2½ in. maximum.

The blowdown tank prevents much damage. Blowing directly to the sewer instead of to the tank blows the hot water and steam into other sewer connections. The blowdown tank is always full of water. When hot water blows in, the cooler water in the bottom overflows to the sewer as it is displaced. A large open vent prevents back pressure, and a small

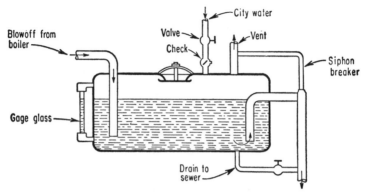

FIG. 2-45.   Blowdown tanks must be piped correctly to prevent explosion.

siphon breaker keeps the tank from siphoning dry during blowdown. A manhole is provided for internal inspection, while a gage glass is used to make sure the tank doesn't run dry. City water, with a check to prevent reverse flow, is used to charge the tank if the water has drained out.

STEAM TRAPS AND EXPANSION JOINTS

Q   Where are steam traps installed?
A   Steam traps are used (1) before the prime movers, (2) at the upward bends or on the vertical headers of steam lines, (3) at the ends of the runs, (4) wherever drainage is needed, and (5) at the exhaust or the return end of heat exchangers (radiators, for example).

Q   How does a float steam trap work?
A   See Fig. 2-46. A metallic float is linked to a valve. When the float rises, the valve opens to discharge condensate. When the float drops, the valve closes. A petcock in the top of the valve must be opened at

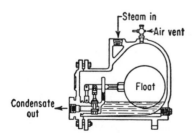

FIG. 2-46.   Float steam trap vents the air, lets only condensate return.

times to vent off the air. To make this valve fully automatic, a thermostatic trap is added at the outlet to vent the air. Such valves are called "float" and "thermostatic."

Q How is the thermostatic trap constructed?

A A metal bellows is filled with a volatile liquid. When steam heats the bellows, the liquid expands, forcing the valve to its seat. The presence of cooler condensate causes the bellows to compress and open the valve, which allows a slight vaccum in the bellows. This causes atmospheric pressure to further contract the bellows (Fig. 2-47).

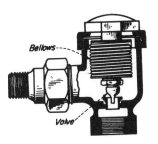

FIG. 2-47. Thermostatic trap has bellows filled with volatile liquid.

Q Describe the operation of a tilting trap.

A A tilting trap has two valves. The one next to the atmosphere allows the body of the trap to fill. When the body is filled, gravity tilts the trap and closes the vent. The steam valve opens and the pressure inside the trap is equalized with the boiler pressure. Gravity allows condensate to flow into the boiler. These traps usually receive condensate from one or more float or thermostatic traps. Tilting traps must be mounted higher than the boiler waterline. Some have been designed to operate an injector and are used for feeding boilers. But for this service they are not as common as electric pumps.

Q Describe the operation of an upright bucket-type trap.

A See Fig. 2-48. Here an upright bucket is used in place of a float. When

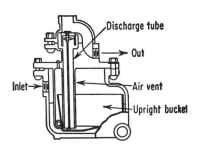

FIG. 2-48. Upright bucket trap has an air vent inside the discharge tube.

the trap is full of air, the bucket is down and the valve is open, allowing air to escape on first start-up. The inflow of condensate partly fills the body and flows into the bucket, causing it to sink and open the valve. When steam enters, condensate is forced up through the tube and out through the valve until the bucket empties and rises, shutting off the valve. After that, the valve won't release air unless it is fitted either with an air vent, as shown, or with a thermostatic air vent that works automatically.

Q How does an inverted bucket trap work?

A See Fig. 2-49. An inverted bucket is linked to a discharge valve in

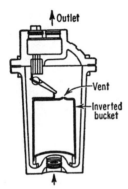

FIG. 2-49. Inverted bucket trap vents the air each time the outlet valve opens.

the top of the trap body. A small air vent is in the top of the bucket. An entering mixture of water, steam, and air is separated. Air enters the bucket, leaks out the vent, and gathers in the top of the trap. The condensate seals the bucket, which when full of steam rises and closes the valve. When it is full of condensate, the bucket sinks and opens the valve to repeat the cycle. If more air discharge is needed, a thermostatic vent is used in the top of the trap to pass air and to seal against steam.

Q How does an impulse trap work?

A See Fig. 2-50. Two orifices in a hollow valve are balanced by the pressure in an upper cylinder. This pressure is controlled by a little condensate that leaks through the tandem orifices. A change in the condensate temperature causes a change in the condensate pressure, which acts to open the valve.

Q Name and sketch at least three methods of providing for expansion in steam pipes.

A See Fig. 2-51. (1) Expansion loops, in which a horseshoe bend allows springing motion to absorb expansion. (2) Corrugated expansion joints, which provide an accordionlike action to absorb expansion. (3) Slip joints,

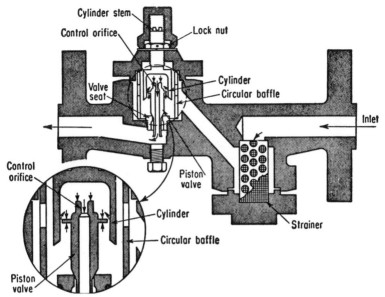

FIG. 2-50.   Impulse trap is simple and compact; it has only one moving part.

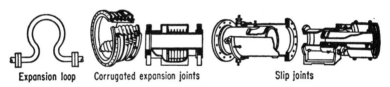

FIG. 2-51.   Expansion joints allow the piping to expand and contract.

which provide a telescoping action of two tubes. These joints require packings and some have piston rings as well as jam-type packing in the stuffing boxes. (4) Swing joints, which combine an expansion loop at a right angle to the flow with a packed or closely fitted joint.

FANS AND BLOWERS

Q   What is the difference between a fan, a blower, and a compressor?
A   There is no definite difference. However, a very-low-pressure machine is often called a "fan." A medium-pressure machine is usually called a "blower." When a machine delivers in pounds per square inch, it is generally regarded as a compressor.

Q Study Fig. 2-52 and then describe (1) static pressure, (2) velocity pressure, and (3) total pressure.

A (1) Static pressure is exerted against the walls as steam pressure against a boiler drum, so that the manometer tube is at right angles. It is this pressure that overcomes the resistance of fire beds or filters. (2) Velocity

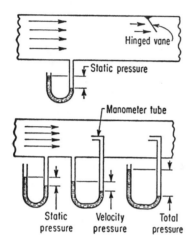

FIG. 2-52. Fan pressure can be measured with manometers shown here.

pressure is over and above static pressure. It is caused by the collision of flowing gases with some object. Think of the hinged vane (shown in the figure). With no flow, the vane is vertical; with fast flow, the vane is blown back. (3) Total pressure is the combination of static pressure and velocity pressure. It can be measured by a manometer that is parallel to and facing the direction of flow.

Q What are the basic types of fans?

A See Fig. 2-53. Two basic types of fans are (1) the centrifugal (radial) flow and (2) the axial flow.

Q Explain the principle of centrifugal fans. How are they used?

A See Fig. 2-54. Centrifugal fans work by the same principle as do centrifugal pumps. Air enters the eye of the fan wheel and is whirled out of the blades into a scroll (volute), or through a diffuser that converts velocity to pressure. Flow is radial to the drive shaft. Centrifugal fans are used for various purposes involving up to 25 in. of water pressure and a wide range of volumes.

Q Describe the blades in a centrifugal fan.

A Centrifugal-fan blades may be either fabricated of sheet metal or cast. They may be straight, or tipped forward or backward.

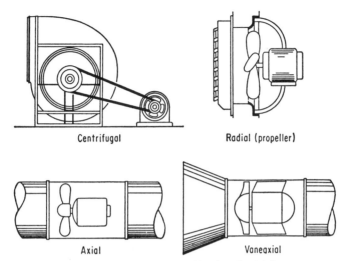

Centrifugal   Radial (propeller)

Axial   Vaneaxial

FIG. 2-53.   Basic fan types are the centrifugal and axial flow.

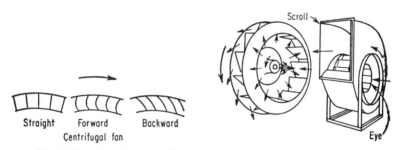

Straight   Forward   Backward
         Centrifugal fan

FIG. 2-54.   Centrifugal-fan blades are straight, forward, or backward.

Q What is a propeller fan?

A A propeller fan consists of a variety of blade shapes, ranging from disk types to elaborately shaped "bent" airplane propellers. Designed for low pressures and a wide range of volumes, it is used mostly as a ventilating fan.

Q What is a tube axial fan?

A It is a propeller fan mounted in a cylindrical shell. The blades may be either disk or airfoil types. Tube axial fans are used at medium pressures for $\frac{1}{4}$- to $2\frac{1}{2}$-in. water static and over a wide volume range.

Q What is a vane axial fan?

A It is a propeller fan set in a cylindrical tube. The tube has airguide vanes either before or behind the propeller to take helical spin out of the air flow. The propellers are usually the airfoil type, having specially shaped, short, stubby blades. Vane axial fans are used up to 60 in. of water pressure, and over a wide range of volumes.

Q What is fan volume?
A Fan volume is the number of cubic feet per minute (ft³/min) expressed at fan-outlet conditions.

Q What is fan total pressure?
A It is the rise in pressure from the fan inlet to the fan outlet.

Q Where are fan static pressure and velocity pressure measured?
A Both static pressure and velocity pressure are averaged at the outlet of the fan.

Q What is the power output of a fan?
A Power output is the horsepower computed from volume and total pressure at the outlet of the fan. Output is divided by power input to get fan efficiency.

Q What is the relationship of horsepower to speed?
A Horsepower changes directly as the cube of the speed. To double the speed, you must have a motor eight times as big.

Q What is the relationship of pressure to speed?
A Pressure changes directly as the square of the speed of the fan. By doubling the speed, you get four times more pressure.

Q What is the relationship of volume to speed?
A Volume changes directly in proportion to the speed of the fan. To get more flow, speed up the fan.

Q Which type of blading (straight, front- or back-tipped) is best for a centrifugal fan used in an air conditioner?
A Back-tipped blading is your best bet because it is the least noisy at its maximum efficiency.

Q What is a lobe blower or Root's blower?
A A lobe blower works on the same principle as a rotary lobe pump. It may have two or more shafts cut with two or more lobes on each rotor. External gears time the lobes for positive rotation. Lobe blowers are used on air conveyors, gas pumps, or as scavengers or superchargers on internal-combustion engines.

Q What is a heat flinger?
A A heat flinger is a small auxiliary fan mounted firmly on a shaft. The flinger protects the bearings from heat by dissipating heat from the main fan service.

Q What does NAFM mean?

A NAFM stands for the National Association of Fan Manufacturers, an organization that sets standards for the industry.

Q What should operating engineers know about standard arrangements for fan drives, rotation, discharge, inlet, or motors?

A The NAFM has a set of code designations to describe the many possibilities of each in relation to the other. Consult their chart when ordering parts or when describing a given installation.

Q In purchasing a fan, what information must you know besides price and space limitations?

A You must know (1) the volume (ft³/min) of air or gas to be moved, (2) the temperature and density of air or gas, (3) the static pressure at fan inlet, (4) the static pressure needed at fan outlet, (5) the driver type, (6) how it is to operate, and (7) what service is required of it each year. Consult with the manufacturer on details.

Q Will the same motor and fan handle the same volume of either air or flue gas under standard conditions?

A No. The standard density of flue gas is heavier than air. (Air = 0.075 lb/ft³; flue gas = 0.078 lb/ft³.) Both densities are standard at 70°F and at sea level (29.92 in. Hg).

Q How are fans controlled?

A Fans are controlled by (1) varying the speed of the drive unit (turbine, motor fluid drive, variable-pitch sheaves); (2) dampers, to throttle the discharge; (3) inlet vanes, which can be adjusted to spin the air entering the fan; (4) variable-pitch blades on the vane axial fans; and (5) spillover, which diverts part of the discharge to the atmosphere or back to the suction of the fan.

Q What is the effect of closing the intake of a large forced-draft blower (especially a centrifugal type)?

A Closing the intake removes the load from the blower and causes the motor to race. Be sure that some important service isn't affected by closing the air intakes. If so, you might have a flareback in the boiler room.

Q How often should the rotating parts of high-speed blowers be painted?

A The rotating parts of high-speed blowers should seldom, if ever, be painted. Paint destroys the balance of these parts. If you do paint, you must balance the fan again dynamically.

Q High-speed propellers are often damaged by foreign objects passing through the blower. What repairs are needed when (1) blades are bent; (2) blades are cut or nicked, damage being more than one-third the distance from the hub to the tip; (3) blades are cut or nicked less than one-third of the distance from the hub to the tip; and (4) the balance weights are loosened?

A (1) If blades are bent, straighten them and use sheet-metal templates to secure their true curve and shape. Some blowers are tinned; so a new metal coating may be needed if heat is used to straighten the blades. Unless cracking is suspected, a 50 percent overspeed test is unnecessary. (2) If damage is more than one-third of the distance from the hub to the tip, straighten as in case 1; then weld cuts or nicks at the edges of the blades. But be sure to file and scrape the blades carefully. Welding is limited to small cuts and nicks less than 1 in. long. While an overspeed test isn't needed, any doubt will be resolved by such a test. (3) If damage is less than one-third of the distance from the hub to the tip, repair as in cases 1 and 2. This condition, however, is far more serious, and an overspeed test should be made. You may have to limit speed to 85 percent after repair, or until the manufacturer or a competent inspection proves that the propeller is safe and reliable. (4) Since the balance weights are welded in most cases, and balanced dynamically, this is a serious repair. An overspeed test of 50 percent is usual. Weights should never be attached by drilling, nor should any holes be drilled in or near the hub, because hub stresses are large at high speed. Call in the manufacturer, for special equipment may be needed.

Q What defects (wear and tear) are apt to occur with turboblower units?
A Defects in turboblowers are apt to be (1) pitting of ball bearings and races, (2) excessive bearing clearance, (3) misalignment of steam nozzles or rotors, (4) oil relief valve and lubricating system laden with dirt, (5) worn parts in oil pump, (6) leaky packings, (7) erosion and corrosion of all parts, and (8) fatigue failure from vibration.

Q Why is the slightest vibration investigated in large high-speed blowers?
A If vibration is not remedied, the high-speed blower will be ruined and may blow apart.

Q List the causes of blower vibration.
A Blowers may vibrate because (1) the main bearings are worn or poorly lubricated, (2) the thrust bearing is worn, (3) parts rub or bind, (4) balance is disturbed, (5) the shaft is misaligned, (6) the shaft is bent, or (7) the foundation is loosened.

Q Why do motors used to drive induced-draft fans need a reserve capacity?
A At times these motors burn up because the density of very cold air in the stack at start-up is much greater than the density of air at normal temperature. The increased weight of the air then overloads the motor

in the fan. Even when operating below nameplate rating, these motors often fail. The only answer is to size draft-fan motors with enough reserve capacity.

REFRACTORIES

Q Why are refractories used?
A Refractories are used to (1) line furnaces with a material that will withstand high heat, (2) confine heat and thus accelerate combustion, (3) guide the flow of combustion gases to desired paths through the boiler, and (4) shield the boiler parts from flame impingement and radiant heat.

Q What are the two basic types of mortar?
A Air set and heat set are the two basic types of mortar. Air set acts like portland cement—it sets up hard by itself after drying for an average period. Heat set, as its name implies, sets with heat and forms a ceramic bond at a high temperature.

Q Are insulating firebrick and refractory firebrick the same thing?
A No. Insulating brick is lightweight and never faces the fire. It is used behind a firebrick facing to insulate the heat.

Q What is a castable refractory?
A A castable refractory is similar to portland cement in that it is air-setting. It is poured into place like construction concrete.

Q What is a plastic refractory? How does it set?
A See Fig. 2-55. A plastic refractory is a mudlike substance that serves the same purpose as firebrick. It is used for patching and to shape burner cones and peepholes.

The plastic refractory is rammed into place either by hand or by air

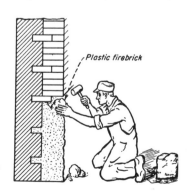

Plastic firebrick

FIG. 2-55. Plastic refractory can be pounded into place.

tool. It must be vented with an ice pick to allow any steam that forms inside to escape when it is heated up for the first time. Firing must be as soon as possible, since a plastic refractory sets up with a ceramic bond. Therefore, a full furnace temperature is needed.

Q   What refractory material is pounded into the stud tubes of water walls?
A   Plastic chrome ore is often pounded in with wooden mallets.

Q   What is refractory tile?
A   It is a preshaped refractory that is fired in a kiln. It is a terra-cotta material, usually provided for various segments of throat openings or for baffles.

Q   What determines the life of a refractory?
A   The following factors influence the life span of a refractory: (1) Quality—the best grade gives the longest life. (2) High temperature—the higher the furnace temperature, the shorter the life of the refractory. (3) Temperature change—frequent and rapid changes from cold to hot, too rapid changes when raising steam, rapid chilling by careless draft regulation when shutting down, all tend to crack the brick. (4) Vibration—poor air-oil rates or allowing the boiler to pant destroys the walls. Furnace explosions do it instantly. (5) Expansion—not enough space for expansion causes the wall to bulge when heated. (6) Slag action—elements in the fuel combine with the brick to give a fluxing action. This lowers the melting point of the refractories. (7) Careless workmanship—too thick joints, lack of bond, poor bricklaying, etc., will shorten the life of a refractory.

Q   What is spalling? Explain the various types of spalling.
A   Spalling is the failure of the brick face. Heat spalling, caused by too rapid a heat change, creates cuplike fractures or radiating cracks in the brick. Chemical spalling is caused by fuel combining with the brick elements and forming a slag. Mechanical spalling, caused by poor workmanship or lack of expansion, results in the corners of the brick cracking and chipping out.

Q   What are some important things to remember when setting up refractory walls?
A   Brickwork must be (1) mechanically strong, (2) as airtight as possible, and (3) flexible enough to permit component parts of the furnace to expand and contract with the rise and fall of temperature. Brick should be laid so that the walls can be repaired or relined as easily as possible and without weakening the wall. Dip the faces of the brick that forms the joint in mortar, and slide and tap the brick firmly into place to make a thin, tight joint. Stagger all joints to cut down on air leakage into the furnace and gas leakage out of it.

Q   What is a pyrometer cone (pyrometric cone)?

A A pyrometer cone is a small cone having a known melting temperature or softening point which is used to compare the performance of materials at high temperatures.

Q What are the trends for brickwork and refractories?

A Brickwork and refractories are being used less and lightweight materials are being used more. The old-time hrt and brick-set water-tube boilers are disappearing. Increasingly, numerous fire-tube "package boilers" and standard-sized water-tube boilers are preassembled at the boiler works as a package. Fire-tube scotch marines have refractory linings to protect the fronts and dry backs. Both water tube and fire tube now use tile openings for burners and other refractory openings. Unit-sized insulated steel casing panels allow greater accessibility for maintenance, decreasing the need for brickwork. Both flue and breeching linings utilize refractories, but newer methods are eliminating brickwork.

Q Discuss the use of refractories in salvage and destructor incinerators.

A As environmental demands increase, so will the need for refractories. The use of refractories in walls and baffles is familiar where waste materials are used to fuel steam boilers. Problems with corrosion and firing equipment are found in steam generators with or without special modifications. However, the increasing use of pyrolytic and destructor incinerators, all of which require refractory-lined chambers and gas passages, has increased the use of refractories.

Q Explain the membrane-wall construction shown in Fig. 2-56.

A In modern boilers, water- or steam-cooled tubes (water walls) are used (instead of massive brick insulation) to form membrane walls, and the basic structure of the enclosure supplies high-temperature areas of setting. Three important types of water-cooled enclosures are used: (1) membrane walls, (2) membrane walls with refractory lining, and (3) flat-stud-tube walls. Figure 2-56 shows a typical furnace wall using membrane construc-

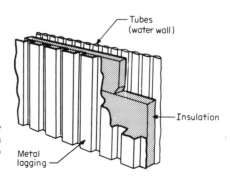

FIG. 2-56. Membrane walls are gastight; they need little insulation because water-wall tubes absorb most of the heat.

tion. These walls are water-cooled walls, constructed of bare tubes joined together by thin membrane bars. The walls thus formed are gastight and require no inner casing to contain the products of combustion. Insulation is placed on the outer side of the wall, and metal lagging protects the insulation. Membrane-wall construction is used today for the furnace walls of our largest high-pressure boilers.

WATER CONDITIONING

Q What are the basic methods of conditioning water by chemicals?

A (1) Internal treatment, where all chemical treatment is conducted inside the boiler, and (2) external treatment, where most chemical treatment is conducted outside the boiler in treatment tanks or in a specially designed softener.

Q What is carry-over?

A Carry-over means that water is entrained in the steam flow. There are two types of carry-over, priming and foaming. Priming is straight mechanical entrainment, usually caused by too rapid a firing rate or an increased change in the firing rate. A sudden load, coupled with excess dissolved and suspended solids in the boiler water, can also cause priming. The effect of fizzing ginger ale, which might be called carry-over into your nose, is something like priming.

Foaming is the formation of unbroken chains of bubbles on the surface of the boiler water. Foaming is always due to organic matter in the boiler water and in almost every case is caused by oil in the water. Foaming may be likened to beer-foam carry-over into your nose.

Q What is the theory of scale control in a boiler?

A Chemicals are used in a boiler to convert the scale-forming salts into nonadherent sludge. Sludge is then removed by blowdown. A short, successive series of bottom blows is more effective than a long blowdown period. Phosphates in an alkaline solution are often used.

Q What are the four major boiler-water control tests used by stationary engineers? State what water condition each test determines.

A See Fig. 2-57. The four major tests are for hardness, alkalinity, chlorides, and pH. (1) Hardness affects scale. (2) Alkalinity indicates required amounts of treatment chemicals (caustic soda or soda ash). (3) Chlorides control the concentration of solids and check on the surface condenser for leaks (especially where sea water is used, as in marine or tidal power plants). (4) pH (hydrogen ion) is a type of alkalinity test having no great value if proper alkalinity control is maintained.

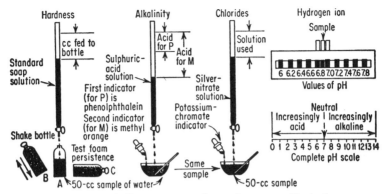

FIG. 2-57. Four major boiler-water control tests that are used by boiler operators.

Q What are the two most common systems of reporting feed-water tests? How are they converted?

A Feed-water tests are usually reported in parts per million (ppm) and in grains per gallon (gpg). To convert ppm to gpg, use the formula 17.1 ppm = 1 gpg.

NOTE: Use 20 for very quick estimates, as an error of 3 ppm is a trifle.

NOTE: The SI metric system is also used, and tests may be reported in mL/L, meaning milliliters per liter. A milliliter is 1/1000 liter (L). If you are not sure which system is being used, watch for gr, which could be either grains or grams abbreviated. The SI metric system is easier to use and more scientific than grains and gallons; ppm is the same in any system. For converting to metric units, see the conversion tables provided in Chap. 7, "Examination Calculations."

Q How is the percent rate of blowdown calculated?

A The percent rate of blowdown is calculated with the aid of a chloride test as follows: The number of concentrations of feed water to boiler water is determined by measuring the chlorides in each

$$\frac{\text{Chlorides in boiler water}}{\text{Chlorides in feed water}} = \text{number of concentrations}$$

The percentage of total blowdown (including carry-over) is calculated by

$$\frac{1}{\text{Number of concentrations}} \times 100 = \text{percent blowdown}$$

EXAMPLE: Calculate the percent blowdown, if the feed water (condensate plus makeup) contains 1.5 gpg chlorides and the boiler-water reading is 30 gpg.

$$\frac{30}{1.5} = 20 \text{ concentrations}$$

$$\frac{1}{20} \times 100 = 5 \text{ percent rate of blowdown}$$

Q Besides hardness, alkalinity, and chloride tests, what other tests are commonly used to control boiler water?
A (1) An excess-phosphate test is used to learn if phosphates are in the control range. (2) An excess-sulfate test is made to see if there is enough sulfite present to control the oxygen and if it is within the control range.

Q What is boiler scale?
A Boiler scale is made up of nonsoluble compounds—usually of calcium, magnesium, and silica. Iron and other salts, and sometimes oil, are also present in boiler scale. Hardness is almost always directly indicative of scale-forming waters.

Q What is the effect of scale in boilers?
A Scale insulates the heating surfaces and wastes fuel, since heat won't transfer through a scale barrier efficiently. This, in turn, may cause metal parts to overheat with dangerous results. Scale also slows down water circulation. It can block all flow, causing overheating of such metal parts as the boiler shells, tubes, economizers, and feed lines. Superheaters are scaled by solids in carry-over, which cause tube failure if the deposits become heavy enough.

REMEMBER: It takes very little scale to cause failure in superheaters.

Q Does boiler scale cause trouble in other parts of a plant besides boilers?
A Yes. Scale in carry-over represents all the solids in the boiler water. Solids build up in all parts of the system, causing trouble in small areas of instruments, traps, valves, condenser tubes, and in machinery. Turbine blades are especially vulnerable to scale. Deposits, especially silica scales, build up on the blades, destroying the efficiency of the machine by blocking off the nozzles and blade-passage areas. Scale also disturbs the balance of a machine.

Q Why does the hardness test indicate scale-forming conditions?
A Soap combines with calcium and magnesium in the hardness-test sample, destroying the lather-forming ability of the soap. The more soap used, the more magnesium and calcium present. These two minerals are the chief scale-forming salts.

Q Explain caustic embrittlement.

A In caustic embrittlement, cracks form along the grain boundaries of the metal in boilers. It occurs in stressed areas, such as on riveted seams and rolled-in tube ends. You also find embrittlement wherever there is (1) a strong alkaline condition with silica, (2) a stressed metal, and (3) a slight leak. A leak allows the water to evaporate and the caustic to concentrate and attack the metal.

Q What is the theory of corrosion control in a boiler?

A Chemicals are introduced to keep the water alkaline. The rate of corrosion is slow in an alkaline solution. Dissolved gases, such as oxygen, are controlled by adding chemicals to combine with the gases to form harmless compounds. Caustic soda (lye), or its close relative sodium carbonate (soda ash), is used to provide alkalinity. The sodium sulfite protects the surfaces from oxygen corrosion by combining with the oxygen.

Q How does water conditioning help control carry-over?

A Dissolved solids are controlled by frequent blowdown in order to limit the amount of salt. Chlorides are the key to the amount of solids concentrating from natural causes. Oil is removed by filters, and every precaution

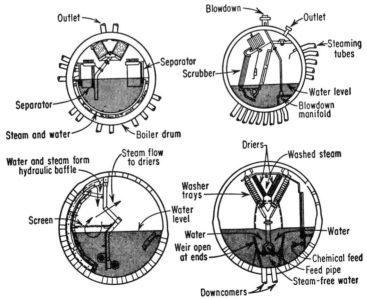

FIG. 2-58. Separators, dry pipes, and scrubbers help to keep the steam dry to machinery.

is taken to keep oil out of the boiler. Some materials, such as starch and other colloids, help to control priming. Boiler treatment is controlled by a test to economize on chemicals used and, even more important, to limit dissolved solids introduced by treatment.

Q What is a dry pipe? What is its purpose?
A A steam-collecting pipe in the top of a boiler is known as a dry pipe. It has perforations (holes) in the top section to collect steam that has the least moisture content.

Q Why are some boiler drums loaded with baffles and scrubbers of various kinds?
A See Fig. 2-58. Boiler drums have baffles and scrubbers to scrub moisture from the steam at high steaming rates. B & W boilers use a cyclone separator. Others use various types of perforated scrubbing sections.

Q By what external methods is oxygen controlled in boiler feed water?
A See Figs. 2-59 and 2-60. Since most oxygen comes from the atmosphere, the boiler feed water is kept as hot as possible to keep the oxygen from dissolving. A modern surface condenser is an effective air remover. Oxygen is further removed by forcing very hot water through the scrubbing

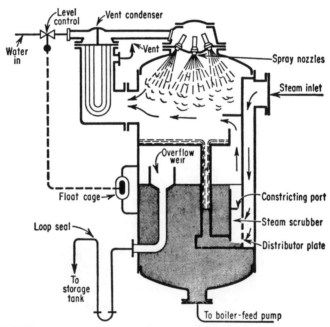

FIG. 2-59.   Entering steam removes the final oxygen by boiling the water.

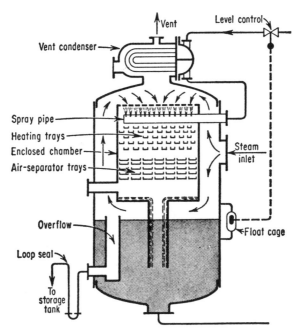

FIG. 2-60. Feed water flows over the trays that break it up into thin films.

baffles to agitate or scrub the dissolved gases loose. The steam blankets the surface of the water, keeping air from contacting it. This is done in tanks to exclude the air.

Q What is a closed heater and what is an open heater?
A A closed heater is a shell-and-tube heater that allows no mixing of water and steam. In an open heater, steam mixes directly with the water it heats.

Q What is a vent condenser?
A Here, cool condensate passes through tubes of a small condenser before going into the deaerator. Gas and steam pass through this condenser before venting to the atmosphere. The idea is to recover the water from the gas and steam and to recover the heat of this mixture.

Q What does a Winkler test represent?
A It determines the amount of dissolved oxygen in water and represents milliliters of dissolved oxygen per liter of water (mL/L).

Q When does a feed water-heater become a deaerator?

A A feed-water heater becomes a deaerator when its design and performance can reduce dissolved oxygen to 0.005 mL/L.

Q What is a tray-type deaerator?
A Here, water is led to a series of trays and falls from tray to tray. Steam blankets the trays and heats and deaerates the falling water.

Q What is a spray-type deaerator?
A Water is sprayed into a steam-filled space. The steam heats and deaerates the spray as the droplets fall. A series of scrubbing baffles with ascending steam further agitates and deaerates the falling water drops.

Q What is a flash-spray-type deaerator?
A Feed water is heated in a closed-type heater after it leaves a booster pump. This heated water is sprayed by a spring-loaded valve into a flash chamber. When pressure is reduced, the hot water flashes into steam and liberates much of the dissolved gases. The hot water is further scrubbed as it falls to the storage area of the tank. The ascending vapor and gas are further scrubbed in baffles before passing to the vent condenser.

Q What is the overall gain in plant efficiency if the feed water can be heated 10 percent higher by exhaust steam?
A The rule of thumb is an overall gain of 1 percent for each 10°F added to the feed-water temperature.

Q What is water clarification?
A See Fig. 2-61. Water clarification is the removal of suspended solids such as mud, leaf mold, slime, and algae. The usual method is to filter or settle the suspended matter. Alum (aluminum sulfate) or some other material may be added to hasten the process by coagulating in jellylike masses, thus trapping the particles as well as the enveloped masses. Since alum has chemical difficulties in acid or in too-alkaline conditions, soda ash is used with it to adjust the pH. This controls water to a pH of 5.7 to 8.0. Most city-water systems have this service, eliminating the need for plant clarification equipment when city water is used.

Q What is the cold-lime and soda softening process?
A See Fig. 2-62. It is a method of treating raw water with lime (calcium hydroxide) and soda (sodium carbonate) to reduce hardness. This system is often used with a sand filter or in a clarifier. The cold system is never a complete treatment and must be supplemented by internal water treatment.

Q What is the hot-lime and soda softening process?
A See Fig. 2-63. This process works at 212°F or higher, using steam as its heat source. Designs may vary, but all use the same basic principles. Some have a deaerating section to remove dissolved oxygen, CO_2, and

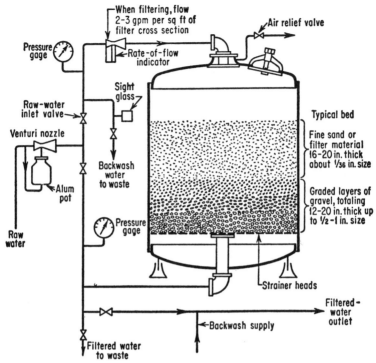

FIG. 2-61. Pressure filter with a simple alum pot is used for water clarification.

other gases. Phosphates are often added to drive hardness to zero and to provide an excess-phosphate internal treatment. Chemical reactions are very rapid and use hydrated lime (calcium hydroxide) and soda ash (sodium carbonate). This process also removes silica.

Q What is a zeolite softener?

A See Fig. 2-64. A zeolite softener is one of the many ion-exchange processes. All salts when dissolved in water tend to form electrically charged particles. Some are positive, others negative, but all are referred to as ions. Positive ions are called cations because the negative electrode (cathode) in an electrolytic solution will gather them. Negative ions are called anions since the positive electrode (anode) will attract them. A natural material called greensand or zeolite has an odd, reversible nature that takes advantage of the ions in the following way. Cations of magnesium and calcium are exchanged for sodium. All the sodium compounds are soluble in boiler water so no scale-forming salts are left. The zeolite (green-

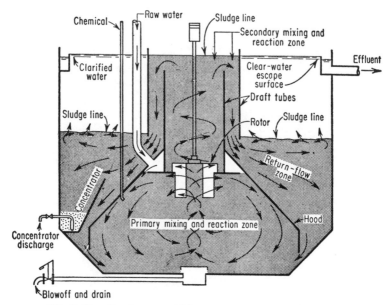

FIG. 2-62.   Continuous cold-lime softener has a sludge blanket.

sand) is recharged with a common-salt (sodium chloride) brine solution, which exchanges the accumulated calcium and magnesium for the fresh brine. Feed water passed through a modern zeolite bed can be treated by various synthetic zeolites to remove nearly all hardness. These devices are very similar in appearance to a rapid sand filter. This process is also known as a base ion exchanger or sodium zeolite.

Q   What is an H-ion (hydrogen-ion)-exchanger zeolite softener?

A   Synthetic zeolites are not affected by acid and can be regenerated with acid instead of sodium, as in the base exchanger. The process is the same, but it causes the salts to become acids since the calcium magnesium and sodium metals are traded for hydrogen ions. The resulting effluent is acid but heat will boil out some of the acid-forming gases, which are expelled to atmosphere. By mixing the effluent of a base-exchanging type (sodium zeolite) which is alkaline with the H-type acid effluent, you obtain a neutral result. The reasons for using an H-type zeolite softener are to reduce the total dissolved solids (some of the product was expelled as gas) and to remove compounds such as sodium bicarbonate that can't be removed by any other method. The equipment is the same as a base exchanger, except that rubber linings, stainless steel, or other acid-resistant materials are used.

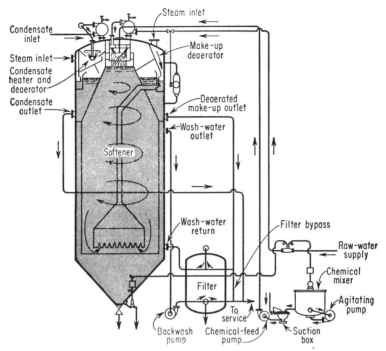

FIG. 2-63. Hot-lime soda has a deaerating section for condensate.

Q How is silica removed from water?

A See Fig. 2-65. The removal of silica is a little more complex, since it doesn't ionize strongly and will pass through ordinary types of cation and anion exchangers. Some chemicals, such as hydrofluoric acid, combine effectively with the silicas, but their use requires a great deal of skill.

Other chemicals, such as ferric sulfate or sodium aluminate, are used effectively in precipitating clarifiers, but the total solids in the effluent necessitate high blowdown rates for the boilers.

A hot-lime and soda softener is often used for silica removal, but even more effective silica-removal results are obtained with dolomitic lime, magnesium oxide, or magnesium sulfate. These are caustic-regenerated, synthetic-resin zeolites that are of a delicate nature. They won't work if strong acids are present; so they are removed in a conventional anion exchanger. In practice, raw water passes successively to a cation exchanger, anion exchanger, degasifier, and then to the silica absorber.

Q What is the electrolytic theory of corrosion?

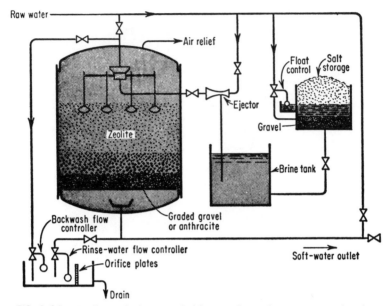

FIG. 2-64. Zeolite tanks have graded layers of gravel, quartz, or anthracite.

A Tiny electric cells are formed by dissimilar bits of metal electrically bonded (as through the steel plate) and in the presence of an electrolytic solution. They act exactly like copper-and-zinc wet cells. The metal plates out and goes into solution from the anode. The electrons flow through the metal to the cathode. The same piece of metal can have dissimilarities because of mill scale, slag, or work-stressed chemical differences. This type of corrosion shows up as pits. The best way to combat it is to use deaerated water and to maintain high alkalinity in order to slow the process.

Q Are there other forms of corrosion in boilers besides the described galvanic corrosion and rusting?
A Yes, here are some of the important ones: Fatigue corrosion: bending a piece of metal back and forth until it breaks. Impact corrosion: pounding until failure. Erosion corrosion: wearing by impact, as water impinging on piping elbows and misaligned joints. Cavitation corrosion: gas bubbles forming and then collapsing on moving metal surfaces, causing hydraulic shock, galvanic action, and erosion, and all combining to pit and wear.

Chemical and/or environmental corrosion: either chemicals in process use or natural elements attacking metal. Hydrogen damage: hydrogen forming from high temperatures breaking down water causes cracks in

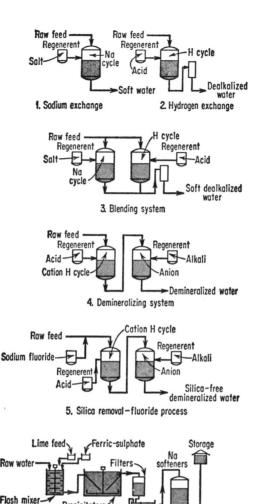

1. Sodium exchange

2. Hydrogen exchange

3. Blending system

4. Demineralizing system

5. Silica removal—fluoride process

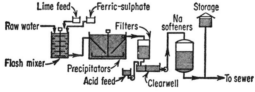

6. Silica removal—ferric-sulphate process

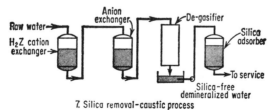

7. Silica removal—caustic process

FIG. 2-65.   Basic hookup of ion exchangers that are used to treat water.

111

metal. The hydrogen penetrates the alloys to interact with and weaken the metal. High-temperature superheaters and refinery vessels are the victims.

Q What is grooving?

A Grooving is deep guttering or lines of pits in piping caused by dissolved gases. In return lines CO_2 and oxygen are the chief offenders. Return lines are usually attacked at the bottom of the pipe. Grooving, usually appearing in the bottom of return lines, is from CO_2 and in steam lines from oxygen with CO_2. A different form of grooving occurs next to riveted seams inside a boiler. It is due to the difference in electric potential of an area, with low oxygen concentrations leaking into areas of high oxygen concentration in the electrolyte (boiler water). The different areas act like dissimilar metals. The low oxygen area acts as the anode. This subjects crevices, such as seams and joints, to corrosion attack.

Q What is cathodic protection?

A A zinc plate (galvanic protection) is usually used to maintain the effect of an electric cell. Galvanic action attacks the zinc instead of the boiler metal or heat exchanger. At times, tanks and piping are protected by a small current flowing in the most favorable direction. The material attacked is the anode and the material protected is the cathode.

> NOTE: Because the symbols used by chemists and physicists are different from those used by electrical engineers, we don't use conventional plus and minus symbols or state negative and positive here. Just remember that the piece corroded is the anode.

Q How is piping protected against corrosion?

A Feed pipes, economizers, etc., are protected against corrosion by recirculating a small quantity of boiler water to boost the alkalinity of the feed water from the feed pump to the drum. Deaerators keep the water free from oxygen. Return pipes are protected by eliminating as much CO_2 as possible. Some engineers introduce ammonia compounds (aminos) to neutralize the CO_2 in the return lines. Oxygen is kept down to a minimum in all parts of the system. Occasionally cathodic protection is needed. One final caution: Don't use or allow the piping to get in a stray electric current flow. As a conductor, the piping may be the anode, or even worse, it may be the boiler that is wasted.

Q What should you know about selecting a boiler-water treatment service?

A You should get a reliable service, including consultations with competent chemists and engineers. There are no secrets, no cure-alls, and no nostrums, for all systems and chemicals in use today are well known. Avoid fantastic gimmicks and devices, one-shot cure-alls, and secret cures.

Buy known chemicals and control the amount fed to your boilers by a chemical test. Some companies sell chemicals and service together. When this is done honestly, you can get a good system, especially in small plants, since this service is fitted to your chemical usage.

BOILER OPERATION

Q What should boiler operators check when taking charge of a steaming boiler?

A They should check the water level by blowing the water column and the steam pressure by reading the gage attached directly to the boiler. They should also read the second gage if one is installed.

Q How should you check the water level in a water column?

A There are two ways to check water level in a water column: (1) In a steaming boiler, blow the column and gage glass. Then observe if piping and connections are free. If they are, water will return quickly to steaming level. (2) In a cold boiler, examine the piping for leaks, cracks, or improper pitch. Verify the relative position of the water column to the heating surface (top of tubes or furnace) of the boiler by sighting or measuring. Then try all valves and gages to make sure they are working freely.

Q What connections are permissible on the pressure piping of a water column?

A The only permissible connections are the steam-gage connection, damper, regulator, and drains, or apparatus that doesn't allow escape of very much steam.

Q What are try cocks and how are they used?

A Try cocks are small test cocks used to verify the water level in steaming boilers. They should be opened slowly, because rushing steam, which siphons water from below the try-cock level, will give a false reading.

Q Two steam gages are exactly alike and both are deadweight-tested to read alike. One gage is mounted near the gage glass of a large boiler, the other on an instrument panel on the operating floor 20 ft below. (1) After a short run, which gage will read high and why? (2) How is this corrected?

A (1) The lowest gage will read high because condensation will collect in the vertical gage line, causing 0.433 psi for each foot of column. (2) To correct this condition, reset the lower gage to read the same as the upper gage. Recheck, as the pressure varies when firing rates change at the upper gage range.

Q Explain how to start up and cut in a boiler with other boilers on the same line. Assume that the boiler has been filled to its air cock with water.
A (1) Run the water level down to about ½ in. from the bottom of the gage glass. Leave the air vent on the steam drum open. (2) Test the main and auxiliary feed systems by using each alone. Raise the water level to about 1 in. from the bottom of the gage glass. (3) Test the water column and gage glass; then check to see that the water returns in the glass in a lively manner. (4) Test the forced-draft equipment so that it also purges the furnace. (5) Light off the burners or follow the manufacturer's instructions for firing up the boiler at a low rate. (6) Check the open drain on the superheater to make sure it is open. (7) If the economizers knock, feed them a little water from time to time. (8) Raise the steam slowly. The firing rate depends on the type of the boiler and the size and thickness of the refractories. Don't overheat superheaters; approximately 900°F is the danger point if the temperature of the gas can be measured. (9) When steam blows freely from the air vent, or at 20 psi, close the vent. (10) Check the gage glass and steam gage by blowing each drain. (11) Open the drain around the nonreturn valve or first steam stop valve, then ease off on the seat by cracking the valve. (12) When the boiler pressure is 90 percent of the line pressure, open the bypass valve around the main stop. When the line is equalized, open the stop. Open the nonreturn valve or gradually open the first stop and allow equalization. The main idea is to drain the water back to the boiler or, if trapped in the line, to force it out the drains. (13) Close the superheater drains. If the superheater temperature is controlled by dampers, adjust the dampers for the desired temperature. (14) Increase the firing rate, as the boiler is ready to take the load. (15) Test the safety valves with the hand release gear. Blow down long enough to clear the seats of scale or dirt. Check the gaskets in all jointed surfaces for leakage. Don't pull up on the joints while under steam pressure. (16) Put all automatic controls in use. Be alert for things that might go wrong.

Q How is low water handled in a steaming boiler?
A (1) Secure the fires—oil, pulverizers, gas, and blowers. To secure the more difficult fuel-bed types, cover the bed with ashes. The next best way is to cover the bed with coal and smother the heat. But, this is dangerous as fuel-bed gases can backfire if all the air is shut off. (2) Secure the feed water. Thermal shock is enough to crack overheated parts, causing disaster. (3) Secure the steam stops to conserve the water in the boiler. (4) When the boiler has cooled, open it for inspection and test hydrostatically to be sure of its condition.

Q What should the operator do if a boiler tube ruptures in a steaming boiler?

A   If a boiler tube ruptures, try to keep water in the boiler and relieve the steam pressure. Stop the combustion of fuel and secure the oil or pulverized-fuel burners. Throw ashes on coal fires. If practical, keep the blowers of oil-burning or pulverized-coal boilers running so that leaking steam blows up the stack. Continue to feed the boiler, but don't flood the plant with scalding water. Open the safety valves to reduce pressure. Continue feeding the boiler until there is no danger of damaging the metal by hot brickwork or coal fire. These precautions apply only to the boiler.

Q   Explain how you would shut down a boiler.

A   (1) Operate all soot blowers, if possible. (2) Reduce the firing rate gradually as conditions permit. (3) Use the manual feed control and be sure that water remains in sight. (4) Secure the burners, but allow the fan to run long enough to purge the furnace before securing. (5) When steam pressure is less than line pressure, the nonreturn valve will close automatically if the boiler is in line with others. If there is no nonreturn valve, close the stop as on a single boiler. If pressure rises, open the stop and try to close it again a little later. Close the spindle on the nonreturn valve. (6) If proper lines are installed, recirculate the economizers. (7) Secure all drains and open the air vent at about 5 psi. (8) If the boiler is to be emptied, wait until setting is cool enough to enter the furnace. (9) If drum is to be inspected, padlock and chain the steam stop, the blowdown, and the feed line. Keep the key in your pocket. Hang a sign outside to warn other employees that the boiler is dry and is not to be fired.

Q   Why are steam generators heated or cooled at a slow, uniform rate?

A   So as to reduce thermal stress and uneven heating of all portions of the boiler and its setting.

Q   What is the effect of having 12 percent CO_2 in flue gas as compared with 13 percent CO_2?

A   For each 1 percent increase of CO_2 the boiler has a change of 2 percent efficiency.

Q   Water causes knocks in steam lines. Explain.

A   Water in steam causes knocks because the steam is moving the water along at a great velocity, slamming it against fittings as the direction of flow changes. One fault is poor drainage. When opening the steam valves, take great care to warm the lines ahead of them slowly enough to allow any condensed steam to drain from the cold line. Design piping runs to avoid low spots and dead ends. Provide enough traps and drains. Carry-over from boilers is another cause of knocking. Slugs of water in the steam are very dangerous. The lines may rupture, or machines and fittings may be destroyed. Slugs of water in reciprocating engine cylinders are very bad, since water is noncompressible. Make sure that cylinder drains are open when warming up their steam lines.

Q What causes water hammer in a steam system? Is it hazardous?
A Water hammer is caused by steam mixing with water in a steam line. A cycle or wave is generated which may rupture fittings and lines or carry into the machines. Find the cause and eliminate it.

Q How would you handle a foaming boiler?
A (1) Reduce the firing rate. (2) Open the surface blow valve. (3) Check the water in the boiler for visual signs of oil. (4) If carry-over is endangering machinery, secure the boiler until the cause of foaming is remedied. (5) Check the feed water equipment for oil or other contamination. (6) Use the bottom blow, if only to get fresh feed into the boiler.

Q How would you handle a priming boiler?
A (1) Reduce the firing rate. (2) Open the surface blow valve. (3) If necessary, increase blowdown, giving a series of short blows at the lowest firing rate, or secure the fires. (4) Take water samples and test them for either chlorides or dissolved solids. (5) If carry-over is endangering the engines, secure the boiler until the cause of priming is remedied.

Q When you notice unusual burning of paint on boiler fronts, doors, or other external parts, what may be wrong?
A Refractory or insulation troubles, overload, or more dangerous, low water.

Q When you notice an unusual burning paint odor, especially from piping, or unusually higher steam temperatures, what may be wrong?
A Low water.

Q What should you look for on the first cold day?
A Vapor revealing steam leaks.

Q You discover any or some of these: foundation shifts, sagging settings, support movement, water not running to blowdown of opened boiler, or unexplained door misfits. What is your concern?
A The piping is overstressed; conversely, if the piping and support hangers are failing, investigate the stability of the foundations, support structure, and walls.

Q Describe the correct method of cleaning a boiler.
A Clean the fireside by removing all soot and other deposits as soon as you can safely enter it after shutdown. In fire-tube boilers, clean tubes with steam, a compressed-air lance, or hand brushes. In water-tube boilers steam-lance and hand-clean—especially the drums and headers.

Watersides are cleaned in various ways. The usual method is to scrape all visible deposits and then use a flexible tube cleaner. These tube cleaners are power-driven with air, water, or electricity. Use brushes or cutters to remove deposits. Take care not to jam the cutters into the tubes and not to cut the tubes by holding the cleaner in one position too long.

Q Why are boilers boiled out?

A There are two reasons for boiling out a boiler: (1) to remove oil, grease, or preservative coatings in a new boiler or following extensive repairs in an older boiler; also to remove oil-grease contamination and (2) to remove sludge or scale deposits.

Q How would you boil out a boiler for oil contamination?

A If no scale is present, it is safe to raise steam when boiling out. But, don't raise steam if scale is present. The scale may be dislodged and may redeposit over the hottest parts of the boiler, causing great damage. The following steps outline the proper procedure for removing oil contamination by boiling out: (1) Either remove the mica in the gage glasses or be prepared to renew it later, because strong caustic will attack the mica. (2) Wipe up as much oil as possible with rags. (3) Fill the boiler with hot water to the upper manhole in the drum or near to the manhole in shell-type boilers. (4) Use a commercial boil-out compound, or dissolve equal parts of soda ash, trisodium phosphate, and caustic soda in a bucket or barrel. Use 6 lb of the mixture for each estimated 1000 lb (125 gal) of water at normal steaming level. Wear safety goggles and protect yourself, as the caustic is dangerous. (5) Close the manhole and raise the water to its normal level. Never flood the superheaters, as they are boiled out separately. Pipe steam to them from another boiler and pump in the mixture, using temporary piping for steam and drain connections. (6) Check all firing equipment and light off fires at the minimum rate. (7) If the setting is to be fired for the first time, observe all instructions and heat gradually to get a good ceramic bond. (8) Raise the steam to one-half of its normal pressure, but don't exceed 300 psi. Keep steam pressure up for several hours. (9) Add water to a level near the top of the glass. Use surface blow to bring the level down to the surface-blow level. Secure the surface blow. Then, in turn, blow the water walls, lower headers, and mud drum. (10) Replenish the chemicals and water, using a chemical feeding system or slug through the feed pump. Continue the process for not less than 48 hr. You can keep tabs on the progress by observing the blowdown. When blowdown samples are clear and remain the same, you can assume that after 48 hr the process is complete. (11) Take care not to overheat the superheaters and economizers. Themocouples can be rigged into the superheaters of large units. Short, 5-min firing rates may be needed. It takes great skill to bring off a new boiler setting properly.

(12) Secure the fires and gradually cool the unit. Open all vents and drains. (13) Open the unit and wipe up any sludge, or hose out the finished job. (14) Inspect all parts of the setting, gas passes, and the fireside of the boiler. (15) Replace the gage-glass mica.

Q How is a boiler boiled out for scale? Does it differ from oil?
A The process for boiling out scale is the same as for oil, except that no steam is raised. The danger here is that the scale may drop or redeposit in a hot zone and cause overheating of the metal.

Q How do you inspect soot blowers?
A Soot blowers need regularly scheduled inspections. Check the tubes near the soot blowers for steam cutting or fly-ash erosion. Check blowing arcs to see that the proper zone is covered by steam jets. Examine the nozzles for impediments. If the tubes are scored from too high a blowing pressure, reduce the blowing pressure.

Check the supports, bearings, and elements for corrosions, warping, or other troubles. If cooling-air vacuum breakers are used, clean them periodically. Check the control valves, cams, and springs on both automatic and semiautomatic types. Make sure all rotating parts are OK.

Q Some gage glasses indicate a color change between the waterline in red and green, or black and white. How do they work?
A The refractive index between the water and the vapor (or air) is different. Colored glass strips or a light beam is positioned to make the gage glass act as a prism. Light is broken down to show the water in green and the vapor in red. This same refractive index shows contrasting black and white. The refractive index causes an apparent bend in a stick when it is placed in clear water. Cut-glass prisms that produce rainbow colors are another example of the refractive index.

Q Why are mica sheets inserted in flat high-pressure gage glasses?
A Mica sheets are used to protect the gage glass from the etching action of the hot alkaline boiler water. Never peel the mica bundle below its original thickness, but replace it when discolored.

Q How are boiler gaskets tightened?
A For inside seats such as a handhole or a manhole, the internal pressure tends to tighten the gaskets. Tighten with a wrench provided for this purpose and retighten again under a hydrostatic test. Never use a pipe, "persuader," or hammer on the wrench. And never tighten boiler gaskets while steam is in the boiler. Bolted flanges (on the safety valves or pipe flanges) tend to open up under pressure. Pull up before and during the hydrostatic test. Tighten up again when the steam pressure is zero, but when the joint is still hot. Pull up evenly by tightening opposite nuts all

around. While tightening, keep the drains open, if possible, as there are dangers.

Q How do you know if a cock is open or closed?

A The ASME code requires that a scored line be marked in the direction of flow on the top of the cock to denote the direction of the cock opening.

See ASME code.

Q How is a boiler chemically cleaned?

A In a chemical cleaning process, acid is used to dissolve the scale. The acid is usually inhibited; that is, it is treated to lessen its affinity for eating steel. Soaking and recirculation are two methods of chemical cleaning. In the soaking method, the boiler, economizer, and superheater are filled with an inhibited acid. Enough time is allowed for the acid to dissolve the scale. Soaking is not as effective as recirculating, but little equipment is needed to do the job. The circulating method uses pumps to circulate an inhibited acid through all parts of the boiler. Tests are made of the cleaning solution to check on the rate that is being used. When the solution shows no signs of weakening, it indicates that all the scale has been dissolved.

After either process, the boiler is rinsed and caustic sode or a soda-ash solution is circulated through it to neutralize the last trace of acid. Chemical cleaning is being used more widely in large and complicated boilers, as it is very effective and cheaper than mechanical cleaning. Some boilers are impossible to clean in any other way. Since chemical cleaning requires special skills and equipment, it is usually done by companies that specialize in this work.

CAUTION: The expelled gas may be explosive.

Q When is it impossible to lay up "wet" a boiler or system?

A Never wet-store any unit or part of the system when there is a chance that temperature will drop to the freezing point. Remember that condensation in valves, engines, and low runs of piping requires careful draining.

Q How do you lay up a boiler for a short period (60 to 90 days)?

A The main idea is to minimize corrosion of both the fireside and waterside during layup. Fill the boiler with boiled or deaerated water until water comes out of the air cock. This forces air out of the boiler. See that alkalinity of water is at least pH 10. Do this with sodium hydroxide (caustic soda) or sodium carbonate (soda ash).

Clean the fireside thoroughly so that soot and ashes on the metal surfaces cannot absorb moisture, and keep the fireside dry. Protect the boiler from extreme temperature changes to prevent condensation or freezing. Seal the furnace against drafts to further exclude moisture-laden air. This is known as the wet method. This is discussed in *Standard Plant Operators' Manual* (see the Suggested Reading section at the end of this chapter).

> WARNING: Sodium hydroxide (lye, caustic soda) is extremely hazardous to skin and eyes. Always add it and any other strong chemicals to water cautiously, protecting eyes and skin.

Q How do you lay up a boiler for a long period?
A Drain the boiler completely through the bottom blowdown valve. Then clean the fireside. Inspect the waterside carefully. Enter the steam drum or shell, using a low-voltage (6-V) electric light. Work safely, using low-voltage lights or properly grounded three-wire 110-V lamps in good repair. Use padlocks and tags on valves before entering. Be sure to ventilate before entering.

> REMEMBER: Rusting requires oxygen, and that and other gases are dangerous in boilers and tanks. Remove any visible corrosion with a scraper. Make sure the valves are tight so that no steam or water enters the boilers.

Next, dry the boiler. One way is to make a light wood fire in the furnace of the empty boiler. Use thin packing-box boards. Because there is no water in the boiler, burn only a few boards at a time to heat the metal only slightly. Another way is to use a hot-air stove. Place quicklime in a wooden tray on top of the tubes in a locomotive boiler. Use about 30 lb of lime for each 100 hp of boiler capacity. Place the lime inside the boiler as soon as it has dried out. Then close the boiler tightly.

In a multidrum boiler, place a tray of quicklime in each drum. The lime is very hygroscopic and absorbs moisture rapidly before moisture can collect on the internal surfaces. In an hrt boiler, place one tray of lime in the bottom of the shell. Close the boiler tightly. If the boiler is idled for a long period, open it every 3 months and replace damp lime. The fireside metal can also be painted or oiled to prevent further corrosion.

Q How do you remove a tube from a fire-tube boiler?
A To remove a tube from a fire-tube boiler cut off the beading with a cold chisel. Then, cut inward 4 in. beyond the tube sheet with a ripping chisel, and fold the metal inward along the rip. Repeat this process at the other end. Then, remove the tube with a chain block or other tackle.

Q How is a water tube renewed?
A To renew a water tube, split the tube ends to the tube sheet in two parallel cuts ¾ in. apart with a flat cold chisel (Fig. 2-66). Using a bar, curl the ¾-in. tongue into the tube and expose the tube seat. Insert an oyster knife (a tool ground to the same curve as the tube hole) and drive

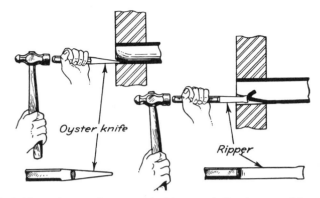

FIG. 2-66. Tubes can be removed with oyster knife, ripper, and hammer.

it in to split the tube up the tongue. Then, use a crimping tool or bar to collapse the belled end inward. Pull the tube out with a chain block.

Q How would you roll a boiler tube into place?

A See Fig. 2-67. (1) Polish the ends of the tube with an abrasive cloth and wire brush, and clean with kerosene. (2) Polish the tube hole with a dulled reamer, abrasive cloth, wire brush, and kerosene. (3) If the tube has been cut to the proper length, slide it into place with the ends polished. Allow ⅜ in. of extra metal on each end for beading. (4) At the other end, tap a soft wedge of brass between the tube and the tube sheet to hold the tube in place. Adjust the tube roller to extend inside the tube (even with the inside of the tube sheet). (5) Roll until tiny flakes of scale start popping off the tube sheet next to the tube. Scale loosens from the tube sheet as it expands. Stop rolling at this point. Overrolling is very harmful.

Q Can cutting torches be used to remove tubes?

FIG. 2-67. Tube is rolled until tiny flakes of scale pop off tube sheet.

A Yes, but only by very skilled and qualified persons. See *Standard Plant Operators' Manual* for detailed how-to-illustrations.

Q In a complete retubing, why is it necessary to keep a few scattered tubes in place?

A To maintain the space relationship of the tube sheets or headers. After a number of new tubes are installed, the old tubes are removed.

Q If radial stays are to be replaced with a larger diameter and the size calculations are approved, what is another problem?

A That the stays will pass between the tubes.

SUGGESTED READING

Elonka, Stephen M., and Anthony L. Kohan: *Standard Boiler Operators' Questions and Answers,* McGraw-Hill Book Company, New York, 1969.

Elonka, Stephen M.: *Standard Plant Operators' Manual,* 3d ed., McGraw-Hill Book Company, New York, 1980.

Elonka, Stephen M.: *Standard Basic Math and Applied Plant Calculations,* McGraw-Hill Book Company, New York, 1978.

Higgins, Alex, and Stephen M. Elonka: *Boiler Room Questions and Answers,* 2d ed., McGraw-Hill Book Company, New York, 1976.

3

STEAM ENGINES

Examiners continue to ask questions about steam engines; some of these engines are continued in use for special purposes and some are on standby, being pressed into service during emergencies.

EXAMPLE: During an electric power failure (with more and more likely to occur each year), a reciprocating duplex steam fuel-oil pump will keep fueling the boiler to generate steam and prevent plant freeze-up or shutdown.

Also, the basics of steam engines are carried into other reciprocating machinery as in compressors, pumps, and diesels. This chapter presents the essential information that will help you better understand other forms of reciprocating machinery and will provide enough answers for most steam-engine-license exams.

BASIC TYPES

Q   Show, by means of a sketch, the principal parts of a simple horizontal slide-valve engine.
A   See Fig. 3-1.

NOTE: Do not be surprised if an OSHA inspector requires additional safety guards on moving parts such as flywheels and belt drives.

Q   Name the function of the following, shown in Fig. 3-1: (1) crosshead;

123

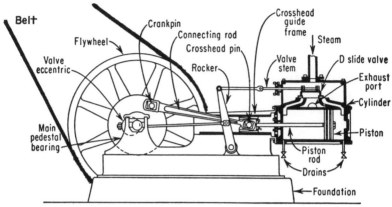

FIG. 3-1.   Basic type of steam engine has a D-type slide valve and supplies power through belting around flywheel for turning factory lineshaft.

(2) crank, crankshaft, and crankpin; (3) flywheel; (4) eccentric; and (5) slide valve.

A   (1) A crosshead translates linear motion into angular motion by oscillating about the wrist pin. (2) A crank and crankpin convert angular motion into continuous rotary motion. A crankshaft provides the bearings and accumulates the torque to drive the flywheel and load. (3) A flywheel smooths out power impulses and absorbs the load by kinetic energy. Some flywheels are used as pulleys for belt drives. (4) The eccentric provides motion at the proper time to actuate the valve gear. (5) A slide valve admits steam and conducts exhaust at the proper time.

Q   Name and describe the sequence of events during the stroke of a steam engine.

A   The stroke sequence of a steam engine is as follows: (1) Admission—the steam port is uncovered, allowing steam to enter the cylinder. (2) Cutoff—steam valve closes, stopping the flow of steam. Steam expands and drives the piston. (3) Release—exhaust port opens and exhaust steam leaves the cylinder. (4) Compression—both the exhaust port and the steam port are closed. Some exhaust steam is trapped and compressed in the cylinder to cushion the end of the stroke.

Q   What advantages do compound engines have over simple engines?

A   See Fig. 3-2. Compound engines have (1) greater steam economy, (2) smoother operation because work is divided between two cylinders, and (3) smaller parts with less wear.

Q   What is a cross-compound engine?

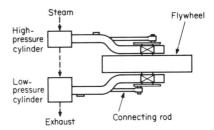

FIG. 3-2. Top view of a simple cross-compound steam engine.

A A cross-compound engine has one high- and one low-pressure cylinder set side by side, driving the same shaft. Cranks are usually set 90° apart for smoother operation.

Q What is a tandem-compound engine?
A See Fig. 3-3. A tandem-compound engine has two cylinders centered on the same piston rod. The low-pressure cylinder is placed nearest the crankshaft.

Q What is an angle-compound engine?
A See Fig. 3-4. An angle-compound engine has two cylinders set at 90°, usually to save floor space.

Q What is meant by a simple-, compound-, triple-, and quadruple-expansion engine?
A The number of times that steam expands names the engine. If steam expands once, it is a simple-expansion engine; twice, a compound unit; three times, a triple unit; four times, a quadruple unit.

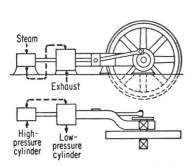

FIG. 3-3. Tandem-compound cylinder arrangement of high- and low-pressure cylinder.

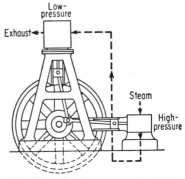

FIG. 3-4. Angle-compound cylinder arrangement used in larger engines.

Q What is the order of steam expansion in a triple-expansion engine?
A Steam is expanded three times in a triple-expansion engine: first, in the smallest, or high-pressure, cylinder; second, in the larger, or intermediate-pressure, cylinder; third, in the largest, or low-pressure, cylinder.

NOTE: Sometimes two low-pressure cylinders are used to reduce the size of one larger high-pressure cylinder.

Q What is a uniflow engine?
A See Fig. 3-5. Steam in a uniflow engine flows in one direction only.

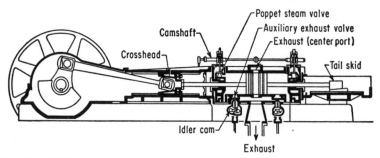

FIG. 3-5.   Uniflow steam engine has a tail skid to help reduce heavy cylinder wear.

It is admitted through a poppet valve at the head end and exhausts through a center port. The admission valves are the double-beat type and are moved by a camshaft. An exhaust port is opened and closed by the piston as it passes over a port that is cut into the cylinder walls.

Q What is a reheater or interheater on a reciprocating engine?
A A reheater consists of several copper coils placed in the receiver between the cylinders of a multiple-expansion engine. The coils carry high-pressure steam to heat the exhaust of the higher-pressure cylinder, thus gaining a thermal advantage. A reheater reduces condensation before steam is admitted into the lower-pressure cylinder.

Q What causes cylinder condensation?
A Cylinder condensation is caused by (1) alternate heating and cooling of steam between the cylinder admission and exhaust, (2) radiating to atmosphere, and (3) conduction through metal parts.

Q What is a receiver on a compound engine?
A A receiver is the space to which higher-pressure cylinders exhaust and store steam for the lower-pressure cylinders.

Q Describe and sketch a D slide valve. Label the parts.
A See Fig. 3-6.

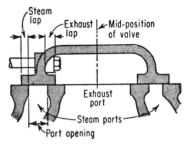

FIG. 3-6. D slide valve at midposition showing the steam and exhaust lap.

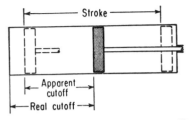

FIG. 3-7. Real and apparent cutoff.

Q What is cutoff and how is it expressed?
A Cutoff is the point at which the steam valve closes the steam port. It is expressed as a fraction of the stroke, thus one-half, three-quarters, etc. It can also be expressed as the apparent cutoff.

Q What is real cutoff?
A Real cutoff is the sum of apparent cutoff plus the percentage of clearance. See Fig. 3-7. The effect of the volumetric clearance is to store steam and to add this to the volume of steam to be expanded in the cylinder. Thus, the greater the volumetric clearance, the less the steam expands in the cylinder. This is known as the real cutoff.

Q For calculating purposes, is the real or apparent cutoff used?
A Real cutoff is used for calculating purposes because it represents the steam admitted.

EXAMPLE: Apparent cutoff is one-fifth of the stroke. Clearance volume is 5 percent of the stroke times the area of the piston (cylinder volume). So real cutoff equals 0.20 plus 0.05, or 25 percent.

Q What is meant by the term *angle of advance* on a plain D slide valve?
A See Fig. 3-8. The cam driving the valve is set 90° ahead of the crank

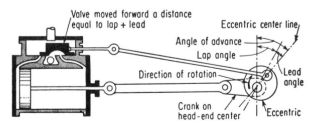

FIG. 3-8. Angle of advance, lap angle, and lead angle are important.

in the direction of rotation. But this is the zero position, and allowance must be made for the valve to be open when the piston is at the top of dead center. The lap of the valve plus the valve lead causes the cam to move forward to give this effect. The amount of cam movement is measured in degrees and is called "the angle of advance."

Q What is steam lap? How is it altered?

A Steam lap is the fraction of an inch that the edge of the valve closes off the port opening when it is in the center of its travel. It can be altered by filing metal from the end of the valve to decrease the lap. To increase the lap, you must weld metal onto the edge of the valve and machine it straight, or use a larger valve.

Q What is valve lead? How is it altered?

A Valve lead is the amount of opening in the steam port when the piston is exactly at the end of the stroke. It can be altered by adjusting the valve gear, moving the cam, or changing the length of the valve rod.

Q What is meant by throw of eccentric? What effect does it have on valve travel?

A Twice the eccentricity of a cam (or crank) is known as the throw. The throw is twice the distance from the center of the crankshaft to the center of the eccentric (cam). Valve travel is not necessarily the same as throw. But for convenience, some examiners give problems in which the valve travels the same distance as the eccentric throw. Linkage may transmit through rocker arms which often reduce the motion. In fact, it is possible to reduce the motion to zero in a reversing link, such as is used on marine engines.

Q Why is compression given to a steam engine?

A (1) To achieve quiet operation. Compressed steam cushions the moving parts when the piston reverses its travel. Without this cushion, the engine pounds and wears excessively. (2) To increase thermal efficiency. Compressed steam fills the clearance spaces before live steam is admitted to the engine.

Q What is a piston valve? What are its advantages?

A See Fig. 3-9. A piston valve is a spool-shaped valve in a cylindrical cage. Its action is similar to that of a D valve. The advantages of a piston valve are: (1) It is simple to construct and maintain; (2) the driving mechanism is simple and there are no difficult adjustments; (3) heat is evenly distributed with little warping effect; (4) a balanced-valve effect is achieved by pressure distributed around the valve; and (5) the inside admission of steam and exhaust at the end is easy on the rod packing.

Q What is a fixed cutoff?

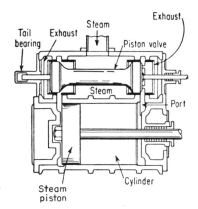

FIG. 3-9.   Piston valve and steam piston.

A   A fixed cutoff maintains the same steam-admission position of a valve, regardless of the load or the speed of the engine.

Q   What is a variable cutoff?
A   A variable cutoff is regulated by a governor to meet changing load conditions.

Q   How does a riding cutoff valve work?
A   The valve mechanism has two separately operated valves, each driven by a separate eccentric. The smaller valve is usually a variable cutoff type and controls the cutoff only. The large lower valve controls admission, compression, and release in the same way as does a D valve.

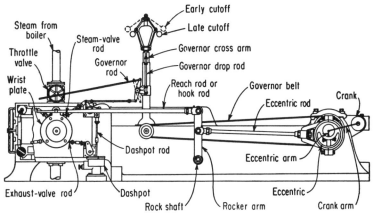

FIG. 3-10.   Corliss engine of the single eccentric type, showing governor and valve gear.

Q Name three ways to obtain variable cutoff with a riding-valve gear.
A (1) Varying the angular advance of the rider eccentric with a shaft governor; (2) using a right- and left-handed screw to control a split riding valve, which, in turn, changes the lap by varying the length of the valve; and (3) using an adjustable link to vary the length of travel of the riding-valve rod.

Q Sketch a single, eccentric corliss engine and show the following parts: (1) steam chest, (2) valve gear, (3) governor, and (4) detail of an admission-valve assembly.
A See Fig. 3-10.

INDICATOR DIAGRAMS

Q Why are indicator cards taken?

Q Indicator cards are taken to (1) prove that the steam and exhaust valves open and close at the proper time in relation to the position of the piston, (2) calculate the power developed by the piston on each side of the cylinder, and (3) calculate the amount of steam consumed by the engine.

> NOTE: The same analysis methods and calculations are applied to diesel engines as are applied to similar problems for reciprocating compressors.

Q What is a steam-engine indicator?
A See Fig. 3-11. A steam-engine indicator is an instrument that draws a diagram on a paper (card) to show the varying steam pressure in a cylinder as the piston moves. The indicator card is driven exactly by the piston rod so that all events can be related and used to make an analysis of the engine.

> NOTE: Indicator cards are also used for diesel engines. See Chap. 10, "Oil and Gas Engines," for indicator applications for compressors.

Q Draw an ideal indicator card for one side of a piston and name the events.
A See Fig. 3-12.

Q What is a reducing motion for indicators?
A It is a device, such as a pantograph, lever, reducing drum, or pulley, used to reduce the motion of the crosshead to an exact stroke that suits the indicator drum.

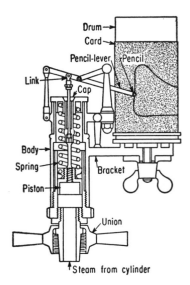

FIG. 3-11.   Steam-engine indicator.

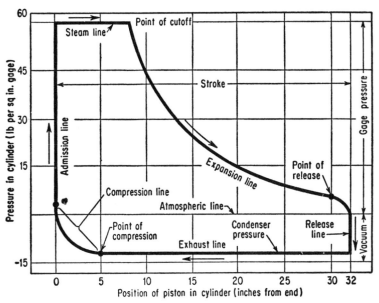

FIG. 3-12.   Ideal indicator diagram for steam engine reveals important data.

Q Draw several variations of admission levels and describe their conditions.
A See Fig. 3-13.

Q What determines the size of a spring to be used in a steam-engine indicator?
A The size of the spring is determined by either boiler pressure or throttle pressure. The spring should not be less than one-half the throttle pressure.

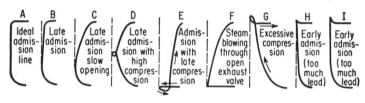

FIG. 3-13. Variations of admission lines from different indicator cards keep informed operators abreast of engine's condition.

To minimize errors, select the spring that gives the largest possible diagram.

Q What is meant by a no. 60 spring?
A The number indicates the scale or stiffness of the spring. A no. 60 spring, therefore, indicates that a pressure of 60 psi will cause the pencil to trace a line 1 in. high on the indicator card and, thus, represent 60 psi in the cylinder.

Q What is a planimeter? How is it used by operating engineers?
A See Fig. 3-14. A planimeter is used to measure the area of an irregular figure. It usually has a measuring wheel fixed to a set of arms. A stylus traces the shape of the figure, which is recorded by a calibrated vernier wheel. The vernier is calibrated to be read in square inches. These instruments are used to measure the work area of indicator diagrams. There are several types; follow manufacturers' instructions when using them.

Q Describe the ordinate method of determining the mean effective pressure (mep) of an indicator diagram.
A See Figs. 3-15 and 3-16. The indicator diagram is divided into 10 vertical lines (ordinates), perpendicular to the atmospheric line on the card. Use the geometric principle of the intercepting diagonal laid across the parallel lines as shown. Note that the two extreme ordinates are spaced to split the space so as to give a better average of the height of the card. This method shows how to use a ruler to locate the ordinates.

To find the mep, use the edge of a paper strip and mark off the length of each ordinate successively on the paper strip. Measure the accumulated

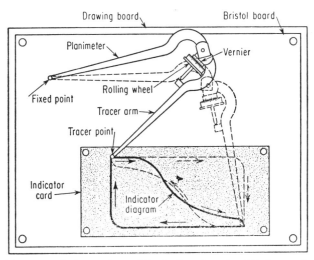

FIG. 3-14. How planimeter is used for finding the area of indicator diagrams.

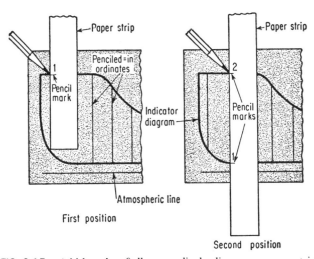

FIG. 3-15. Add lengths of all perpendicular lines on a paper strip.

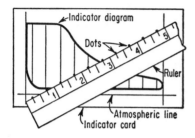

FIG. 3-16.   Ordinate method for determining the mean effective pressure.

lengths and divide by 10 to find the mean or average height. Multiply the mean height by the spring number; the answer is the mep.

CALCULATIONS

Q   What is the basic formula for calculating engine horsepower?

A $hp = \dfrac{2 \times PLAN}{33,000}$ for double-acting piston

where $P =$ mep, psi

$L =$ length of stroke, ft $\left(\dfrac{L}{12}\text{ if given in inches}\right)$

$A =$ area of piston (0.7854 $\times$ diameter D squared)
$N =$ revolutions per minute
$D =$ diameter of piston
$33,000 = 1$ horsepower (hp)

Q   Calculate the indicated horsepower (ihp) of an engine having a double-acting piston diameter of 14 in., stroke of 30 in., speed of 125 r/min, and mep of 75 psi.

A $ihp = \dfrac{2 \times PLAN}{33,000}$

$= \dfrac{2 \times 75 \times 2.5 \times 0.7854\,(14)^2 \times 125}{33,000}$

$= 218.662$ *Ans.*

Q   What is the horsepower of an 18 × 20 in. double-acting engine, running at 200 r/min with mep of 47 psi?

A $hp = \dfrac{2 \times PLAN}{33,000}$

$\quad = \dfrac{2 \times {}^{20}\!/_{12} \times 0.7854 \times 18 \times 18 \times 200 \times 47}{33,000}$

$\quad = 241.61 \qquad Ans.$

Q What are engine constants?
A Known factors are constants which allow a formula to be shortened for a series of calculations. Here is an example of figuring ihp:

$ihp = \dfrac{2 \times PLAN}{33,000} = \dfrac{2 \times P \times L/12 \times 0.7854 \times D^2 \times N}{33,000}$

$\quad = \dfrac{0.1309 \times PLD^2N}{33,000} = 0.000003936 \; PLD^2N$

Thus, in calculating the constant of any engine, the variables would be the mep, length of stroke (in inches for this formula), cylinder bore, and revolutions per minute. For all practical purposes 0.000004 may be used instead of 0.000003936.

EXAMPLE: Determine the ihp of an engine (when mep = 47 psi, length of stroke = 20 in., cylinder bore = 18 in., and r/min = 200).

SOLUTION:

$ihp = 0.000004 \times 47 \times 20 \times (18)^2 \times 200$

NOTE: Use 4 to multiply and let experience place the decimal point.

$ihp = 4 \times 47 \times 20 \times 324 \times 200$
$\quad = 243.64 \qquad Ans.$

Although this method is not quite accurate, it is a quick way to find the approximate ihp.

Q What is meant by the term *engine constant* when the ihp of a specific engine is calculated?
A The term *engine constant* means that the engine has fixed dimensions of bore and stroke which can be precalculated. Two constants are really needed, since the area at the crank end of the piston is reduced by the diameter of the piston rod. A further gimmick is to run the engine at the same speed when testing. With uniform speed, the only variable is the mep. Here is an example for determining the constant: In an 18 × 20 in. engine running at 200 r/min, we get

$$hp = \frac{2 \times PLAN}{33,000}$$

$$= \frac{P \times 20\!/\!_{12} \times 0.7854 \times 324 \times 200 \times 2}{33,000}$$

$$= P \times 5.140$$

then 5.140 = constant for this engine

If this engine produces an mep of 47 psi, determine the ihp.

$$ihp = P \times constant$$
$$= 47 \times 5.14$$
$$= 241.58 \qquad Ans.$$

Q What does a loop in an indicator diagram mean?
A A loop in an indicator diagram means that there is a loss of power in the engine because steam has expanded and then been compressed by the piston. Such areas are measured and subtracted from the mep.

Q What is the efficiency of an engine which has an ihp of 275 and a brake horsepower (bhp) of 210?

A Percent efficiency $= \dfrac{hp\ developed}{hp\ indicated} \times 100$

Percent $E = \dfrac{bhp}{ihp} \times 100$

$$= \frac{210}{275} \times 100$$

$$= 76.36 \qquad Ans.$$

Q (1) What is the water rate of a reciprocating engine? (2) What is a normal or good-average water rate?
A (1) The water rate is the actual measured pounds of water used by the engine to produce 1 ihp/hr. To determine the water rate, you must know the ihp and the amount of water used in a given time. (2) A normal or good-average water rate depends on the type of the engine and the exhaust pressure.

NONCONDENSING ENGINES		CONDENSING TO 26 IN. VACUUM
Uniflow	20½ lb	12½ lb
Corliss, 4 valve	22 lb	20½ lb
Slide valve	26½ lb	23 lb

ENGINE GOVERNORS

Q How does a governor control the speed of an engine?
A A governor uses centrifugal force to control the position of the admission valve or to throttle the steam line supplying the engine. As the engine speed changes, the governor positions the control to keep the engine speed constant.

Q Why are governors needed on steam engines?
A Governors are needed on steam engines to maintain a fairly constant speed for all loads. Should the load suddenly cease because a belt breaks or an engine-driven generator trips out, the governor prevents the engine from overspeeding.

Q Sketch and explain a flyball governor.
A See Fig. 3-17. A flyball governor has weights mounted on the pendulum

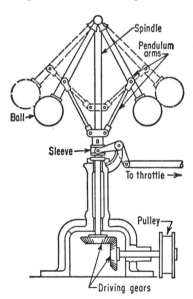

FIG. 3-17. Simple flyball (pendulum) governor on many engines.

arms. As a spindle revolves, the centrifugal force causes the balls to raise and lift the sleeve. A clevis fork throttles the steam supplied to the engine.

Q Describe the Pickering governor.
A See Fig. 3-18. A Pickering governor has flyballs mounted on the spring leaves instead of on the pendulum arms. The balls operate a stationary spindle and throttle the steam directly to the engine.

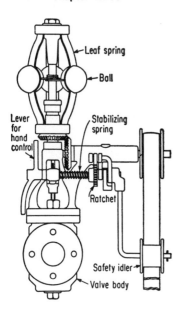

Leaf spring

Ball

Lever for hand control

Stabilizing spring

Ratchet

Safety idler

Valve body

FIG. 3-18. Pickering governor with safety idler for preventing runaway engine.

Q What is an inertia-type governor?
A See Fig. 3-19. An inertia-type governor has a weighted arm mounted on a pivot. Inertia tends to keep the weights moving at a constant speed. If the engine speeds up, the weight lags behind the wheel. The weighted arm positions the cam and controls the valve gear. The point of cutoff is thus varied to suit the load conditions. A spring is used to hold the weighted arm in balance against the centrifugal force and to position the arm for inertia force.

NOTE: Inertia is the force that throws you off balance when a bus starts or stops suddenly.

Q Why are inertia-type shaft governors preferred to centrifugal types?
A Inertia-type governors depend on the inertia of a moving mass that is arranged to shift the point of cutoff. This results in either an increase or decrease of steam expansion to match the load requirements of both power and speed.

Centrifugal units depend on centrifugal force to govern the throttle steam and to reduce or increase the steam pressure supplied from the steam line. This isn't efficient.

Inertia-type governors are preferred because (1) the mass rate of steam flow is varied instead of the pressure and (2) they have greater sensitivity to load change, which gives closer control of engine speed.

Q What is a Rites governor?

A See Fig. 3-19. A Rites governor is an inertia shaft governor.

Q What basic governor troubles are apt to occur?

A (1) Hunting—alternate speeding and slowing of the engine—which means that the governor is too sensitive to load changes. (2) Sticking—

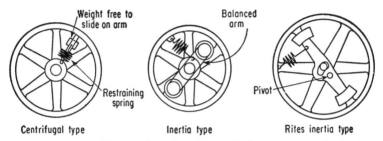

Centrifugal type   Inertia type   Rites inertia type

FIG. 3-19.   Centrifugal and two inertia-type shaft governors on flywheel.

failure to control speed, allowing the engine to run away or slow down—which means that the governor is not sensitive to load changes.

Q What is a governor safety stop?

A On throttling-type governors, the safety stop is a weighted arm that needs the support of a governor belt. If the belt breaks, the idler arm drops and shuts the steam supply valve to the engine. On corliss units, the flyballs fall to the lowest position and knock off the safety cams; the cams disengage the catch blocks on the steam intake valves so that no steam is admitted to the engine.

NOTE: The principles of governors are applied to many different machines such as overspeed control; indeed these devices are used to control electrical switches, auto ignition spark advance, etc.

OPERATION AND MAINTENANCE

Q How would you start a slide-valve-type or piston-valve-type steam engine?

A (1) Make sure that the engine is lubricated properly and that it is free to turn. (2) Drain the steam lines up to the throttle valve. (3) Open the exhaust valve, if the engine has one. (4) Crack open the cylinder drains. (5) Open the steam-chest drains. (6) Crack open the steam stop just enough to raise it off the seat. (7) Set up the lubrication system. (8) Open the throttle bypass to admit steam to warm the engine. If there isn't any bypass, crack the throttle slightly. (9) Open wide the steam stop on the boiler. (10) Allow enough time for the engine to warm up slowly, 10 to 20 min for 100-hp engines. (11) Bar the engine to be sure it is free, and leave it about 20 to 30° past dead center. (12) Admit a puff of steam to roll the engine past the first dead center, but close the throttle if the engine starts too rapidly. Keep the engine rolling slowly for a few turns. (13) Close the drain cocks when they begin to blow dry steam. (14) Bring the engine up to speed and control by the governor. (15) Adjust all the lubricators. (16) Check the engine frequently, during the first hour of operation. Follow the manufacturers' instructions.

Q How would you stop a steam engine?
A (1) Close the throttle. (2) Close the steam stop valve. (3) Open the cylinder and valve-chest drains. (4) Close the exhaust valve, if one is provided. (5) Secure the lubricating system. (6) Wipe the engine clean.

Q How is a corliss engine started? How is it secured?
A A nonreleasing corliss engine is started and stopped in the same way as a piston or slide-valve engine. A releasing corliss engine is drained, and the lubrication setup checked in the same way as that described for a slide-valve engine. Many corliss engines have no cylinder drains; drainage is through exhaust valves at the bottom of the cylinders.

To start a corliss engine do the following: (1) Detach the hook rod and latch out from the wrist plate. (2) Use the starting lever on the wrist plate and quickly admit steam to both ends of the cylinder. Keep the engine still for a brief period; then admit enough steam to rock the engine back and forth a partial stroke. (3) With a warmed-up engine, open the proper valves to rotate the engine in the right direction. Allow the engine enough speed to carry it through a half revolution. (4) Latch in the hook rod and open the throttle a little more to allow the engine to run slowly. (5) Remove the starting lever. (6) Increase the speed slowly until the governor takes control. Then give the engine full throttle.

To secure a detaching corliss engine, close the throttle and immediately throw the starting cam (block) of the governor into the starting position. Hold the block in place by hand until the governor weights come to rest on the block. This will allow you to bring the engine to rest in a good position so that you can restart it without having to use a bar to jack it.

Q What is piston clearance? Why is it necessary?
A Head clearance or striking clearance is the minimum distance between the piston assembly and the inside of the cylinder head. This space provides for steam compression as well as clearance for moving parts.

Q What is counter bore? Why is it desirable?
A Counter bore is the flaring at the end of the piston-ring travel in a

cylinder. It helps to prevent ridges from forming near the ends of the cylinder bore. Ridges would damage the piston rings. This is equally true for all reciprocating machinery rings in diesels, compressors, and pumps.

Q How is a slide valve adjusted?
A A slide valve can be adjusted by (1) adjusting the cam to time all events either earlier or later or (2) changing the length of the valve rod, which changes the events at one end of the cylinder at the expense of the other end.

Q What are common causes for hot bearings in reciprocating engines?
A Hot bearings in reciprocating engines can be caused by (1) lack of lubrication, (2) wrong or dirty lubrication, (3) misalignment of parts, (4) misfitted parts, and (5) excessive load or speed.

Q How would you find a faulty bearing?
A You can tell a great deal by sound and feel. Any deviation of sound from a regular sequence should be investigated.

Sudden quiet almost always indicates that a large bearing is hot, and the smell of hot oil will soon confirm this. Pounding in the main bearings or crankpins can be heard as a heavy thump, which occurs just after the crank passes dead center. A main-bearing knock can be felt at both the shaft and the bearing. It sounds duller and more severe than a crankpin knock. A crosshead knock is sharp and not as severe as the others. Sometimes you can flood a suspicious bearing with oil and reduce the noise enough to determine the trouble in the crosshead bearing. A sudden rise in bearing temperature is a certain indication of trouble. Water in a cylinder is a frequent cause of knocks. Since this is a very dangerous condition, open the cylinder drains immediately.

Q How is wear taken up in steam-engine bearings?
A Shims or liners are removed from between the halves to allow a closer fit between the journals and bearings. At times, brasses (bearing metal) are scraped to allow better fitting. Prussian blue and bearing scrapers are used in this process.

Q What is meant by the term *wiredrawn?*
A When steam pressure is reduced by flowing through a narrow passage, such as a partly closed valve, the steam is said to be "wiredrawn." Scars on valves resulting from such a condition are also referred to as "wiredrawn."

Q Why is condensation or excessive carry-over dangerous to reciprocating engines?
A Because water is noncompressible. If an excessive amount of water gets into the cylinder, it will wreck the engine (Fig. 3-20).

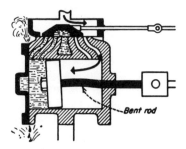

FIG. 3-20. Bent piston rod is common when water carries over into steam cylinder.

Q Why are piston rings used in most forms of reciprocating machinery such as steam engines, diesels, pumps, and compressors?

A Piston rings maintain a seal and act as a readily replaceable wearing surface between the piston and the cylinder sleeves (liners) to further restore efficiency economically, eliminating reboring and fitting oversized pistons and rings.

Q Describe a snap ring and restraining piston ring.

A A snap ring is a plain one-piece ring with a gap, similar to a common automobile-engine piston ring, and is made of cast iron (Fig 3-21). A restraining ring is a composite-type piston ring usually furnished with an adjustable spring to control the fit of the ring within the cylinder bore.

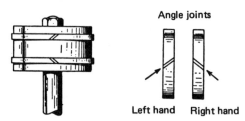

FIG. 3-21. Piston rings are flexible; they maintain seal between cylinder and piston.

Q Describe jam-type and segmental-metallic-type piston-rod packing.

A Jam-type packings of woven or twisted asbestos are often reinforced with lead, babbitt, copper alloys, or synthetic material. They seal by being compressed around the rod. Rings of packing are squeezed by a gland into a stuffing box.

Segments of metallic packings are shaped to fit the rod and are held against the shaft by garter springs. The various rings form a labyrinth shape in a split packing box, thus reducing pressure of steam leakage as it passes each ring.

Q What should you check when installing a new rod packing?

A When installing a new rod packing, be sure that (1) the proper packing is used, (2) the rod isn't bent, scored, or rusted, (3) the gland is true, neither bent nor cocked, (4) the stuffing box and gland are not scored. (5) the gland is in alignment with the shaft, (6) all old packing is removed, (7) the lantern ring, if used, is positioned under the lubrication inlet, and (8) the threads for tightening the gland are in good condition.

Q How is a rod packing (Fig. 3-22) installed?

A To install a rod packing, cut it around a mandrel or size it around

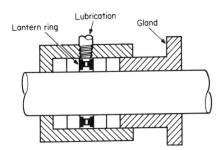

FIG. 3-22. Lantern ring, if used, must be at lubrication inlet.

the rod. Cut the ends square across. Install each ring separately with the joints staggered. Press each turn of packing into place. Next, draw up with a wrench, then back off on the completely packed box until the nuts are finger-tight. Leakage will be greater while the packing is seating. Never tighten packing to the point where there is no leakage; the packing set acts like a bearing, and must leak slightly to be lubricated by the fluid or gas that it seals. You need little or no lubrication other than what is already in the packing. Jamming the gland too tight will score the rod and overheat the packing. Be sure that you don't cock the gland.

Q Suppose that you must have a very strong metal-to-metal fit. What are the general rules for a cast-iron hole and steel hole members using a shrink fit? The plug member (shaft) is of steel.

A For cast iron, make a plug one-thousandth of an inch greater for every 2 in. of bore diameter. For steel, make the plug one-thousandth of an inch greater for each 1 in. of bore diameter.

Q Calculate the shrink fit of an 8-in.-diameter steel crankshaft to be fitted into a steel web.

A The rule for steel is to use one-thousandth of an inch interference for every inch of bore diameter. So, bore the hole 0.008 in. undersize, or 7.992 in., to receive the 8-in.-diameter shaft.

Q What is an oil separator in a steam system?

A An oil separator is either a series of baffles or a centrifugal separator designed to separate oil from the exhaust steam. Towel cloth, charcoal, or some other substance capable of separating oil and withstanding both heat and abrasion of steam is used to further remove the oil. As another refinement, diatomaceous earth, sponges, towel filters, or flotation separators are used to filter feed water because the least amount of oil is harmful in a boiler.

SUGGESTED READING

Elonka, Stephen M.: *Standard Plant Operators' Manual,* 3d ed., McGraw-Hill Book Company, New York, 1980 (has over 2000 detailed how-to illustrations—from boring cylinders to setting valves to packing stuffing boxes, etc.).

4

STEAM TURBINES

Turbine is the family name for most machines having a bladed (vaned) rotor rapidly spinning in a closely fitted casing. Turbines range in sizes from dentist air-driven drills to the giant megawatt steam turbines in central power plants. Turbines are possibly the most trouble-free and efficient machines in use.

Emergencies require prompt action to avert serious casualties. Most large repairs require special equipment and skills, usually performed by outside specialists. License examiners ask questions on the classification, safe operation, and lubrication of turbines. As steam engine questions disappear, turbine questions are their replacements.

FUNDAMENTALS

Q What is a steam turbine?
A A steam turbine is a rotary-motion machine that converts a jet of steam into useful work.

Q What advantages has a turbine over a reciprocating engine?
A (1) A turbine delivers a smooth, uninterrupted flow of power at high rotative speeds instead of a series of power impulses at low speeds. (2) There is a better use of heat energy contained in steam, since the turbine metal can withstand high steam temperature and exhaust at very low pressure (vacuum). (3) There is no boiler-water contamination from lubricating

oil as there is in a steam engine. (4) Turbines have less weight per horse-power and fewer wearing parts.

Q Give an example of an impulse force.

A A jet of water from a fire hose moves debris along the ground. Direct this jet of water against a water wheel and the wheel will revolve; this is an impulse force.

Q Give an example of a reaction force.

A The kick of a shotgun, or the push of a high-pressure fire hose that requires several people to hold the nozzle, are two examples of a reaction force. A reaction force causes a lawn sprinkler to rotate.

Q What are the two basic types of turbines?

A The two basic turbine types are the impulse and the reaction.

Q What is the operating principle of an impulse turbine?

A The basic idea of an impulse turbine is that a jet of steam from a fixed nozzle pushes against the rotor blades and impels them forward. The velocity of the steam is about twice as fast as the velocity of the blades. Only turbines utilizing fixed nozzles are classified as impulse turbines.

Q Describe the operating principle of a reaction turbine.

A A reaction turbine utilizes a jet of steam that flows from a nozzle on the rotor. Actually, the steam is directed into the moving blades by fixed blades designed to expand the steam. The result is a small increase in velocity over that of the moving blades. These blades form a wall of moving nozzles that further expand the steam. The steam flow is partially reversed by the moving blades, producing reaction on the blades. Since the pressure drop is small across each row of nozzles (blades), the speed is comparatively low. So more rows of moving blades are needed than in an impulse turbine.

Q Are turbines all impulse or reaction?

A No. There are many forces at work, and each turbine is classified by the principal force at work inside the machine.

Q Describe an impulse nozzle that is suitable for a small single-stage turbine.

A A convergent-divergent impulse nozzle in which steam expands to exhaust pressure is suitable for a small single-stage turbine. Here, a jet of steam is directed against the moving blades or buckets at a very high velocity.

Q What is velocity compounding?

A See Fig. 4-1. Velocity compounding is a method of absorbing the high velocity of the steam jets by redirecting the flow across the blades. In

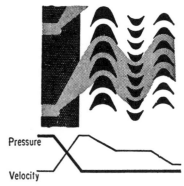

Pressure

Velocity

FIG. 4-1. Velocity compounding absorbs the jet velocity of steam in small steps.

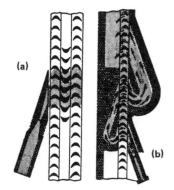

(a)

(b)

FIG. 4-2. Conventional velocity compounding *(a)*, and axial reentry *(b)*.

axial-flow turbines, the first row of blades receives the jet of steam from the nozzles. A stationary row of blades reverses the steam flow and directs it against the next row of moving blades. This is called a Curtis stage; it is one of several methods of velocity compounding.

Q Describe two methods of velocity compounding other than the Curtis stage.

A See Figs. 4-2, 4-3, and 4-4. The reentry method of velocity compounding uses the reversing chambers to redirect the steam flow against the same row of buckets. A second method of velocity compounding calls on tangential or helical flow in which the flow sets a corkscrew path between

FIG. 4-3. Solid wheel produces helical flow pattern.

FIG. 4-4. Reversing blading is attached to high-expansion ratio of steam nozzle.

the moving buckets and the casing. This is referred to as a "Terry solid-wheel turbine."

Q Describe the "solid-wheel" turbine illustrated in Fig. 4-3.

A A solid-wheel turbine is an impulse, helical-flow type, used mostly for noncondensing service. Steam issues from the expanding nozzle at high velocity and enters the side of the wheel bucket. There steam direction is reversed 180°. The stationary reversing chamber returns steam to the moving wheel, where the process is repeated until most of the steam's energy is spent.

These machines are sturdy and compact and can take a lot of abuse. The blades and wheel are one piece, and the blades have large clearances, with double-rim protection. End play won't damage the turbine, and the blades won't foul.

Close blade clearance isn't too important because the power-producing action of steam acts on curved surfaces at the back of the buckets. Blade wear has little effect on performance. Steam enters and leaves at right angles to the shaft; so there is almost no end thrust. The rotor can be removed from the shaft because it's not shrunk on.

If not loaded, the turbine can be started up cold in a few seconds. (But always warm it up, if possible.) With large wheel clearance and little load on thrust, danger of the blades rubbing is small. But because of all these features, this turbine is often neglected and abused.

Q What is a backpressure turbine?

A A backpressure turbine is designed to exhaust steam above atmospheric pressure.

Q What is a straight condensing turbine?

A A straight condensing turbine exhausts steam below atmospheric pressure (to a vacuum).

Q Are turbines classified by staging?

A Turbines are often classified by staging; for example, single stage, two-stage impulse, Terry wheel, etc.

Q What are topping turbines and superposed turbines?

A Topping turbines and superposed turbines are high-pressure, noncondensing units that can be added to an older, moderate-pressure plant. Topping turbines receive high-pressure steam from new high-pressure boilers. The exhaust steam of the new turbine has the same pressure as the old boiler and is used to supply the old turbines.

Q What is an extraction turbine?

A In an extraction turbine, steam is withdrawn from one or more stages, at one or more pressures, for heating or plant process needs. They are often called "bleeder turbines."

Q What is a mixed-pressure turbine?

A A mixed-pressure turbine works on a principle directly opposite to that of an extraction turbine. Here, steam left over from plant process is led to a lower stage in the turbine to generate power as it expands to condenser pressure.

Q For a given horsepower, why does a reaction turbine have more rows of blades than an impulse turbine?

A Since each stage in a reaction turbine has little steam-pressure reduction, many stages are needed. Impulse turbines have the greatest pressure drop in the nozzle; so fewer stages are needed.

Q Make simple sketches of several types of turbines.

A See Figs. 4-5 and 4-6.

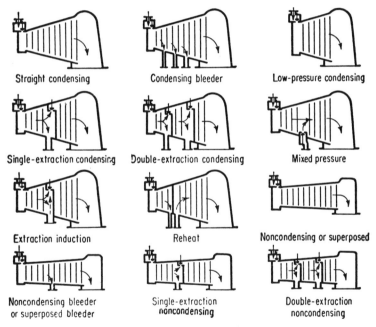

Straight condensing Condensing bleeder Low-pressure condensing

Single-extraction condensing Double-extraction condensing Mixed pressure

Extraction induction Reheat Noncondensing or superposed

Noncondensing bleeder or superposed bleeder Single-extraction noncondensing Double-extraction noncondensing

FIG. 4-5. Basic turbine types are named according to steam flow through unit.

Q Why is high superheat associated with higher pressures? How is this applied to turbines?

A Briefly, entropy causes more moisture to form at the low-pressure end of a turbine when higher boiler pressures are used. To offset this moisture, superheat is used to furnish additional Btu to the steam. Addi-

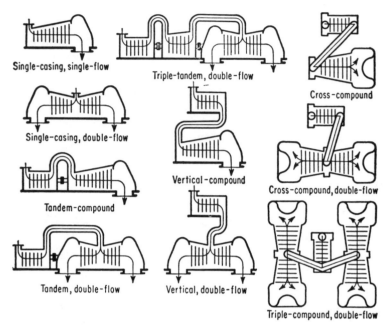

Single-casing, single-flow

Triple-tandem, double-flow

Cross-compound

Single-casing, double-flow

Vertical-compound

Cross-compound, double-flow

Tandem-compound

Tandem, double-flow

Vertical, double-flow

Triple-compound, double-flow

FIG. 4-6.   Large turbine units feature double-flow and compound arrangements.

tional heat delays the moisture from forming in the last stages. Most turbines are designed for 10 to 12 percent moisture in the last stage.

Q What is the difference between a bucket and a blade?
A See Fig. 4-7. Buckets are the moving elements of an impulse turbine.
They are usually crescent-shaped but are not always symmetrical. Blades
are the moving elements of a reaction turbine. They are teardrop-shaped,
bent to a curve with the blunt end forward. While the term *bucket* applies
to impulse turbines, buckets are often called "blades" in impulse machines.

Q What is a radial-flow turbine?
A In a radial-flow turbine, steam flows outward from the shaft to the
casing. The unit is usually a reaction unit, having both fixed and moving
blades. They are used for special jobs and are more common to European
manufacturers.

Q What is a stage in a steam turbine?
A In an impulse turbine, the stage is a set of moving blades behind
the nozzle. In a reaction turbine, each row of blades is called a "stage."
A single Curtis stage may consist of two or more rows of moving blades.

Q What is a noncondensing turbine?

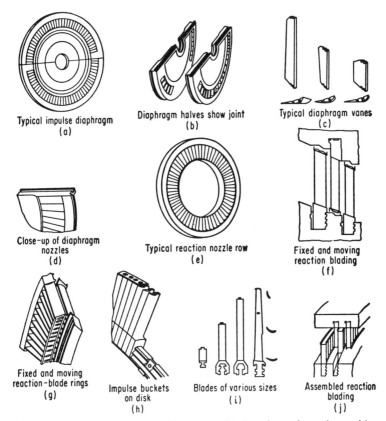

Typical impulse diaphragm
(a)

Diaphragm halves show joint
(b)

Typical diaphragm vanes
(c)

Close-up of diaphragm
nozzles
(d)

Typical reaction nozzle row
(e)

Fixed and moving
reaction blading
(f)

Fixed and moving
reaction-blade rings
(g)

Impulse buckets
on disk
(h)

Blades of various sizes
(i)

Assembled reaction
blading
(j)

FIG. 4-7.   Diaphragms, nozzles, and blades used in impulse and reaction turbines.

A   A noncondensing turbine exhausts steam above atmospheric pressure. Its exhaust steam is usually used for process or plant heating.

Q   Why are gears used with turbines?

A   Since the turbine is efficient only at high, rotative speeds, reduction gears must be used if the driven machine is to run at lower speeds.

Q   Which is more efficient, a good geared turbine or an electric generator and motor drive?

A   This depends on the application. For marine work, a turbine with reduction gearing is more efficient than an electric generator and motor. The reasons for this are: (1) a gear is 90 percent plus efficient, (2) a generator is from 80 to 85 percent efficient, and (3) a motor is from about 80 to 85 percent efficient. Therefore, 85 percent of 85 percent is 72.25 percent efficient as compared with 90 percent.

SEALING GLANDS

Q Why are sealing glands needed in a turbine?

A See Fig. 4-8. Sealing glands in a turbine do one of two jobs: (1) they prevent steam from leaking out of the casing along the shaft at the steam end, or (2) they stop air from leaking into the casing at the vacuum end.

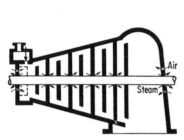

FIG. 4-8. Leakage of air into and steam out of casing is shown by arrows.

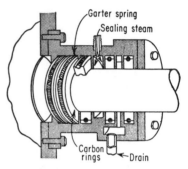

FIG. 4-9. Carbon sealing rings are in segments, held by springs around rings.

Q Name and describe four types of turbine seals.

A See Figs. 4-9, 4-10, and 4-11. (1) Carbon rings—segments of carbon fitted around the shaft with very little clearance. The segments are held together by garter or retainer springs. The rings are spaced into the grooves of a split box, similar to piston rings. (2) Labyrinth packings—a series of rings machined with serrations of V grooves, sometimes mated to serrations on the shaft. They are held in place by a casing. Clearances between the Vs and the shaft are close, forming a series of pockets that throttle the steam. This throttling causes a pressure drop past each serra-

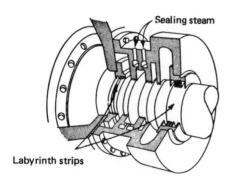

Labyrinth strips

FIG. 4-10. Labyrinth seals are circular strips or serrations almost touching shaft.

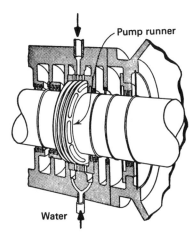

FIG. 4-11. Water seal has pump runners on shaft to hold water at periphery.

tion. (3) Water seals—a shaft-mounted runner acts as a pump impeller to create a ring of water under pressure at the end of the runner, thus sealing the gland. Clean water must be used because deposits cause trouble. (4) A stuffing box—woven or soft packing rings are stuffed in a box, then compressed with a gland. These are the same as stuffing boxes in other machines.

Q What is a diaphragm?
A See Fig. 4-7. Partitions between pressure stages of an impulse turbine are called "diaphragms." They hold the vane-shaped nozzles and seals between the stages. Usually labyrinth-type seals are used. One half of the diaphragm is fitted into the top of the casing, the other half into the bottom.

Q What is a shield strip?
A See Fig. 4-12. It is a strip used on high-pressure reaction blading to help direct steam flow.

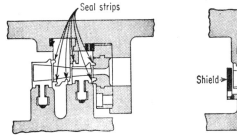

FIG. 4-12. Seal strips and shielding for impulse buckets reduce clearances.

Q What are sealing strips?

A They are thin strips fastened to the blading of reaction turbines to prevent steam from leaking. Shroud rings are used to mate the casing strips with little clearance. The parts are made thin to prevent damage if they should rub.

Q What is a shroud?

A See Fig. 4-13. It is a band used to connect the tips of the blades to

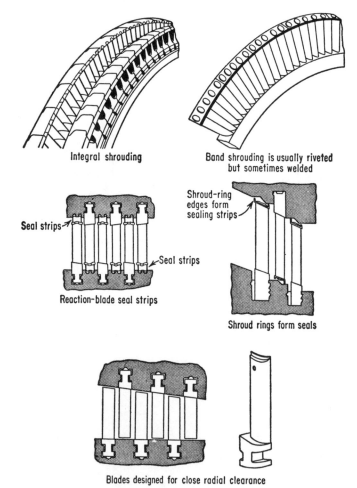

Integral shrouding

Band shrouding is usually riveted but sometimes welded

Seal strips

Reaction-blade seal strips

Seal strips

Shroud-ring edges form sealing strips

Shroud rings form seals

Blades designed for close radial clearance

FIG. 4-13.   Details of shrouding, shielding, and sealing arrangments for turbines.

give them more rigidity. It may be either welded or riveted to the blade tips. Some short blades have an integral shroud. Shrouds also help to prevent steam spillover.

Q In which turbine is tip leakage a problem?

A Tip leakage is a problem in reaction turbines. Here, each vane forms a nozzle; steam must flow through the moving nozzle to the fixed nozzle. Steam escaping across the tips of the blades represents a loss of work.

Q What are two types of clearance in a turbine?

A Turbine clearances are designated as (1) radial, the clearance at the tips of the rotor and casing, and (2) axial, the fore-and-aft clearance, at the sides of the rotor and the casing.

BEARINGS

Q Name four types of thrust bearings.

A Thrust bearings are classified as (1) babbitt-faced collar bearings, (2) tilting pivotal pads, (3) tapered land bearings, and (4) rolling-contact (roller or ball) bearings.

Q What is the function of a thrust bearing?

A Thrust bearings keep the rotor in its correct axial position.

Q Describe a pivotal-plate thrust bearing.

A See Fig. 4-14. A Kingsbury pivotal-plate unit has a collar on the shaft which faces a number of thrust shoes (pads). These shoes are supported on pivots (buttons) which allow the shoes to tilt and form an oil wedge between the collar and the tilting pad. The thrust load is carried on these oil wedges.

Q What is a balance piston?

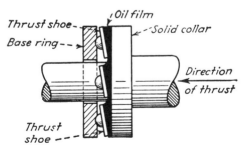

FIG. 4-14. Kingsbury thrust bearing uses thrust shoes.

A Reaction turbines have axial thrust because pressure on the entering side is greater than pressure on the leaving side of each stage. To counteract this force, steam is admitted to a dummy (balance) piston chamber at the low-pressure end of the rotor. Some designers also use a balance piston on impulse turbines that have a high thrust.

Q Describe a combination thrust and radial bearing.

A This unit has the ends of the babbitt bearing extended radially over the end of the shell. Collars on the rotor face these thrust pads and the journal is supported in the bearing between the thrust collars.

Q Describe a tapered-land thrust bearing.

A The babbitt face of a tapered-land thrust bearing has a series of fixed pads divided by radial slots. The leading edge of each sector is tapered, allowing an oil wedge to build up and carry the thrust between the collar and pad.

Q Why is the term *roller-contact bearing* preferred to *antifriction bearings*?

A Antifriction is a catchall term for ball, roller, and needle bearings. But it is erroneous, since all bearings create friction. Roller-contact bearing is the correct designation.

Q What is important to remember about radial bearings?

A A turbine rotor is supported by two radial bearings, one on each end of the steam cylinder. These bearings must be accurately aligned to maintain the close clearances between the shaft and the shaft seals, and between the rotor and the casing. If wear lowers the rotor, great harm can be done to the turbine.

Q What is the maximum safe temperature of a babbitt bearing?

A The safe temperature limit depends on the kind of babbitt used. Usually, a range of from 150 to 175°F is the maximum for lead base. Tin-base babbitt is good up to 200°F.

GLAND SEALS

Q What is gland-sealing steam?

A See Fig. 4-15. It is the low-pressure steam that is led to a sealing gland. The steam seals the gland, which may be either a carbon ring or labyrinth type, against air at the vacuum end of the shaft.

Q What is the function of a gland drain?

A The function of a gland drain is to draw off water from sealing-gland cavities created by the condensation of the sealing steam. Drains are led to either the condenser air-ejector tube nest or the feed-water heaters.

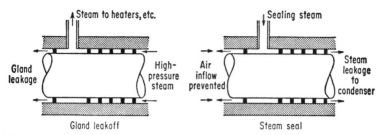

FIG. 4-15.   Gland leak-off and steam seals are used to improve turbine performance.

Often, gland drains are led to a low-pressure stage of the turbine to extract more work from the gland-sealing steam.

Q   What is leak-off steam?

A   Leak-off steam is about the same thing as gland-sealing steam, and it serves the same purpose. However, leak-off steam is from the high-pressure area of the turbine.

Q   What is an air ejector?

A   An air ejector is a steam siphon that removes noncondensable gases from the condenser.

GOVERNORS

Q   How many governors are needed for safe turbine operation? Why?

A   Two independent governors are needed for safe turbine operation. One is an overspeed or emergency trip that shuts off the steam at 10 percent above running speed (maximum speed). The second, or main governor, usually controls speed at a constant rate; however, many applications have variable speed control.

Q   What are the main parts of a governor and what purpose does each serve?

A   A governor is made up of: (1) A speed-sensing mechanism which may consist of centrifugal weights or flyballs, or a hydraulic pump pressure system. (2) Linkage that transmits the motion of the weights to the steam control valves. Hydraulic systems use fluid and pressure piping as well as linkage to accomplish this. (3) Steam control valves that regulate steam flow by various means, such as by throttling or opening more nozzles as the load requires.

Q   How is a flyball governor used with a hydraulic control?

A   As the turbine speeds up, the weights are moved outward by centrifugal force, causing linkage to open a pilot valve that admits and releases oil on either side of a piston or on one side of a spring-loaded piston. The movement of the piston controls the steam valves.

Q How does a hydraulic governor system work?
A See Fig. 4-16. An impeller mounted on the end of the turbine rotor acts as a speed-sensing element. As the turbine speeds up, the oil pressure

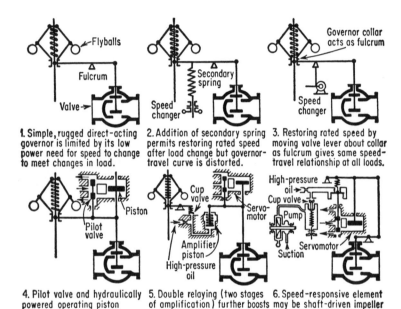

FIG. 4-16.   Six basic speed-governing arrangements are used for steam turbines.

increases. This pressure controls a cup valve that controls a pilot valve. The pilot valve positions the large piston, which is moved by high-pressure oil from the turbine bearing-lube system. The piston controls the movement of the steam valve.

Q What is a multiport governor valve? Why is it used?
A In large turbines, a valve controls steam flow to groups of nozzles. The number of open valves controls the number of nozzles in use according to the load. A bar-lift or cam arrangement operated by the governor opens and closes these valves in sequence. Such a device is a multiport valve. Using nozzles at full steam pressure is more efficient than throttling the steam.

Q What is a servomotor?
A See Fig. 4-16, no. 6. A servomotor is a hydraulic system in which a pilot valve positions a piston by admitting or releasing pressure on two sides of the cylinder.

Q What is the safe maximum tripping speed of a turbine operating at 2500 r/min?
A The rule is to trip at 10 percent overspeed. Therefore, $2500 \times 1.10 = 2750$ r/min.

Q What is meant by critical speed?
A It is the speed at which the machine vibrates most violently. It is due to many causes, such as imbalance or harmonic vibrations set up by the entire machine. To minimize damage, the turbine should be hurried through the known critical speed as rapidly as possible.

CAUTION: Be sure vibration is caused by critical speed and not by some other trouble.

LUBRICATION

Q Sketch a complete lube-oil system from the sump to the turbine.
A See Fig. 4-17.

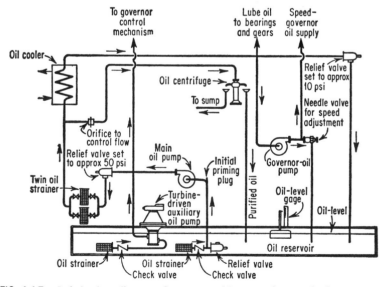

FIG. 4-17.   Lubricating-oil system for steam turbine may also supply the governor.

Q Describe each of the following lube systems: (1) grease, (2) drip, (3) ring, (4) splash, and (5) forced feed.

A See Chap. 18, "Lubrication and Bearings."

Q How is oil pressure maintained when starting or stopping a medium-sized turbine?

A An auxiliary pump is provided to maintain oil pressure. Some auxiliary pumps are turned by a hand crank; others are motor-driven. This pump is used when the integral pump is running too slow to provide pressure, as when starting or securing a medium-sized turbine.

Q Why is it poor practice to allow turbine oil to become too cool?

A If a turbine is allowed to become too cool, condensation of atmospheric moisture takes place and starts rust on the polished surfaces. Condensed moisture may also interfere with lubrication.

Q How is the oil temperature of a large turbine controlled?

A The turbine oil temperature is controlled by circulating cooling water into an oil cooler of the coil or shell-and-tube type. The water flow is regulated to maintain the correct oil temperature.

Q What would you do if you noticed an abnormal rise in bearing temperature?

A If there is an abnormal rise in bearing temperature, make an immediate check of the lubrication system. If a quick check doesn't show the cause, shut down.

Q Steam blowing from a turbine gland is wasteful. Why else should it be avoided?

A It should be avoided because the steam usually blows into the bearing, destroying the lube oil in the main bearing. Steam blowing from a turbine gland also creates condensate, causing undue moisture in plant equipment.

Q Besides lubrication, what are two functions of lubricating oil in some turbines?

A In larger units, lube oil cools the bearings by carrying off heat to the oil coolers. Lube oil in some turbines also acts as a hydraulic fluid to operate the governor speed-control system.

OPERATION AND MAINTENANCE

Q What is meant by the water rate of a turbine?

A It is the amount of water (steam) used by the turbine in pounds per horsepower per hour.

Q Name three types of condensers.

A (1) Surface (shell-and-tube), (2) jet, and (3) barometric. See Chap. 14, "Heat Exchangers."

Q What is a relief valve on a turbine?

A The turbine casing is fitted with spring-loaded relief valves to prevent damage by excessive steam pressure, especially at the low-pressure end. Some casings on smaller turbines are fitted with a sentinel valve which serves only to warn the operator of overpressure.

Q What is a steam strainer?

A Any device that separates moisture carry-over from steam is called a "steam strainer." They all work on the principle of an abrupt change in the direction of the steam flow. Because water is heavier than steam, it flies off and drains out, while steam flows through.

Q Name and describe two basic types of turbine couplings.

A Rigid and flexible are the two basic types of turbine couplings. Rigid types have the rotor shaft and drive member coupled together as one piece. Flexible couplings allow for slight misalignment (very slight).

Q Sketch the water cycle of a condensing turbine plant. Use blocks and label the path of each medium.

A For the water cycle in Fig. 4-18:

1. Boiler drum
2. Superheater
3. Turbine
4. Condenser
5. Condensate pump
6. Air ejector
7. Air-ejector drain coolers, gland coolers, first-stage water heater

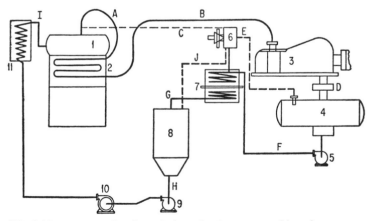

FIG. 4-18. Water cycle of a typical condensing steam-turbine plant system.

8. Deaerating tank
9. Feed-booster pump

10. Feed pump
11. Economizer

A. Saturated steam
B. Superheated steam
C. Low-pressure steam to air ejectors and heaters
D. Exhaust at vacuum
E. Air and noncondensable gases to air ejectors
F. Condensate to air-ejector coolers and to heater

G. Heated water to deaerating feed-heater tank
H. Feed water to feed-booster pump and feed pump
I. Feed to boiler
J. Exhaust steam (low-pressure steam) to deaerating feed heater

Q List the sequence of operations in starting and shutting down a condensing turbine.

A For starting the system in Fig. 4-19:

1. Start auxiliary oil pump and check oil pressure.
2. Check level in oil reservoir.
3. Open all cylinder drain valves.
4. Open gland leak-off valves.
5. Drain condensate from the main steam header and the steam leads.
6. Establish circulating-water flow through condenser.
7. Start condensate pump.
8. Establish seal on high-pressure gland for starting condition.
9. Establish seal of low-pressure gland for starting condition.
10. Start condenser air ejector and close vacuum breaker.
11. Close cylinder drains to stages under vacuum.
12. With partial vacuum established, quickly admit enough steam to start rotor and then shut off.
13. Listen for rubs on casing and at seal locations.
14. If no rubs are evident, admit enough steam to establish rotor

speed of about 200 r/min. Maintain about ½ hr to warm up rotor and casing evenly.

15. Trip emergency hand control to check operation.
16. Reestablish steam flow and slowly increase speed toward rated revolutions per minute during next 15 min. If rotor vibrates severely, decrease speed and continue warming up until no objectionable vibration appears on speed increase.
17. Adjust high-pressure and low-pressure seals for operating condition.
18. When cylinder condensation ceases, close drain valves.
19. Turn on cooling water to oil cooler to maintain about 110°F outlet oil temperature.
20. As turbine reaches rated speed make sure that the governor takes control.
21. Place unit on line quickly and apply about 20 percent load.
22. Open bleed-line valves and place heaters in operation.

For shutting down the system in Fig. 4-19:

A. Reduce turbine load gradually to zero and quickly take the unit off the line.

B. Close bleed-line valve and take heaters out of service.

C. Shut off steam by manual tripping of overspeed trip.

D. Open vacuum breaker.

E. Shut off air ejector.

F. Check that auxiliary oil pump starts at proper speed.

G. Shut off gland-seal water.

H. Shut down condensate pump.

I. Shut off gland-sealing steam.

J. Open all atmospheric drains.

K. Shut off water to oil coolers.

L. Shut down condenser circulating-water pumps.

M. Keep auxiliary oil pump in operation until unit is cool.

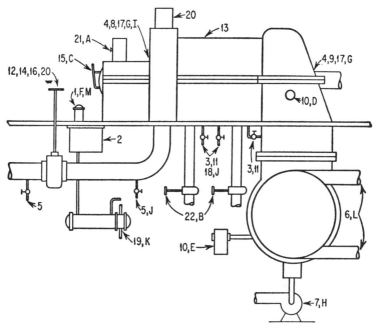

FIG. 4-19.   Sequence of operations in starting and shutting down a condensing turbine system. Follow above numbers for starting sequence, letters for shutting-down sequence.

Q   Why must steam turbines be warmed up gradually?

A   Although it is probable that a turbine can, if its shaft is straight, be started from a cold condition without warming up, such operation does not contribute to continued successful operation of the unit. The temperature strains set up in the casings and rotors by such rapid heating have a harmful effect. The turbine should be warmed as slowly as local conditions permit because of close clearances, in larger units especially.

Q Does the sound of a turbine mean anything?

A No unusual sound is too trivial to be neglected. Any change from the normal operating sound should be investigated. If you hear rubbing or grinding, shut down at once.

Q How are clearances checked while the turbine is running?

A Radial clearance is checked by micrometers built into the main bearing caps. These readings are checked against a master reading, the last reading taken under the same operating conditions, while both hot and cold. Axial clearance is verified in the same way—by an indicator at the end of the rotor-bearing cap.

Q What would you do if you lost vacuum while operating a condensing turbine plant?

A If vacuum is lost, shut down immediately. The condenser cannot stand steam pressure; the condenser tubes may leak from excessive temperature. Excessive pressure will also damage the shell, the exhaust, and the low-pressure parts of the turbine.

Q What are the main causes of turbine vibration?

A Turbine vibration is caused by: (1) unbalanced parts, (2) poor alignment of parts, (3) loose parts, (4) rubbing parts, (5) lubrication troubles, (6) steam troubles, and (7) foundation troubles.

Q What is the purpose of a turning gear?

A Heat must be prevented from warping the rotors of large turbines or high-temperature turbines of 750°F or more. When the turbine is being shut down, a motor-driven turning gear is engaged to the turbine to rotate the spindle and allow uniform cooling.

NOTE: Marine turbines are usually warmed up with the turning gear and low-pressure steam to prevent surging the ship on its moorings.

Q What inspection must be made hourly or at shorter intervals on turbines during operation?

A At short intervals check the oil temperature and pressure at the inlet and outlet of the turbine bearings, cooler, and pumps; steam temperature and pressure at the throttle and various turbine stages; water temperature and pressure at the cooling-water inlet and outlet; pressure of the condensate; load conditions on the machine; and operating sound for any abnormal noises.

Q What inspections should be made monthly?

A (1) Trip the emergency governor by overspeeding the turbine 10 percent if possible. (2) Check the steam strainer for cleanliness. (3) Measure alignment and clearances with gages provided for rotors, couplings, or foundation alignment. (4) Send a lube-oil sample to the lab or test lube oil according to the oil company's directions.

Q What inspections should be made annually or at longer periods?
A (1) Dismantle and clean all parts by raising the casing and bearings. (2) Replace or rebuild all worn and eroded parts. (3) Align and balance all parts after repairs are made.

NOTE: Some large utilities open turbines only once in 5 years and are trying to stretch this to 10 years. However, insurance firms usually insist on yearly inspections.

Q What is a bridge gage and how is it used?
A See Fig. 4-20. A bridge gage is used on large, plain bearings and

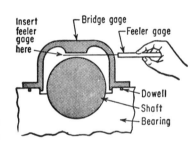

FIG. 4-20. Bridge gage is used with feeler gage to measure bearing wear.

journals to detect wear. To use it, remove the top bearing cap and clean the flange of the lower bearing housing and journal. Set the gage on its feet into dowel holes, if provided. Use feelers to measure the clearance between the shaft and the top and side reference surfaces of the bridge gage. This reading should agree with either the manufacturer's or the recorded measurements. Lube oil under the journal affects the reading; so wait as long as practical—24 hr after shutting down—to take the reading.

SUGGESTED READING

Elonka, Stephen M.: *Standard Plant Operators' Manual,* 3d ed., McGraw-Hill Book Company, New York, 1980.

Elonka, Stephen M.: *Standard Basic Math and Applied Plant Calculations,* McGraw-Hill Book Company, New York, 1979 (has a chapter on horsepower and heat engines).

5

PUMPS

For over two thousand years human beings have used the pressure of the atmosphere to help raise water to a higher level. Today, the pump ranks second only to the electric motor as the most widely used industrial machine. If a material will flow, it can be pumped, from highly volatile ether to coal slurry thick sludges. Even molten metals and liquids at 1000°F or higher are moved by modern pumps.

Pumps range from tiny adjustable displacement units to giants handling over 100,000 gal of fluids per minute. Designs differ in many ways, some in very slight details, others in the entire principle of operation.

Here we cover a few of the important basic types in common use. The better you know this faithful workhorse, the better care you as an operator of energy systems can give it, thus preventing unexpected problems and shutdowns. This chapter will help you pass license examinations with flying colors.

PUMPING THEORY

Q How does a pump "lift" liquid?
A We live on the floor of an ocean of air, which at sea level exerts a force of 14.7 lb on every square inch of surface. Because air has this weight, we can use it to force liquids up a tube by reducing the pressure between the liquid level and the suction side of a pump. And so a pump does not "lift" the liquid; atmospheric pressure forces it up into the partial vacuum created by the pump.

Q Classify the major types of pumps.

A (1) Reciprocating, (2) rotary, (3) centrifugal, (4) propeller, and (5) jet.

Q Do all types of pumps use the same principle to move liquids?

A No. Piston pumps exert a pressure directly on the fluid being pumped. Centrifugal pumps exert the pressure indirectly by gradually arresting the momentum of the fluid given to it by rapid rotation of an impeller.

The water inlet and discharge of the piston pump are controlled by valves which open and close intermittently; in the centrifugal pump the entry and discharge are continuous with no valves and no pump-controlling devices. Some rotary pumps combine the positive-pressure method of the piston pump with the continuous entry and discharge of the centrifugal pump with rotating impellers of screws.

Vacuum pumps of the hydraulic air type remove air and vapors from steam condensers with a rapidly rotating impeller, which hurls thin sheets of water through water passages into a venturi-shaped cone, where the high-velocity water stream enters the air from the condenser.

Q What is meant by static suction lift in connection with pumps and injectors.

A Static suction lift is the vertical distance in feet (Fig. 5-1) from the

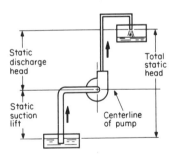

FIG. 5-1. Static suction lift, static suction head, and total static head.

surface of the liquid supply to the intake of the injector or centerline of the pump suction, when the pump or injector is placed above the source of liquid supply.

NOTE: Always slope suction lines upward toward the pump to avoid air pockets forming at the high point and thus reducing pump capacity.

Q Explain why pump elevation affects a unit's capacity.

A Many pumping installations have the liquid supply subjected to atmospheric pressure. The pressure available to force the liquid into the pump's suction is the atmospheric pressure minus the vapor pressure of the water, minus the friction-head losses, minus the vertical distance the center of the pump is above the supply level, or plus the distance it is below this level, all expressed in consistent units. Since atmospheric pressure decreases with an increase in altitude above sea level, the permissible suction lift, or required submergence, will vary with the altitude at which the pump is installed. See Fig. 5-2 and also the Calculations section in this chapter.

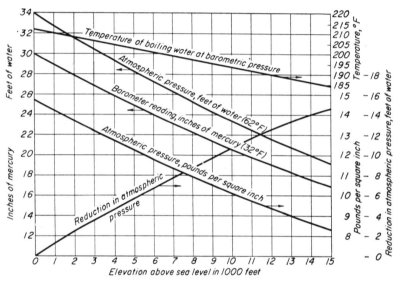

FIG. 5-2. Atmospheric pressure at various altitudes must be known when purchasing pump capacity for a given location.

RECIPROCATING PUMPS

Q Describe the principal steam parts of a direct-acting steam pump.

A See Fig. 5-3. (1) The steam cylinder that serves as the bored casting for the piston. (2) The steam piston which fits snugly into the cylinder and is sealed with piston rings. (3) The steam valves that admit and release steam to either side of the piston. (4) The piston rod which continues on to the liquid end of the pump to work a plunger. (5) The valve mechanism which is driven by piston rods through links.

Q What is a valve deck?

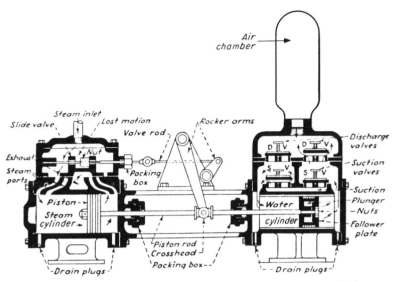

FIG. 5-3.   Reciprocating duplex direct-acting pump is simple, reliable.

A   A valve deck is a plate that contains either the suction or discharge valves of a direct-acting pump.

Q   What kind of valves are used on the water end of a direct-acting pump?
A   Disk valves are used on the water end of a direct-acting pump.

Q   How many ports are there in a duplex pump?
A   There are five ports in each cylinder of a duplex pump—two steam, two exhaust, and one main exhaust, or a total of 10.

Q   What is the least number of valves used in the water end of a duplex pump?
A   See Fig. 5-4. At least eight valves are used in the water end of a duplex pump—four suction and four discharge.

Q   How can you tell a hot-water valve from a cold-water valve, a high-pressure valve from a low-pressure valve?
A   You can distinguish the type of service the valve is suited for by the materials used. For cold water, hot water to 200°F, and for low pressures, rubber or fiber valves are used. For high pressures and water above 212°F, bronze or steel valves are used.

Q   Describe the motion of a steam valve on a duplex pump.
A   See Fig. 5-5. A spool on each piston rod moves a bell-crank lever that passes through a shaft and bearing to a small lever on the other side. The small shafts are transverse to the piston rods. The small lever

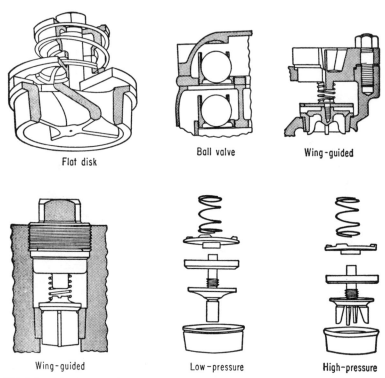

Flat disk

Ball valve

Wing-guided

Wing-guided

Low-pressure

High-pressure

FIG. 5-4.   Liquid valves for direct-acting and power pumps come in various designs.

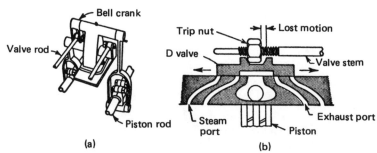

(a)

(b)

FIG. 5-5.   (a) Linkage of duplex pump. (b) When D valve is in center position, ends of valve just barely cover the steam ports.

moves the valve rod, which in turn moves the valve. With this arrangement, each moving piston rod works the steam valves of the opposite cylinder.

Q Discuss the outside and inside lap of D slide valves on a steam-driven pump.

A See Fig. 5-5. D slide valves on a steam-driven pump have neither outside nor inside lap because there is no flywheel to carry the pump beyond dead centers. Early cutoff is impossible. When the valves are in the center position, the steam ports on the opposite end are barely covered.

Q How would you set the steam valves on a duplex pump?

A The first step is to place the pistons in their central positions. They should be at midtravel when rocker arms are vertical, but simply moving the pistons until the arms are vertical cannot be depended upon, since the crossheads may have moved on the piston rods from their original setting. The correct procedure is as follows:

1. Push one of the pistons back until it strikes the cylinder head (Fig. 5-6).

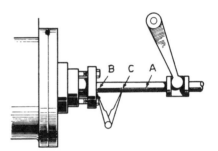

FIG. 5-6. Setting valves of duplex reciprocating steam pump.

2. Scribe mark A on the piston rod at the face of the packing gland.

3. Pull the same rod out until the piston strikes the opposite cylinder head.

4. Scribe another mark B on the piston rod at the face of the same packing gland.

5. Find the center of the distance between these two points and mark this central point C.

6. Move the rod back until the central mark is at the face of the gland, and the piston will be exactly at midstroke. Repeat this process for the other side of the pump.

7. Set the slide valves exactly in the center of their travel. In this position they will just cover the steam ports with no overlap.

8. Divide the lost motion evenly on each side of the nut or nuts on the valve rod that moves the valves.

9. The setting is now complete, but before replacing the valve-chest cover, be sure to move (with a finger) each valve as far as it will go, in opposite directions, so that the steam ports are uncovered; otherwise the pump will not start when steam is turned on.

To summarize, valves are properly set if they just cover the steam ports, with lost motion equally divided, when the pistons are at midtravel. The term *lost motion* refers to the space between the lugs on the back of the valve and the nuts on the valve rod that moves the valve. This slack is necessary to let the piston almost complete its stroke before the crosshead, rods, and rocker arms move the valve. If no lost motion were provided, the pistons would either remain stationary or make a very short stroke.

Q   What are the effects of too much or too little lost motion in the side-valve linkage?
A   See Fig. 5-5. Too much lost motion in the slide-valve linkage causes the piston to strike the heads; too little lost motion causes the piston to short stroke. These conditions can be corrected by using the trip nut or spacers of the correct width.

Q   Why can a direct-acting feed-water pump, using 200 psi steam, force water into the boiler that supplies its steam?
A   This happens because the steam piston is larger in area than the liquid plunger. For example, if the steam area (not the diameter) of this same pump is twice that of the liquid area, the pump will build up a pressure of 400 psi.

Q   What cause operating failures of simplex steam-operated valves?
A   Simplex steam-operated valves fail because of (1) worn valve seats, (2) worn or broken valve rings, (3) worn trip rods and bearings, (4) misaligned rods, (5) scored valve cylinders, (6) scored rods, (7) worn packing, (8) bent or deformed parts, (9) tight packing, (10) no lubrication, (11) low steam pressure, (12) water in steam spaces, and (13) trip nuts slipping out of adjustment.

Q   Why is the suction piping larger than the discharge on reciprocating pumps?
A   Design experience has proved that flow in the suction pipe of reciprocating pumps should not exceed 200 ft/min, nor should these pumps discharge at more than 500 ft/min (duplex units) or at 400 ft/min (simplex double-acting types). Suction is very critical in all types of pumps. It is usual to design larger suction lines to reduce friction to the water flow.

Q   What causes poor suction capacity in a direct-acting pump?
A   Poor suction is caused by (1) leaks in suction piping, stuffing boxes, castings, or joints; (2) restricted flow, due to suction piping that is too long, or too small in diameter; (3) vapor flashing, due to high-temperature water; (4) air binding; and (5) mechanical faults, such as worn valves, rings, packings, bent rods, or other defective parts.

Q   What are the theoretical and practical limits of suction lift for direct-acting pumps?

A Theoretical suction lift for direct-acting pumps is 33.9 ft; practical suction lift is only 24 ft. Table 5-1 shows the maximum theoretical suction lift with water at various temperatures, and the maximum practical lift ordinarily possible, but only at sea level. The higher the altitude, the lighter the air available to force water through the pump.

WARNING: Table 5-1 is based on safe values. Many pump manufacturers recommend a more conservative lift to ensure good operation at all times.

TABLE 5-1   Maximum Suction Lift for Water
Assumed barometer reading 30.0 in. Hg at sea level

Water temperature, °F	Maximum theoretical lift, ft of water	Maximum practical lift, ft of water
60	33.4	30
80	32.8	29
100	31.8	27
120	30.0	25
140	27.3	22
160	23.0	17
180	16.7	10
200	7.3	1

Q Why are cushion valves used on steam cylinders?
A Cushion valves provide an adjustable steam cushion for the piston. They ensure a full-length working stroke and prevent the piston from striking the cylinder heads when the pump is working under widely varying conditions of load.

Q How can you know by sight whether a direct-acting pump is a high- or low-pressure machine?
A On high-pressure pumps the liquid cylinders usually have a smaller diameter than the steam cylinders. Low-pressure pumps usually have larger water cylinders than steam cylinders (depending on steam pressure).

Q What is the difference between an air-bound pump and a steam- or vapor-bound pump?
A "Air-bound" means that the pump is filled with air (loss of prime). "Steam-bound" means that the water is too hot for the suction pressure. As pressure is reduced, water flashes into steam.

Q What are the evils of short stroking?
A When a pump is short stroking, it delivers less than rated flow. Steam clearance spaces increase, but steam is wasted since it does no useful work in this increased clearance volume. Also, cylinder walls wear, forming

a ridge at either end that can break the piston rings when the pump is full stroking.

Q Why is an air chamber used on direct-acting pumps?

A An air chamber is designed to minimize pulsation by cushioning the delivery of water. Trapped air is compressed as the pressure increases, absorbing the shock. As pressure drops, air expands and tends to keep a uniform pressure in the system (see Fig. 5-3).

Q What are the advantages of single-action outside-plunger pumps?

A These pumps are externally packed, allowing the plunger packings to be replaced without dismantling the water end of the pump.

Q What would you do if your large duplex pump began to knock?

A (1) Drain condensation from the steam lines and cylinders. (2) Purge the water end of air, and check for vapor binding. (3) Inspect valve mechanism and linkage for lost adjustment. (4) Examine the various sections for defective parts. (5) Check the water flow to and from the pump.

Q Describe the power-driven pump in Fig. 5-7, which is a vertical gear-driven triplex power pump often used as a boiler feed pump.

A Strictly speaking, all pumps are power-driven in some fashion, but the term *power pump* is usually limited to a pump of the reciprocating type that is driven by a belt or gears from an engine, motor, or line shaft. The pump may have one, two, three, or more cylinders, and the cylinders may be single- or double-acting. The *triplex* is a very common form of

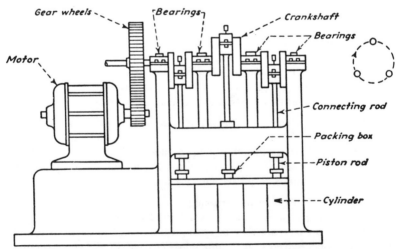

FIG. 5-7. Vertical, triplex reciprocating pump can be used for high pressures.

power pump. It has three cylinders set side by side, with their plungers connected to a three-throw crankshaft. The cranks are set 120° apart to ensure a fairly steady flow of water. Plungers are usually *single-acting;* that is, the upward stroke is a suction stroke and the downward stroke is a discharge stroke, the upper end of the cylinder being open.

Q Describe the plunger-type controlled-volume pump illustrated in Fig. 5-8.

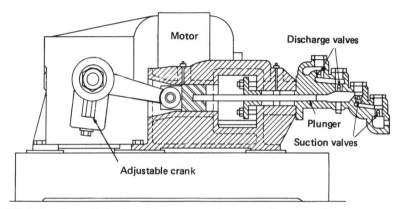

FIG. 5-8. Controlled-volume plunger pump has screw adjustment of stroke length. Change of crankpin position alters capacity of pump.

A These compact units, also known as controlled-volume, chemical-feed, variable-displacement, and metering pumps, find many applications in industry today. They are widely used for metering feed-water chemicals into higher-pressure boilers while steaming. An adjustable crank, driven by an electric motor, reciprocates a rod which acts as the plunger. The stroke of the pump can be varied by adjusting the crank throw. Simple metal ball-type suction and discharge valves assure minimum leakage problems.

CENTRIFUGAL PUMPS

Q How does the centrifugal pump differ from positive-displacement (rotary and reciprocating) types?

A Unlike the positive-displacement types, the centrifugal pump operated at constant speed delivers any capacity from zero to a maximum, depending on head, design, and suction conditions. Characteristic curves (Fig. 5-9) show the interrelation of head, capacity, power, and efficiency, for a specific impeller and casing.

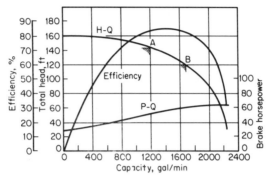

FIG. 5-9. Characteristic curves for a given impeller size and design show head, horsepower, capacity, and efficiency.

This head-capacity curve, labeled H-Q, shows the relation between capacity and total head; the curve may be rising, drooping, steep, or flat, depending on the impeller type and design. At A in the curve, note that head is 144 ft and capacity is 1200 gal/min. But at 120-ft head, B, the capacity, rises up to 1680 gal/min.

Usually, one plots head, power, and efficiency against capacity at constant speed, as in this curve. But in special cases, it is possible to plot any three variables against a fourth.

Q Why is a check valve placed in (1) the discharge and (2) the suction of a centrifugal pump?

A A check valve is placed in the discharge of a centrifugal pump to prevent other pumps or pressures from other sources from backing into the pump and out through the suction. In the suction line, a check valve acts as a foot valve and holds prime in the pump during shutdown.

Q Will a centrifugal pump that is fully primed and operating at full speed require more or less power if the discharge valve is closed?

A A centrifugal pump uses much less power when the discharge valve is closed. The effect is used in starting very large pumps, especially with ac induction motors. The discharge is opened gradually after the pump is working at full speed.

> CAUTION: Be sure not to churn the water long enough to cause overheating. As a safeguard, small recirculating lines are often used to permit some flow when starting the pump with the main discharge closed.

Q In centrifugal pumps, what is the theoretical relationship between (1) pressure head and impeller speed and (2) power and impeller speed?

A The pressure head of a centrifugal pump varies directly as the square of the impeller speed. The power needed varies directly as the cube of the impeller speed.

Q What is meant by single suction and double suction?

A See Figs. 5-10 and 5-11. If the liquid enters from one side (eye) of the impeller, it is a single-suction pump. If the liquid enters from both sides of the impeller, it is a double-suction pump.

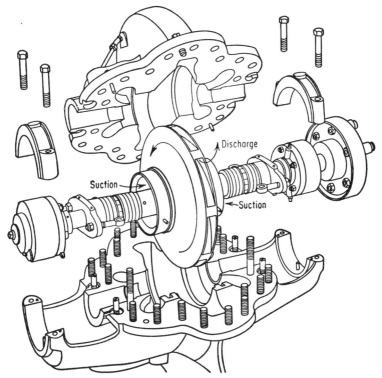

FIG. 5-10. Single-stage centrifugal pump components with double-suction impeller.

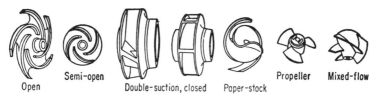

FIG. 5-11. Impellers for centrifugal pumps come in correct design for service.

Q How does a volute-type centrifugal pump work?

A See Fig. 5-12. Volute-type centrifugal pumps have impellers that discharge into a progressively widening spiral casing where the velocity of the liquid is converted to pressure.

Q What is a diffuser pump?

A See Fig. 5-13. A diffuser pump converts velocity into pressure inside a diffuser ring.

FIG. 5-12. Volute converts velocity energy into static pressure.

FIG. 5-13. Diffuser changes flow and helps convert velocity to pressure.

Q What is a turbine pump?

A See Fig. 5-14. A turbine pump converts water velocity into pressure inside a diffuser ring instead of a volute. Water is gathered in impeller vanes and whirled at high velocity for most of a revolution in an annular channel.

FIG. 5-14. Turbine pump adds energy to liquid.

Q Why must a centrifugal pump have prime?

A Since centrifugal pumps are not self-priming, some means of priming and air venting must be provided. Besides, packing is water-lubricated and clearance rings or labyrinth rings have very little clearance. These surfaces will score and overheat, ruining the pump if it is operated without water.

Q How are centrifugal pumps primed?

A Centrifugal pumps may need (1) a priming tank, (2) a foot valve, (3) a filling line, or (4) in some special designs, a priming chamber. The pump must be filled with water before starting. An air vent is usually provided at the top of the casing.

Q What is meant by a centrifugal pump termed "single stage," "two stage," "three stage," etc?

A See Fig. 5-15. In a single-stage centrifugal pump, water flows through one impeller into one volute or diffuser. A two-stage pump has two separate impellers, each in a separate volute or diffuser. A three-stage unit has three separate impellers, each in a separate volute or diffuser, etc.

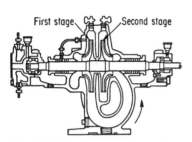

FIG. 5-15. Two-stage pump forces liquid from first stage to second stage.

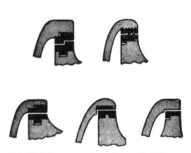

FIG. 5-16. Wearing rings of different designs reduce leakage and are renewable as rings wear from abrasion, erosion.

Q What is a flinger ring?

A It is a flanged ring fitted to the pump shaft between the pump gland and the bearings. Any leakage through the seals (leak-off) runs up to the flinger ring, where it is thrown off by centrifugal force. This action keeps water out of the bearings.

Q Why are wearing rings used in centrifugal pumps?

A See Fig. 5-16. Wearing rings are used to provide tight seals at the running joints between the impeller and the casing. These rings are usually removable, and can be replaced with new, tight rings at a nominal cost without replacing expensive casings.

Q Why are pumps multistaged?

A There are limits to the pressure and volume at which each single-stage pump works most efficiently. Multistaging divides each stage into a separate pump, allowing unlimited pressure or volume to be attained.

Q What happens to a high-speed centrifugal pump when it is operated with the discharge valve closed?

A Water is soon churned into steam, and the pump is damaged because of lack of water lubrication and cooling. Pump parts may actually fuse together from friction heat.

Q What is a propeller pump?

A See Fig. 5-11. It is a pump having an impeller shaped like a motorboat propeller. They are also called "axial-flow pumps" and are used for pumping great volumes at low head pressure.

Q What is a macerating pump?

A This pump is used to move, mix, and beat pulpy effluents such as sewage wastes into thinner and better-flowing liquids. Some impellers are open, for example, the paper-stock, mixed-flow, and open impeller. See Fig. 5-11. Some very viscous products such as brewery yeast, dog food, and other pasty and sometimes abrasive corrosive products are pumped into a stainless-steel case that is rubber-lined and has a stainless-steel screw. See Fig. 5-17.

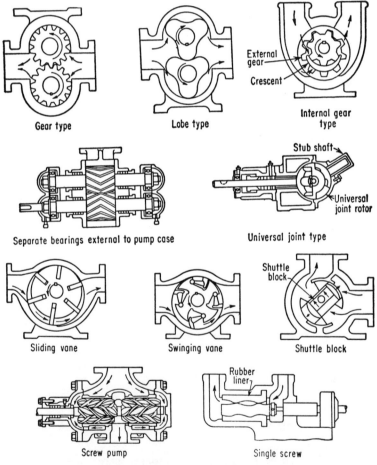

Gear type

Lobe type

External gear

Crescent

Internal gear type

Separate bearings external to pump case

Stub shaft

Universal joint rotor

Universal joint type

Sliding vane

Swinging vane

Shuttle block

Shuttle block

Rubber liner

Screw pump

Single screw

FIG. 5-17.   Rotary pumps come in various designs for many services.

ROTARY PUMPS

Q What three design features are common to all types of rotary pumps?
A See Fig. 5-17. (1) All rotary pumps are positive-displacement units that deliver a smooth constant flow. (2) They all have moving parts with tight clearances on all sides. (3) They all deliver flow by trapping a quantity of liquid at one side of the casing and discharging it at the other side.

Q What advantages do rotary pumps have?
A Rotary pumps are self-priming, are capable of high suction lifts, have low net positive suction head (NPSH), can handle high-viscosity liquids at high efficiency, have a wide speed range, and are available for low-capacity, high-head or high-capacity, high-head applications. Only some of the many designs are illustrated in Fig. 5-17.

STEAM JET AND AIR (VACUUM) PUMPS

Q What is the function of an air pump in a steam plant?
A An air pump removes air and noncondensable gases from the condenser, as these gases destroy vacuum. Some older pumps are reciprocating. Modern plants remove air with ejectors, hurling-water pumps.

Q What is a jet pump?
A Fig. 5-18. A jet pump consists of a suction line that opens into a

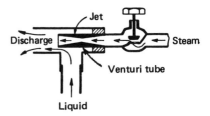

FIG. 5-18. Simple jet pump has no working parts, works best with venturi tube.

suction chamber, a jet or nozzle, and a diffuser. A jet of water, steam, or air is forced out the nozzle and passes through the diffuser at high velocity. Water or air in the suction chamber mixes with the jet and is forced out, causing a suction and discharge action to and from the suction chamber. Jet pumps are used as simple siphons, air ejectors, educators, etc. They may operate while completely submerged.

Q What is an injector and how does it work?
A See Fig. 5-19. An injector is designed to siphon and force water into

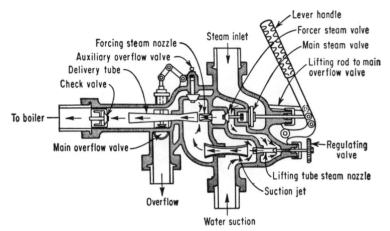

FIG. 5-19. Double-tube injector forces feed water into live boiler using boiler's steam.

the boiler. It is usually installed on smaller boilers as an auxiliary or emergency feeding device. A group of nozzles are arranged so that a jet of steam imparts velocity and energy to the water that is lifted into the injector. Then, the weight of water plus velocity overcome boiler pressure, and the water is forced into the boiler that supplies the steam to the jet. The essential parts are the steam jet, suction jet, and the combining and delivery tube.

Q Describe the "hurling-water" type of centrifugal displacement pump (Fig. 5-20) used as an air (vacuum) pump in steam plants.
A This vacuum pump, also known as a *liquid-piston air pump*, has a round multiblade rotor revolving freely in an elliptical casing, which is partially filled with liquid. The curved rotor blades project radially from the hub

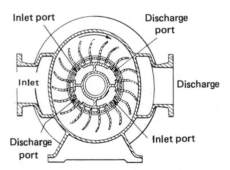

FIG. 5-20. Liquid-piston air pump used to create high vacuum in steam-turbine plants.

to form, with the side shrouds, a series of pockets or buckets around the periphery.

The rotor revolves at a speed high enough to throw the liquid out from the center by centrifugal force. The result is a solid ring of liquid revolving in the casing, at the same speed as the rotor, but following the elliptical shape of the casing. This forces the liquid to alternately enter and recede from the rotor buckets, twice in each revolution.

As the liquid withdraws from the rotor, it pulls the noncondensable gases, along with some vapor, from the condenser through the inlet port. As rotation continues, the converging wall of the casing forces the liquid back into the rotor chamber, compressing the gas trapped in the chamber and forcing it out through the discharge port.

PACKING AND MECHANICAL SHAFT SEALS

Q　Explain how jam-type mechanical packing seals.

A　Packing is wasted, rods and shafts scored, and packing needlessly burned up because few mechanics understand how packing seals. Figure 5-21 shows a stuffing box filled with five rings of new packing. This braided packing is saturated with lubricant, coated throughout with graphite, and takes up about 9 in.³ of space in the box. Here, the gland nuts are only hand-tight because the new packing has just been installed. The lower drawing shows the same packing completely compressed until it takes only 5.4 in.³. Volume is less because all saturant has been melted, squeezed, or washed out. Because packing can't be compressed further, it has reached the end of its useful life. You must renew it or it will burn up and score the shaft, causing more damage than the cost of the most expensive packing.

Q　Explain in detail why jam-type packing fails.

A　Figure 5-22 shows new packing before the gland has been tightened. As the machine runs, some saturant in the packing is washed or squeezed out. As saturant is lost, packing shrinks away from the shaft because its volume has been reduced. Here, the operator usually tightens the gland, stopping all fluid flow. With no leakage, there is no lubrication from fluid flow out of the pump. As a result, the rod heats up and the temperature of the packing rises. That is when lubricant, placed inside the packing material by the manufacturer, goes to work (Fig. 5-22b). The high temperatures start to melt oil out of the packing, which lubricates the shaft for just such an emergency. Because more oil has oozed out of the packing, space taken by it is again reduced. This starts a flow of liquid from the

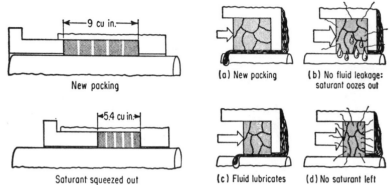

New packing

FIG. 5-21.   New packing comes saturated with about 30 percent lubricant.

(a) New packing

(b) No fluid leakage: saturant oozes out

Saturant squeezed out

(c) Fluid lubricates

(d) No saturant left

FIG. 5-22.   When all saturant is squeezed out, packing fails, wears rod excessively.

casing, which again lubricates the rod and packing, also carrying away heat (Fig. 5-22*c*).

Here is where trouble can start. If the operator tightens the gland enough to stop leakage again, the liquid flow is lost. Again, high temperature melts more packing lubricant, reducing volume and starting flow from the casing automatically, as before. This can go on until no saturant is left in the packing or until the pack volume of the packing cannot be further reduced. When the gland is tightened further to stop leakage, the packing burns up and the rod scores (Fig. 5-22*d*).

Q   How should you tighten packing?

A   If the joint leaks too much, tighten each hexagon nut only one flat. This is one-sixth of a turn. Then wait for about 10 min, because it may take this long for the packing to adjust itself and to reduce excessive leakage. After 10 min, the packing has distributed itself in the box and you can tighten the nuts another flat if leakage is still too much. The glands are usually tightened when the machine is shut down overnight in order to prevent leakage. But the trouble is that the operator starting the machine the next time does not loosen the gland. This is a common cause of packing failure and of grooved shafts. Hang a sign on the machine reading, "Loosen packing gland before starting this pump."

Q   What is a shaft sleeve?

A   See Fig. 5-23. Removable shaft sleeves are used to protect the shaft against wear, corrosion, or erosion. They are placed in stuffing boxes or in interstage glands. As with wearing rings, worn sleeves can be replaced at a nominal cost.

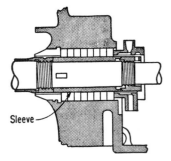

FIG. 5-23. Shaft sleeve protects shaft against wear from packing.

Q What is a lantern ring?
A See Fig. 5-24. It is a ring of cage construction that is inserted between the turns of the shaft packing. A sealing liquid from the pump or some other source is conducted through the side of the stuffing box and led to the lantern ring. The ring distributes the sealing water around the

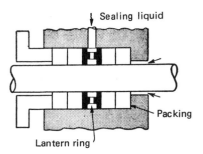

FIG. 5-24. Lantern ring helps keep abrasive liquid inside casing and packing cool.

shaft. The sealing water prevents air from leaking into the pump and also lubricates the packing. Lantern rings are made of soft materials—white metal, brass, or plastic—to prevent scoring the shaft. Be careful not to crush the rings when tightening the gland.

Q Which ring in a stuffing box does most of the work?
A See Fig. 5-25. Most sealing in a typical stuffing box is done by the ring next to the gland. In all metallic sets, the pressure drop across the set is more uniform, but the ring next to the casing breaks down most of the fluid pressure. The reason for this is that mechanical pressure is higher at the gland because the friction on the outside of the packing against the stuffing box is much greater than the friction along the rod. This would be true if the bore had the same fine finish as the rod. It follows that the more rings the gland tries to force against the bottom of the box, the greater the pressure will be on the first ring it presses

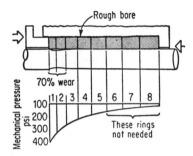

FIG. 5-25. Ring nearest gland does the most work. Renew it oftener to reduce shaft wear.

against. If a set of several rings of the same density isn't seated ring by ring, but all sealing is done by the gland at the same time, the rings nearest the gland will be highly overloaded. Then, because of pressure decay, the rings in the bottom of the box may do no sealing whatsoever. Where a combination set of soft and hard packing is used, the softer rings in the set normally do most of the sealing. That is why dense rings must be seated correctly in the box—to keep the fluid pressure and the gland pressure from being exerted against the softer rings, which would extrude through the joint opening. Test results show that on both centrifugal and reciprocating pumps about 70 percent of the wear is on the first two packing rings nearest the gland. The question, then, is why not have two rings only, or at most three, since they do most of the sealing? The answer is that each additional ring does throttle some fluid pressure, and most machines must have enough rings so that if one fails another does the sealing without shutting down the machine. This is one of the biggest advantages of mechanical packing over mechanical seals.

Q How would you fit new jam-type packing into a stuffing box?
A See Fig. 5-26. To fit new jam-type packing into a stuffing box, first remove all the old packing (Fig. 5-26a). Aim a packing hook at the bore of the box to keep from scratching the shaft. Clean the box thoroughly so the new packing won't hang up. Check for bent rods, grooves, or shoulders. If the neck-bushing clearance in the bottom of the box is great, use a stiffer bottom ring or replace the neck bushing. Revolve the rotary shaft; if the indicator runs out over 0.003 in., straighten the shaft, check the bearings, or balance the rotor. A gyrating shaft beats out the packing. Wind the packing, needed for filling the stuffing box, snugly around the rod (Fig. 5-26b). It is cut through each turn while coiled, as shown. If the packing is slightly too large, never flatten it with a hammer. Place each turn on a clean newspaper and roll it out with a pipe as you would with a rolling pin (Fig. 5-26c). Open the ring joint sidewise (Fig. 5-26d), especially with lead-filled and metallic types. This prevents distorting the

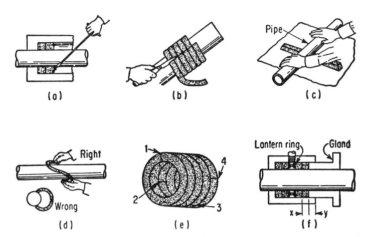

FIG. 5-26. Removing old packing and installing new must be done properly.

molded circumference and breaking the ring opposite its gap. Stagger the joints 180° (Fig. 5-26*e*) if only two rings are in the stuffing box. Space at 120° for three rings and at 90° if four rings or more are in the set. Be sure to install packing so that the lantern ring lines up with the cooling-liquid opening (Fig. 5-26*f*). Also, remember that this ring moves back into the box as the packing is compressed. Therefore, leave space for the gland to enter, as shown.

Q Describe mechanical seals.

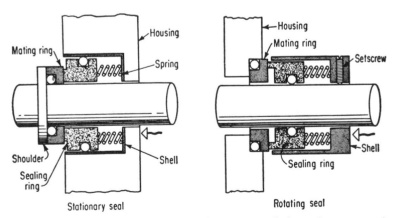

Stationary seal   Rotating seal

FIG. 5-27. Mechanical shaft seals come in numerous designs, do not wear the shaft.

A All mechanical seals have two flat sealing faces at right angles to the axis of rotation. One face is allowed axial motion in order to permit sealing faces to remain in contact despite shaft end play, face wear, and face runout. This rotating face is flexibly mounted; it is also known as the seal ring.

There are two basic types of mechanical seals: stationary and rotating (Fig. 5-27). In a stationary seal, the sealing ring is in the machine housing and does not move. In a rotating seal, the sealing ring turns with the shaft. Mechanical seals need no adjustment; many jam-type packing applications are being taken over for this reason. But the operating engineer must understand how they work to get the best service from them.

CALCULATIONS

Q What data are used for pump calculations?
A To calculate pumps, you should know that

8.33 lb of water = 1 gal (U.S.)
231 in.³ = 1 gal (U.S.)
1 ft³ of water = 1728 in.³
1 ft³ of water = 7.48 gal
1 ft³ of water = 62.5 lb
1-ft column of head of water = 0.434 psi
1 hp = 33,000 lb lifted 1 ft/min
1 hp = 746 W

Q What does 10 × 8 × 12 mean on the nameplate of a steam pump?
A Reciprocating pumps are sized according to the steam cylinder bore, water cylinder bore, and length of the stroke. Thus, 10 in. is the diameter of the steam cylinder, 8 in. is the diameter of the water cylinder, and 12 in. is the stroke.

NOTE: This is a simplex pump. A duplex pump would be described as 10 × 8 × 12 *duplex.*

Q What pressure results from a 60-ft-high vertical pipe filled with water?
A One foot of water weighs 0.434 psi; so 60 × 0.434 = 26.04 psi.   *Ans.*

Q How high will 75 psi of steam force water in a 10 × 8 pump? Assume that there is no loss.
A The formula for calculating pressure balance is

$$P' = \frac{PA}{A'}$$

P' = pressure of total head of water
P = steam pressure
A' = area of water piston
A = (steam piston area) = $10 \times 10 \times 0.7854 = 78.54$ in.²
A' = (water piston area) = $8 \times 8 \times 0.7854 = 50.2656$ in.²

$$P' = \frac{78.54 \times 75}{50.2656} = 117.1 \text{ psi}$$

Water pressure ÷ 0.434 = height of column of water

$$\frac{117.1}{0.434} = 269.6 \text{ ft} \qquad Ans.$$

Q What is the formula for calculating the gallons of water pumped by a reciprocating pump?

A $G = \dfrac{ALNE}{231}$ *Ans.*

G = gal/min
A = area of water piston
L = length of stroke, in.
N = number of strokes
E = efficiency of pump
231 = constant (1 gal = 231 in.³)

Q How many gallons of water per minute will be discharged by a pump with a water cylinder of 8 in. diameter, stroke of 12 in., and 48 double strokes per min? Assume that the pump has 7 percent slip.

A $G = \dfrac{ALNE}{231}$

$A = (8)^2 \times 0.7854 = 50.2656$
$L = 12$ in.
$N = 48 \times 2 = 96$
$E = 100 - 7 = 93$ percent
231 in.³ = 1 gal

$$G = \frac{50.2656 \times 12 \times 96 \times 0.93}{231} = 233.1 \text{ gal/min} \qquad Ans.$$

Q A centrifugal pump delivers 125 gal/min against a head of 75 ft. The efficiency of the pump is 65 percent and motor efficiency is 83 percent. (1) What size motor should be used? (2) How much does it cost to run this pump if the electric current costs 9.8 cents per kilowatthour?

A $hp = \dfrac{WH}{E \times 33,000}$

1 gal = 8.33 lb
$W = 125 \times 8.33 = 1041.25$
$H = 75$
$E = 65$ percent

$hp = \dfrac{1041.25 \times 75}{0.65 \times 33,000}$

hp = 3.64 theoretical requirement
Motor efficiency = 83 percent

$\dfrac{3.64}{0.83} = 4.38$ hp used

(A 4-hp motor is probably OK. See Chap. 8, "Electricity and Electronics," for reasons.) Assuming that the cost of current is 9.8 cents per kilowatthour,

1 hp = 746 W
$4.38 \times 746 = 3267.48 = 3.27$ kW
9.8 cents $\times 3.27 = 32.046$ cents per hour   *Ans.*

Q A pump delivers 125 gal/min against a pressure of 62 psi; suction pressure is 12 psi. If the pump is 60 percent efficient, what horsepower is needed?

A The formula for calculating horsepower is

$hp = \dfrac{W \times H}{33,000 \times E}$

W = total weight, lb of water
H = total head, ft = (water pressure ÷ 0.434)
E = efficiency of pump
Head = total height that water is forced
62 − 12 (suction pressure) = 50 psi
8.33 lb = 1 gal water
$W = 125 \times 8.33 = 1041.25$ lb
$H = 50 \div 0.434 = 115.207$
$E = 60$ percent

$hp = \dfrac{1041.25 \times 115.207}{33,000 \times 0.60} = 6.05$ hp   *Ans.*

Q What will theoretical discharge pressure be if an 1800-r/min pump, with discharge of 60 psi, has its speed doubled to 3600 r/min?

A Since the pressure varies as the square of the speed,

$$\frac{60}{X} = \frac{1800^2}{3600^2} = 240 \text{ psi} \qquad Ans.$$

Q Calculate the power of the foregoing problem if the original power was 3 hp.

A Since power increases directly as the cube of the impeller speed,

$$\frac{3}{X} = \frac{1800 \times 1800 \times 1800}{3600 \times 3600 \times 3600} = \frac{5832}{46,656}$$

$$X = \frac{3 \times 46,656}{5832} = 24 \text{ hp} \qquad Ans.$$

Q Is there a simple formula for calculating the impeller size of centrifugal pumps?

A Yes. If the rated revolutions per minute and the head in feet are known, the diameter of the impeller equals $1833 \times \sqrt{\text{head}} \div \text{r/min}$.   *Ans.*

Q What is the formula for estimating the revolutions per minute of a centrifugal pump?

A $\text{r/min} = \dfrac{1833 \times \sqrt{\text{feet of head}}}{\text{diameter of impeller (in.)}}$ *Ans.*

Q Calculate the revolutions per minute of a centrifugal pump with an impeller 12 in. in diameter, forcing water to 80 ft total head.

A $\text{r/min} = \dfrac{1833 \times \sqrt{\text{head of water}}}{\text{diameter of impeller}}$

$H = 80$
$D = 12$ in.

$$\text{r/min} = \frac{1833 \times \sqrt{80}}{12} = \frac{1833 \times 8.94}{12}$$

$$= 1366.2 \qquad Ans.$$

Q A pump is located at an elevation of 10,000 ft above sea level. What is its maximum theoretical suction lift at this level when handling 62°F water? How does this compare with the maximum lift at sea level?

A Figure 5-2 shows that the reduction in atmospheric pressure is 10.6 ft of 62°F water at 10,000-ft altitude, and that the atmospheric pressure at this altitude is 23.3 ft of water. So the maximum theoretical lift at 10,000 ft above sea level is 23.3 ft of 62°F water. The maximum lift at sea level is 33.95 ft with 62°F water. Lift at the elevated location is 10.6 ft less than the maximum at sea level.

Q If this pump is to operate with a 4-ft suction lift at 10,000-ft altitude, what lift must it have at sea level?

A Its lift at sea level must equal the sum of its actual lift and the reduction in atmospheric pressure between sea level and the elevated position, or 4 + 10.6 = 14.6 ft of water. Note that the chart in Fig. 5-2 can be used for water at any temperature between 32 and 80°F. Above 80°F, correction for the temperature must be made.

SUGGESTED READING

Elonka, Stephen M.: *Standard Plant Operators' Manual*, 3d ed. McGraw-Hill Book Company, New York, 1980 (has over 2000 illustrations).

Elonka, Stephen M.: *Standard Basic Math and Applied Plant Calculations*, McGraw-Hill Book Company, New York, 1979.

6
INSTRUMENTS

Instruments and control are interrelated: Instruments sense, and controls decide and act. In manual operations, you read an instrument, and then decide what, if anything, should be done. Automatic controls receive information signals from a sensing instrument, and then decide what action, if any, is needed. Only then do they proceed with the proper function. Instruments sense and report heat, speed, electric current, color, chemicals, gases, sound, and many, many mediums.

The slow-moving manual control systems are today rapidly disappearing, and, instead, solid-state electronic devices for sensing, as well as deciding, are becoming more numerous yearly. Here we touch upon instruments not covered in other chapters in this book.

PRESSURE-MEASURING INSTRUMENTS

Q Describe a steam gage.

A See Fig. 6-1. A steam gage, properly called a "Bourdon gage," has a hollow circular spring which deforms when subjected to internal pressure. This deformation causes a pointer hand to rotate on a graduated dial. The hand can be removed to set the gage to agree with a test gage or a known pressure from a deadweight gage tester. Besides the hollow spring or Bourdon tube, a link to a sector gear and a pinion gear to move the hand are used. Since the movement of the spring is proportional to the outside and inside pressures, the gage indicates pressure above atmosphere. A vacuum gage is the same as a pressure gage except that the excess pressure is outside the Bourdon tube.

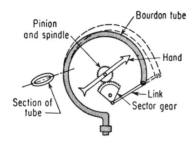

FIG. 6-1. Bourdon tube tends to round out and straighten as pressure increases.

Q What is the difference between a compound gage and a duplex gage?
A The compound gage has a single spring (tube) and hand to show both vacuum and pressure. The duplex gage has two hands and two springs. The hands are fitted like the hour and minute hands of a clock, and one spindle is hollow and the other is solid. Each hand shows pressure on the same dial. This is a convenience for pressure differences for pump suction to discharge, for filter drop, and wherever difference is a concern.

Q Sketch a manometer draft gage and explain how it is read.
A See Fig. 6-2. One end of the U-shaped glass tube is inserted into the air duct; the other end is open to atmospheric pressure. The total distance between the two levels of liquid in the U tube is the pressure. If water is used, read the gage in inches of water. If mercury is used, read the gage in inches of mercury.

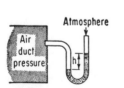

FIG. 6-2. Manometer uses water or mercury in U tube.

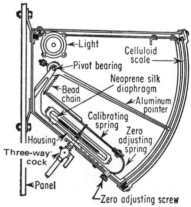

FIG. 6-3. Diaphragm-type draft gage.

Q Sketch a diaphragm-type draft gage and describe how it works.
A See Fig. 6-3. A pressure line (pipe) leads from the duct to the diaphragm chamber. One side is duct pressure and the other is atmosphere. The

diaphragm moves toward the spring when the duct pressure pushes it up. Linkage from the spring allows the pointer to move, thus indicating the pressure.

TEMPERATURE-MEASURING INSTRUMENTS

Q How does a glass-and-liquid thermometer work?
A A glass tube with a bulb at the bottom end (Fig. 6-4) contains mercury or some other liquid which expands when heat is applied and thus rises in the tube. The graduations on the tube denote temperature.

Q What is the difference between a thermometer and a pyrometer?
A There is no difference between a thermometer and a pyrometer, unless a fine distinction is made. Instruments used to check flame temperatures are pyrometers, but so are instruments that measure temperatures over 600°F, and all of them are forms of a thermometer.

Q What is a thermocouple?
A See Fig. 6-5. Two dissimilar metal conductors joined at two points form a thermocouple. When one of these points is heated, a small electric current flows that is directly proportional to the heat. By measuring the current on a calibrated meter, the amount of heat can be determined accurately at some distance and over a wide temperature range.

Q What is meant by the coefficient of lineal expansion?
A Most solids expand when heated. A metal rod heated evenly over its full length expands and becomes longer. Iron has a coefficient of 0.0000067 in./(in.)(°F); steel, 0.0000061 in./(in.)(°F); and brass, 0.000010 in./(in.) (°F), etc.

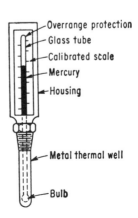

FIG. 6-4.   Mercury-in-glass is a popular type of thermometer.

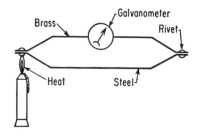

FIG. 6-5. Thermocouple is a circuit of two dissimilar metals; heat causes electron flow.

Q What is a bimetallic strip?

A A bimetallic strip consists of two dissimilar metals, such as brass and steel, of the same length. The strips are fastened together by welding or riveting. When the strips are heated, the brass expands more than the steel, causing the strip to bend. This bending action is used to control switches by opening or closing electric contacts at a given temperature.

Q How does heat affect helixes (spirals)?

A Spirals uncoil when heated. If one end is fixed, the other is free to turn a spindle, such as the thermometer in Fig. 6-6 or a stack switch. Many bimetallic industrial thermometers have helical elements as shown in the illustration.

Q How does heat affect the electrical resistance of metal?

A Heating causes a direct increase in the electrical resistance of most metals. By measuring current change, calibrated instruments can accurately measure temperatures over wide ranges, from deep cold (cryogenic) to extremely high heats.

Q Are there other instruments for measuring temperature?

A Yes. Since thermocouples are unsatisfactory for measuring temperatures above 3000°F, instruments that use the radiation from a hot body are used. The radiation pyrometer measures the intensity of all radiations. Another device, the optical unit, measures the intensity of those of a particular wavelength.

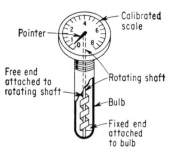

FIG. 6-6. Helical bimetallic element moves pointer to tell temperature.

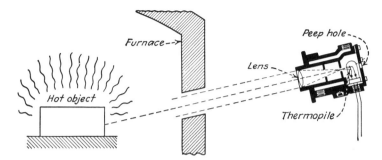

FIG. 6-7. Pyrometer uses a lens to concentrate rays on a thermopile.

The total-radiation pyrometer concentrates the rays from a particular area of the hot body on a thermocouple or thermopile (a group of thermocouples in series), and the thermocouple potential indicates the intensity of all radiation reaching it. In Fig. 6-7 a lens is used to concentrate the rays on a thermopile, which has a nickel coil to compensate for variations in cold-junction temperature. The peephole is for aiming the pyrometer at the hot body. Devices of this kind are available as indicators, recorders, and controllers.

LEVEL-MEASURING INSTRUMENTS

Q *Level* is the height of a liquid in a vessel above a reference or datum line. Measuring level helps determine the volume or weight of liquid in a vessel. Level is expressed directly in units of liquid and can be calibrated to express volume (cubic inches or cubic feet), weight (pounds and tons), and capacity (gallons and barrels). Describe an indicator used for level

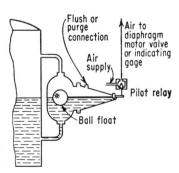

FIG. 6-8. Level indicator for closed vessel can be wired for remote reading.

measurement in vessels where pressures are greater than atmosphere, or under vacuum conditions.

A A cage-type float-operated level gage is often used to measure level in tanks under vacuum or pressure. In Fig. 6-8 the float cage is mounted on the outside vessel wall. The lower connection is from the cast metal cage's bottom into the liquid, and the upper connection is into the vapor. As the level in the tank changes, the level in the cage changes an equal amount. The metal ball float in the cage rises or falls with the liquid surface. The float's movement is transmitted through a packed rotary shaft, to move a valve stem or to operate a pneumatic pilot relay. In this design, the maximum range is limited to 15 in. by practical cage size.

FLOW-MEASURING INSTRUMENTS

Q What principle is often used to operate fluid recording meters?
A Fluid recording meters are often operated by a measuring chamber which is filled and then discharged. A mechanical counter records the number of times the chamber is filled. The principle is the same as that employed in a positive-displacement or piston pump acting in reverse. Here, a liquid pressure causes the piston to move and a counter records the number of strokes.

Q What is a pitot-tube meter?
A See Fig. 6-9. A pitot-tube meter is used to measure the flow of a gas or liquid. It consists of two tubes connected to a pressure gage; a simple manometer is for low-pressure work. One tube is bent and faces the stream of flow. The velocity of the flow forces the liquid in the pitot tube to rise until the weight of the column balances against the force of the flow. A second tube, part of the closed circuit, balances the pressure of the stream against the pressure of the flow. This prevents loss of the measuring fluid.

Q How does a venturi meter work?

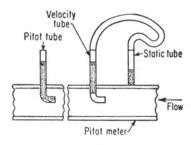

FIG. 6-9. Pitot meter measures flow of gas as well as liquid.

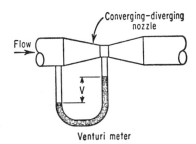

FIG. 6-10. Venturi meter's converging-diverging nozzle creates pressure drop.

A See Fig. 6-10. The flow of a fluid carries energy in the form of pressure and velocity. When a restriction to this flow is met, the velocity increases and pressure decreases. The drop in pressure is measured both before and after flow contraction. This indicates the velocity and can be translated on a calibrated gage as flow in gallons per minute.

Q How does an orifice meter work?
A See Fig. 6-11. An orifice meter operates in the same way as a venturi meter, except that an orifice is used to contract flow instead of the converging-diverging nozzle of the venturi meter.

Q Describe a fluid recording disk-type meter.
A See Fig. 6-12. Fluid enters the measuring chamber under the disk. Pressure causes the disk to push the pin about the bearing. As the disk revolves, it wobbles. At one-half a revolution, the upper part of the case fills and continues to rotate the disk. Since a definite quantity of fluid must flow to complete the revolution, a train of gears operates the pointers on the dials of the meter. The meter is calibrated to read in gallons.

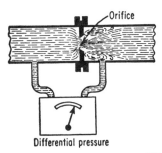

FIG. 6-11. Orifice meter uses differential pressure method.

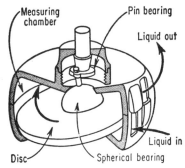

FIG. 6-12. Fluid recording disk-type meter.

INSTRUMENTS THAT MEASURE FLUE-GAS QUALITY

Q What is a combustion, or CO_2, indicator?

A Any device that measures, records, or visually tells of flue-gas conditions is a combustion, or CO_2, indicator. There are several measuring methods in use:

1. *Visual.* Black smoke indicates poor combustion, usually caused by insufficient air. A malfunctioning oil atomizer is a frequent cause. White smoke is caused by excess air. Overheated oil can be a cause. Brown haze is undesirable nitrogen oxide (NO_x), which is an irritant-gas nuisance that will cause EPA action. A clear stack with the least amount of excess air and no brown haze is desired. Periscopes are used for monitoring the breeching, with either an operator seeing the color of gas flow or instrument and automatic scanning control or both. Increasingly, video television cameras monitor critical areas and inform the operators.

2. *Chemical test.* The absorption of CO_2 in a caustic solution is the basis of this test—usually an orsat or Fyrite device. The resulting vacuum is measured in a glass tube calibrated to read the percentage of CO_2. Some chemical types also work continuously.

3. *Electrical measurement.* An analyzer has two cells with an electric heating element in each. One cell is filled with air, the other with flue gas. Each gas has a different specific heat and cools the coils accordingly. Since the electrical resistance of the coils varies with temperature, it is measured and the difference is read on the dial of the instrument as the percent of CO_2.

4. *Density of flue gas as compared with density of air.* This type of CO_2 indicator has two chambers with a rotating and a fixed fan mounted in each chamber. Air is circulated in one chamber and flue gas in the other in a continuous process. Both fans rotate at the same speed and discharge toward the fixed fans. The fixed fans are linked together and balanced to measure the difference of impact of heavy CO_2 against the air. The linkage moves the pointer across a dial calibrated in percent CO_2. (See Chap. 12, "Fuels and Firing.")

INSTRUMENTS THAT MEASURE STEAM AND OIL QUALITY

Q What is a steam calorimeter?

A A steam calorimeter is used for measuring the quality of steam. Three basic types are used: condensing, separating, and throttling.

Q What is a bomb calorimeter?

A A bomb calorimeter is used for measuring the Btu content of a fuel sample. A measured quantity of fuel is placed in a small crucible inside a strong steel shell (bomb). Oxygen is pumped into the shell, and a small electric element dips into the fuel sample to start combustion. Heat given off is measured in a water jacket that surrounds the bomb. The rise in temperature of the known weight of water is calculated to give the Btu content of the weighed sample. All internal parts of the bomb are corrosion-proof to prevent damage by oxygen.

Q How is oil viscosity measured?

A See Fig. 6-13. In this country, oil viscosity is measured in seconds Saybolt, either Saybolt Seconds Furol (SSF) for heavy fuels or Saybolt Seconds Universal (SSU) for lighter fuels. Bearing oil is heated to 130°F and diesel oil to 210°F, and their viscosity is expressed as the number of seconds needed for 60 cc to flow through an orifice about $\frac{1}{16}$ in. in diameter at the test temperature.

Q How is pour point measured?

A See Fig. 6-14. Pour point is measured by cooling the oil to a low temperature, under controlled test conditions, until it will barely flow.

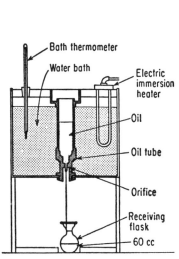

FIG. 6-13. Saybolt universal visco-simeter.

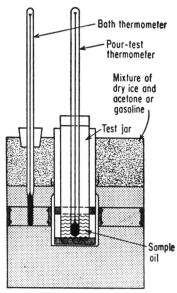

FIG. 6-14. Apparatus tells pour point.

MISCELLANEOUS INSTRUMENTS

Q How does a servomotor work?
A See Fig. 6-15. A servomotor is a hydraulic device that positions valves or other mechanisms by means of a pilot valve. By so doing it controls the oil flow and pressure to a larger cylinder.

Q Explain a hydrometer and describe its use for several engineering applications.
A A hydrometer is a float with a graduated stem and with a weight at its bottom end. It is commonly used for testing battery acid. More refined models have a thermometer to give two simultaneous readings of specific gravity and temperature to correct the density. These are used to read in (1) degrees Baumé, for oil; (2) grains of salt or dissolved solids, for boiler water; (3) specific gravity, for various tests such as storage batteries; and (4) strength of brine solutions, etc.

Q What is a dynamometer used for?
A A dynamometer is used to measure the power output of a machine. There are two broad classes: (1) One is the absorption type by which the power measured is converted into some usable form. A prony brake is an example. (2) The other is the transmission type by which power is passed on unchanged. An electric generator under maximum load for the machine can have power output measured electrically.

Q What is the difference between a revolution counter and a tachometer?
A A revolution counter shows the cumulative number of revolutions, while a tachometer shows instantaneous revolutions per minute.

NOTE: Most automobiles use a tachometer as a speedometer, which reads miles or kilometers per hour. However, the total mileage of travel is shown on a revolution counter.

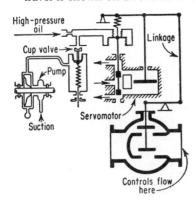

FIG. 6-15. Servomotor hydraulically actuates a final control element.

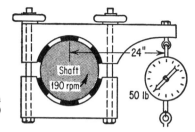

FIG. 6-16. Prony brake shown with 50-lb load calculates to 3.6 hp at 190 r/min.

Q What is a prony brake?
A See Fig. 6-16. A prony brake consists of a brake band wrapped around a pulley that is placed on the shaft of a machine being tested for power output. When the brake band is compressed, the long arm fastened to the brake presses against a scale which measures torque. Calculations and tests give you the bhp.

ELECTRICAL INSTRUMENTS

Q What is a voltmeter?
A A voltmeter connects across the line to measure voltage. High-resistance windings are used in these instruments.

Q What is an ammeter?
A An ammeter is connected in a series or through a shunt connected to one side of a circuit to measure current flow. Current transformers are used for high-voltage alternating current (ac).

Q What is a wattmeter?
A A wattmeter is a combination of a voltmeter and an ammeter calibrated either to read directly in watts or to record wattage on a series of dials. It is used to measure power either instantaneously or on a cumulative time basis.

Q What is an internal shunt?
A It is a shunt installed inside an ammeter case. It has a fixed value and is always part of the meter circuit. The meter scale is calibrated to read the actual meter current times the multiplier. If more than one internal shunt is supplied, either the readings are multiplied or more than one scale of calibrations is used on the instrument.

Q What is an external shunt?
A An external shunt is any shunt installed outside the meter box, regardless of whether it is on the meter case or behind the switchboard. External shunts are used to extend the range of the meter.

Q An ammeter has a range of 0 to 10 A and a resistance of 0.1 Ω (ohms). If the range is to be extended from 0 to 100 A, what size shunt is needed?

A Formula for calculating shunt, measured in Ω:

$$R_s = \frac{R_m}{N-1}$$

where R_s = resistance of shunt
R_m = resistance of meter
N = multiplier

The first step is to find the multiplier. Our instrument has a range of 0 to 10 A, and we want 0 to 100 A, or 10 times as much. So, the multiplier in this case is 10. Therefore,

$$R_s = \frac{R_m}{N-1} = \frac{0.1}{10-1} = \frac{0.1}{9} = 0.011 \ \Omega \qquad Ans.$$

NOTE: Always try to keep the multiplier simple by choosing a shunt that is an easy fraction of the total resistance.

Q What is a permanent-magnet moving-coil meter?

A See Figs. 6-17 and 6-18. This instrument consists of a permanent magnet and a moving coil on a pivoted staff. The pointer on the staff moves

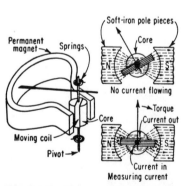

FIG. 6-17. Permanent-magnet moving-coil instrument has pointer on staff.

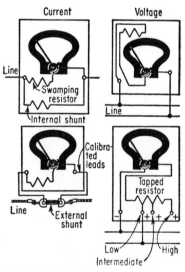

FIG. 6-18. Measuring range is extended by shunts and series resistors shown here.

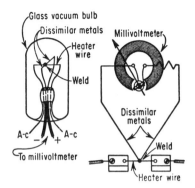

FIG. 6-19. Vacuum (left) and open-air thermocouple (right) for high frequency.

over a calibrated dial. Springs are used to oppose the torque and to carry the current in and out of the coil. This instrument properly connected can be designed to measure direct current (dc) and dc voltage. Ac measurement is more difficult but is practical if used for high-frequency work, such as with radios. Two systems are used for alternating current: (1) A thermocouple is buried in a heating element and the thermocouple effect is measured (Fig. 6-19). (2) A copper oxide disk rectifier is used, and the resulting direct current is measured (Fig. 6-20).

Q What is a moving-iron instrument?

A See Fig. 6-21. A moving-iron instrument consists of a fixed solenoid coil and a moving plunger; it is used for measuring alternating current. A shaft is pivoted and carries the pointer across the calibrated dial. Springs

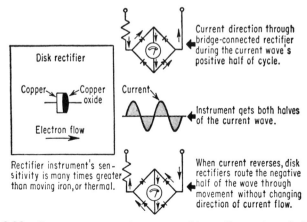

FIG. 6-20. Permanent-magnet instrument with rectifier works as indicated.

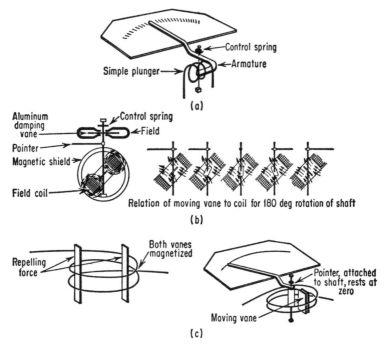

FIG. 6-21. Moving-iron instruments are used for measuring alternating current.

are used to oppose the movement of the plunger as the alternating current is passed through the solenoid. This instrument is also used for dc measurements. While not as accurate as the moving-coil instruments, it is adequate for most practical dc measuring requirements.

In contrast to the moving-coil type, moving-iron instruments have a fixed coil and a soft-iron member, with a shaft and free-moving pointer attached. An inclined coil is another member of the moving-iron family. It provides a long, well-distributed scale in both ac portable and switchboard instruments. The operation of a repulsion instrument depends on the repelling force set up between two adjacent pieces of soft iron that are subjected to the same magnetic field.

Q Are other heat effects used for instruments?
A Yes. Heat has electrical and photoelectrical effects that are useful no matter how feeble the current, as in a thermocouple (Fig. 6-5). Another example is the radiation pyrometer, which is an optical device for measuring very high temperatures. It utilizes a lens system to both cool and focus heat radiation on a thermocouple.

Q Explain the combustion safeguard system in Fig. 6-22.

A This system is based on the rectified impedance principle for oil-fired burners, which states that either a flame or a photocell sited at a flame is capable not only of conducting an electric current but also of rectifying an alternating current. The system utilizes this principle by applying alternating current to either a flame electrode inserted in the flame or a photocell sited at the flame. And so the resultant rectified current, which can be produced only when flame is present, is in turn detected by the relay.

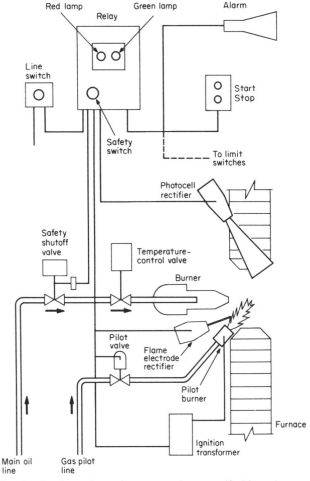

FIG. 6-22. Combustion safeguard system works on rectified impedance principle.

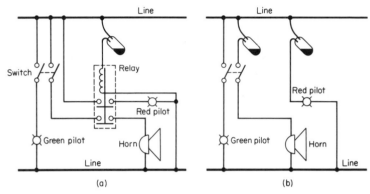

FIG. 6-23.   Emergency warning systems are used to warn or shut down malfunctioning equipment.

The actual flame-detecting units consist of flame-electrode and photocell rectifier assemblies, and the protecting relay. The flame-electrode type is commonly used for nonluminous flames such as oil flames.

Q   Why can a flame conduct an electric current?

A   Because when fuels are burned, a dissociation of the components of the fuel takes place and leaves free, within the flame boundary, a concentration of ions, which carry electric charges. These ions are produced by splitting the neutral particles which make up the gas into positive and negative parts. The splitting-up process takes place constantly during the burning of the fuel.

And since an electric current is a flow of charged particles through a substance, a flame which is made up of a concentration of charged particles may conduct an electric current.

Q   Why are emergency instrument systems important?

A   An emergency system's main purpose is to sound an alarm or shut down equipment when abnormal operation occurs. Figure 6-23 shows two systems. Usually the same kind of device built for control service can also be used for an emergency trip or alarm, but it is best not to use the same unit for both services.

When selecting equipment for alarms, consider the following functions that may be required: (1) high and low pressure, (2) high and low level, (3) high and low temperature, (4) high and low flow rate, (5) electric-circuit characteristics, (6) chemical change, and (7) movement.

For notifying an operator in an emergency, use the audible and visual methods shown (Fig. 6-23). In system *a*, a mercury switch controls a relay to operate the light and alarm. System *b* is the same except that two mercury switches operate simultaneously instead of the relay. Instead of lamps, an annunciator board can mount a series of tabs, which drop out to an open position when energized to identify the instrument concerned.

SUGGESTED READING

Elonka, Stephen M., and Alonzo R. Parsons: *Standard Instrumentation Questions and Answers*, Krieger Publishing Company, Inc., Melbourne, Fla., 1979.

Elonka, Stephen M.: *Marmaduke Surfaceblow's Salty Technical Romances*, Krieger Publishing Company, Inc., Melbourne, Fla., 1979 (has 122 stories on solving technical problems).

7

EXAMINATION CALCULATIONS

Our latest survey of license requirements for boiler operators and stationary engineers in the United States and Canada (see Chap. 21) indicates that because of the energy crunch, causing industry to convert from oil to coal, more and more examiners are asking questions on the firing and burning of coal. Included in the problems are questions that have appeared in examinations. Also, there are some questions and calculations that will enable you to burn coal more efficiently.

Because examiners may not allow the use of electronic calculators, we strongly advise, before you apply for a license examination, that you play it safe and work all the problems in this book without your calculator.

CONVERSION FACTORS

1 mil = 0.001 inch
2000 pounds = 1 short ton
2240 pounds = 1 long ton
5280 feet = 1 statute mile
6080 feet = 1 nautical mile

Cross-sectional area in circular mils = diameter of round wire in mils squared.

To convert degrees Fahrenheit to degrees Celsius (Centigrade), use the following equation:

$$°F = \frac{9}{5} °C + 32$$

Atmosphere (standard) = 29.92 inches of mercury
Atmosphere (standard) = 14.7 pounds per square inch
1 horsepower = 746 watts
1 horsepower = 33,000 foot-pounds of work per minute
1 British thermal unit = 778 foot-pounds
1 cubic foot = 7.48 gallons
1 gallon = 231 cubic inches
1 cubic foot of fresh water = 62.5 pounds
1 cubic foot of salt water = 64 pounds
1 foot of head of water = 0.434 pound per square inch
1 inch of head of mercury = 0.491 pound per square inch
1 gallon of fresh water = 8.33 pounds
1 barrel (oil) = 42 gallons
1 long ton of fresh water = 36 cubic feet
1 long ton of salt water = 35 cubic feet
1 ounce (avoirdupois) = 437.5 grains
1 therm-hour = 100,000 Btu per hour
1 brake horsepower = 2544 Btu per hour

$$1 \text{ brake horsepower} = \frac{2544}{100,000} = 0.02544 \text{ therm-hour}$$

$$1 \text{ therm-hour} = \frac{100,000}{2544} = \frac{39.3082 \text{ brake horsepower}}{(40 \text{ hp is close enough})}$$

$$1 \text{ therm-hour} = \frac{100,000}{33,475} = \frac{2.9873 \text{ boiler horsepower}}{(3 \text{ hp is close enough})}$$

EXAMPLE: How many therm-hours in a 100-hp engine?
$100 \times 0.02544 = 2.544$ therm-hours   *Ans.*

1 boiler hp = 33,475 Btu per hour
= 34.5 lb steam per hour at 212°F
= 139 ft^2 EDR (equivalent direct radiation)
1 EDR = 240 Btu per hour
1 kW = 3413 Btu per hour
3413 British thermal units (Btu) = 1 kilowatthour (kWh)
1000 watts = 1 kilowatt (kW)
1.341 horsepower (hp) = 1 kilowatt
2545 Btu = 1 horsepower-hour (hp-hr)
0.746 kilowatt = 1 hp
1 micron (micrometer) = one millionth of a meter (unit of length)

METRIC CONVERSION

NOTE: Now that most countries have converted to the metric system, these conversion factors are important to know.

METRIC TO ENGLISH CONVERSION

To convert	into	Multiply by
Centimeters	Inches	0.3937
	Feet	0.0328
	Yards	0.010936
Kilograms	Pounds	2.205
Liters	Cubic feet	0.03531
	Cubic inches	61.02
	Quarts (U.S.)	1.057
	Gallons (U.S.)	4.228
Meters	Inches	39.37
	Feet	3.281
	Yards	0.9144

ENGLISH TO METRIC CONVERSION

To convert	into	Multiply by
Inches	Centimeters	2.54
Inches	Meters	0.0254
Square inches	Square centimeters	6.45
Cubic inches	Cubic centimeters	16.39
Feet	Centimeters	30.48
Feet	Meters	0.3048
Yards	Meters	1.0936
Pounds	Kilograms	0.4535
Quarts (U.S.)	Liters	0.946
Gallons (U.S.)	Liters	0.2365
Tons (short)	Kilograms	907.03
Atmosphere	Centimeters of mercury	76.0
Pounds per square inch	Kilopascals[1]	6.8947

EXAMPLES:

To convert 70 in. to centimeters:

$$70 \times 2.54 = 177.8 \text{ cm}$$

[1] The kilopascal (kPa) is the unit used for measuring pressure and stress. The conversion from pounds per square inch (psi) to kilopascals is unfamiliar to most of us. The ASME code will show *psig* followed by *kPa,* which is an approximation (to convert psig to kPa, multiply by 7 to get a rough equivalent). Check the ASME code for metrication. Note that the unit *bar,* which you may encounter, is the same as kPa.

To convert 6 m to inches:

$6 \times 39.37 = 236.22$ in.

To convert 60 kg per square centimeter to pounds per square inch or psi, three steps are necessary:

1. Convert kilograms to pounds:

   $60 \times 2.205 = 132.30$ lb

2. Convert square centimeters to square inches:

   $0.3937^2 = 0.155$ in.²

3. Then

   $$\frac{60 \text{ kg}}{\text{cm}^2} = \frac{132.3 \text{ lb}}{0.155 \text{ in.}^2} = 853.6 \text{ psi} \qquad Ans.$$

NOTE: By dividing 2.205 by 0.155, a factor of 14.226 is obtained, which if used will give pounds per square inch directly from kilograms, that is, $60 \times 14.226 = 853.6$ psi.

BURNING COAL

Q A full trimmed coal bin is 12 ft long and 8 ft wide. One end is 9 ft high, and the other is 7 ft high. If the coal weighs 40 lb/ft³ how many tons are in the bin?

A Average height $= \dfrac{9 + 7}{2} = 8$ ft

ft³ $= 12 \times 9 \times 8 = 864$
$864 \times 40 = 34{,}560$ lb
$34{,}560 \div 2000$ lb/ton $= 17.28$ tons $\qquad Ans.$

Q Given: Coal of 62 percent carbon; rate of combustion $= 11.75$ lb/(hr) (ft² of grate surface); size of grate $= 6 \times 6$ ft; volume of 1 lb of air at $62°F = 13.14$ ft³; 150 percent air supplied. How many cubic feet of air are required per minute? (11.58 lb of air will theoretically burn 1 lb of carbon.)

A $6 \times 6 = 36$ ft² of grate
$36 \times 11.75 = 423$ lb of coal on the grate per hr

$\dfrac{423}{60} = 7.05$ lb of coal per min

7.05 × 0.62 = 4.371 lb of carbon in coal
4.371 × 11.58 = 50.616 theoretical lb of air
50.616 × 1.5 = 75.924 lb of air supplied at 150 percent air supply
75.924 × 13.14 = 997.64 ft³/min air   *Ans.*

Q Coal costs $55 per ton and has a heating value of 12,500 Btu per pound; overall efficiency of the boiler is 70 percent. At what price per gallon would fuel oil break even with the coal? Assume that the fuel oil has 140,000 Btu/gal and the overall boiler efficiency is 80 percent with oil. Disregard all other items, such as storage and ash handling.

A 12,500 × 0.70 = 8750 Btu available per lb of coal
8750 × 2000 = 17,500,000 Btu per ton

$$\frac{17,500,000}{55 \times 100} = 3181.8182 \text{ Btu per 1 cent}$$

140,000 × 0.80 = 112,000 Btu available per gallon

$$\frac{112,000}{3181.8182} = 35.2 \text{ cents per gallon} \qquad Ans.$$

Q Using coal of 13,210 Btu and 75 percent overall boiler efficiency from and at 212°F, what is the evaporation per pound of coal?

A $W = \dfrac{HE}{970.4}$

where W = lb of water evaporated per lb of coal
H = total heat available in 1 lb of coal
E = efficiency of boiler
970.4 = Btu required to evaporate 1 lb of water from and at 212°F

$$W = \frac{13,210 \times 0.75}{970.4}$$

= 10.209 lb of water evaporated per lb of coal   *Ans.*

Q Calculate the evaporation per pound of 12,000 Btu coal that is 80 percent combustible, from and at 212°F.

A $W = \dfrac{\text{Btu}}{R \times 970.4}$

where W = lb of water per lb of combustibles
R = percent combustible in coal
970.4 = latent heat of steam at atmospheric pressure (0 gage pressure)

$$W = \frac{12,000}{0.80 \times 970.4}$$

= 15.457 lb of water   *Ans.*

Q Calculate the number of pounds of coal needed to heat 32,660 lb of water from 70 to 150°F. The efficiency of the heater is 65 percent and the coal has a value of 13,000 Btu/lb.

A $W = \dfrac{W' \times \text{TR}}{H \times E}$

where W = lb of coal required
W' = lb of water heated
TR = temperature rise of water
H = Btu/lb of coal
E = efficiency of the heater
$150 - 70 = 80°F$ temperature rise to be added by heating

$$W = \frac{32,660 \times 80}{13,000 \times 0.65}$$

$= 309.2$ lb of coal   *Ans.*

STEAM GENERATION

Q What is boiler horsepower? How does it differ from engine horsepower?

A Boiler horsepower is an arbitrary unit involving 10 ft² of heating surface, or 33,479 Btu (33,480 used in calculations), or the evaporation of 34.5 lb of water from and at 212°F. This is the potential of energy developed. Engine horsepower is 33,000 ft·lb of work per minute.

Q Give three formulas for calculating the horsepower rating of boilers.
A H = total Btu used
W = equivalent evaporation of water in pounds
S = ft² of heating surface of boiler

1. $\text{hp} = \dfrac{H}{33,480}$

2. $\text{hp} = \dfrac{W}{34.5}$

3. $\text{hp} = \dfrac{S}{10}$ or $\text{hp} = \dfrac{S}{11.5}$

NOTE: Some authorities use 10; others use 11.5. For your exams, find out from the experienced workers before you go for exams.

Q What is the percent output of rating of a boiler containing 850 ft² of heating surface, and generating 3200 lb of steam per hr at 95 psig, when the feed-water inlet temperature is 190°F and the steam quality is 97 percent? Use formulas 1 and 3 in preceding question.

A Ten square feet of heating surface = 1 hp. Convert gage pressure to approximate absolute pressure by adding 15 psi. 95 + 15 = 110 psia. For accuracy, use 14.696 or 14.7 instead of 15, which is an approximation.

Latent heat at 110 psia = 883.2 Btu/lb
Heat of liquid at 110 psi = 305.66 Btu/lb
883 × 0.97 steam quality = 856.5 Btu latent heat/lb
856.5 + 305.6 + 1162.1 Btu/lb at 97 percent dry
190°F − 32°F = 158 Btu/lb of feed water
1162.1 − 158 = 1004.1 Btu total heat needed
3200 lb/hr × 1004.1 = 3,213,120 Btu/hr

(Formula 1) $hp = \dfrac{H}{33,480}$

$H = 3,213,120$ Btu

$\dfrac{3,213,120 \text{ Btu}}{33,480 \text{ Btu/hp}} = 96 \text{ hp}$

(Formula 3) $hp = \dfrac{S}{10}$

$S = 850 \text{ ft}^2$

$hp = \dfrac{850}{10} = 85$

$\dfrac{96}{85} = 1.13$

$1.13 \times 100 = 113$ percent of rating   *Ans.*

Q What is the meaning of the term *factor of evaporation?* State the formula.
A The factor of evaporation is the ratio of the actual amount of water evaporated at the boiler conditions to the equivalent evaporation of water from and at 212°F.

The formula is: $F = \dfrac{H - q}{970.4}$

$F =$ factor of evaporation
$H =$ Btu required for steam under actual boiler operation
$q =$ Btu heat of liquid of feed water
970.4 = latent heat of steam at 212°F

NOTE: Always subtract 32°F from the temperature of the feed water.

Q Calculate the equivalent evaporation of 4500 lb of water. Steam pressure is 100 psia and feed water is 180°F.

A The formula for calculating the factor of evaporation is as follows:

$$F = \frac{H - q}{970.4}$$

where F = factor of evaporation
H = total heat in 1 lb of steam
q = heat of liquid of feed water
970.4 = latent heat of 1 lb of steam, Btu

Consult the steam table and note that 1 lb of steam at 100 psia has a total heat of 1187.2 Btu. This is H.

180 − 32 = 148 Btu/lb heat of liquid water (note that 32 is always subtracted).

$$F = \frac{1187.2 - 148}{970.4}$$

$$= 1.071$$

The formula for calculating the equivalent evaporation in pounds of water is as follows:

$W' = WF$

where W' = equivalent evaporation, lb of water
W = actual evaporation, lb of water
F = factor of evaporation
$W' = 4500 \times 1.071$
$= 481.9$ *Ans.*

Q A boiler evaporates 5000 lb of water per hr under actual load. The factor of evaporation is 1.06. How many pounds of fuel are consumed to evaporate this water from and at 212°F if each pound of fuel has 18,000 Btu and the overall boiler efficiency is 80 percent?

A $W' = W \times F$
$W' = 5000 \times 1.06$
Equivalent weight of water = 5300 lb
Btu available per lb of fuel at 80 percent efficiency = 18,000 × 0.80 = 14,400
Latent heat of steam at 212°F = 970.4 Btu
5300 × 970.4 = 5,143,120 heat units needed, Btu

$$\frac{5,143,120}{14,400} = 357.16 \text{ lb of fuel} \qquad Ans.$$

Q How many pounds of steam at 15 psig are needed to heat 100 lb of feed water from 60 to 180°F at atmospheric conditions?

A 180 − 60 = 120 Btu/lb needed
100 × 120 = 12,000 Btu needed
15 psig + 14.7 = 29.7 psia
Total heat of steam at 29.7 = 1163.8 Btu   (steam table)
The steam temperature is lowered to that of a water-steam mixture as follows:
180 − 32 = 148 Btu/lb heat of liquid
1163.8 − 148 = 1015.8 Btu available for heating water for each lb
of 15 psig steam
12,000 ÷ 1015.8 = 11.8 lb of 15 psig steam needed   *Ans.*

Q In a properly operated boiler the amount of blowdown is adjusted to some percentage of the steam flow. This is approximated by tests to keep the boiler-water solids concentration at or below some set limit. Suppose that 850 ppm solids is the limit—30 percent makeup with 110 ppm solids. Determine how many pounds of blowdown are needed for each 1000 lb of steam generated.
A 110 × 0.30 = 33 ppm solids in feed water

$$\frac{850 \text{ ppm solids}}{33} = 25.75 \text{ concentrations}$$

$$\frac{1}{25.75} \times 100 = \text{percent blowdown} = 3.8 \text{ percent}$$

1000 lb × 3.8 percent = 38 lb blowdown   *Ans.*

NOTE: Total dissolved solids (TDS) is more accurate than a chlorides test. TDS requires more skill and more equipment than the simple chlorides test.

VACUUM

Q How many inches of mercury will balance a column of water 26 ft high?
A 1 in. Hg (mercury) = 0.491 psi
1 ft water = 0.443 psi

Find a factor: $\dfrac{0.433}{0.491} = 0.8818$ Hg per ft of water (use 0.882)

0.882 × 26 = 22.93 in. Hg   *Ans.*

Q The vacuum gage on a condenser reads 27 in. Hg and the atmospheric barometer reading is 29.8 Hg. What is the absolute pressure in inches of barometer and in pounds per square inch in the condenser?

A 29.8 Hg in atmosphere − 27.0 Hg in condenser = 2.8 Hg absolute
   pressure
   1 in. Hg = 0.49 psi
   2.8 × 0.49 = 1.37 psia   *Ans.*

PUMPING

Q One pump can empty a tank in 8 hr 15 min, while another takes 11
hr. If both pumps are used together, how long will it take to empty the
tank?
A The amount emptied in 1 hr by both pumps = 1/8.25 + 1/11. Use
lowest common denominator (LCD) = 33.

$$\frac{4+3}{33} = \frac{7}{33}$$

To find the amount of time, invert to 33/7 = 4.714 hr.

   0.714 hr × 60 min = 42.84 min
   0.84 min × 60 sec = 50.4 sec
   4 hr 42 min 50 sec = time for both pumps to empty the tank   *Ans.*

Q What is the relationship between head in feet and pounds pressure
per square inch?
A 1 lb pressure per in.^{2} = 1 ÷ 0.434 = 2.3 ft of head.
   1 ft of head = 1 ÷ 2.3 = 0.434 psi   *Ans.*

Q Tabulate some common data used in pumping calculations.
A Some of the principal constants used in pumping calculations and
their equivalent values in common units of weight and volume are as
follows:
   1 lb pressure per in.^{2} = 2.3 ft of head
   1 ft of head = 0.434 psi
   1 ft^3 of water weighs 62.4 lb
   1 ft^2 of water contains 7.48 U.S. gal
   1 ft^3 of water contains 6.24 imperial (imp.) gal
   1 U.S. gal weighs 8.33 lb
   1 imp. gal weighs 10 lb
   1 U.S. gal contains 231 in.^{3}
   1 imp. gal contains 277 in.^{3}
   1 ft^3 of hot water weighs approximately 60 lb
   1 boiler hp is equivalent to the evaporation of 34½ lb of water from
water at 212°F into saturated steam at 212°F.
   1 ft · lb is the mechanical work done when a weight of 1 lb is lifted
through a height of 1 ft, or work done when a force of 1 lb is exerted
through a distance of 1 ft. It is the unit of mechanical work.

In addition to the above quantities, the following formulas relating to circles and cylinders are used in many pumping calculations.

The area of a circle is 78.5 percent of the area of the square it fits into. That is the diameter squared and then multiplied by 0.785, or

$$A = D^2 \times 0.785$$

The diameter of a circle is equal to the square root of the quotient of the area divided by 0.785, or

$$D = \sqrt{A \div 0.785}$$

The volume of a cylinder is equal to the area of the end multiplied by the length, or

$$V = A \times L$$

The values given have been carried to three significant figures only. Practically all pumping calculations are based on very approximate data and observations. Using more exact values would therefore mean a great deal more arithmetical work with no real advantage in the accuracy of the final result. For the same reason it is a mere waste of time to take approximate measurements and work an answer out to some such figure as 24,689.764 when all we can be reasonably sure of is that the quantity is somewhere around 24,700.

Q If fuel oil expands 0.0004 volume for each degree Fahrenheit, determine how many gallons should be paid for if 12,000 gal were received at 150°F.

A In the United States we usually calculate oil at 60°F; therefore,

150 − 60 = 90°F difference
0.0004 × 90 = 0.036 vol
12,000 × 0.036 = 432 gal
12,000 − 432 = 11,568 gal   *Ans.*

VELOCITY AND CENTRIFUGAL ENERGY

Q What are the maximum safe speeds for flywheels cast in one piece of (1) cast iron and (2) steel?

A (1) 6000 ft/min rim speed
(2) 8000 ft/min rim speed

NOTE: Consult *Marks,*[2] as there is much to know about flywheels.

---

[2] Theodore Baumeister, *Marks' Standard Handbook for Mechanical Engineers,* 8th ed., McGraw-Hill Book Company, New York, 1978.

Q A cast one-piece flywheel has a 9-ft diameter. What is its maximum speed for either iron or steel?

A Circumference = $3.1416 \times$ diameter

$C = 3.1416 \times 9 = 28.274$ circumference of rim

For cast iron, $r/min = \dfrac{rim\ speed}{circumference}$

$$= \frac{6000}{28.274} = 212\ r/min \qquad Ans.$$

For steel, $r/min = \dfrac{8000}{28.274}$

$$= 282\ r/min \qquad Ans.$$

Q What is the formula for calculating the energy stored in a rotating flywheel rim?

A $E = \dfrac{WV^2}{2g}$

where E = kinetic energy
W = weight of rim
. V = rim speed, ft/sec
g = 32.2 ft/sec acceleration due to gravity

Q What energy is stored in a 9-ft flywheel rim weighing 10 tons and revolving at 125 r/min? Neglect the spokes.

A Circumference = $3.1416 \times 9 = 28.274$

$$\frac{r/min}{60\ sec} = ft/sec$$

$$\frac{125}{60} = 2.083$$

$$2.083 \times 28.274 = 58.895\ velocity$$

$$E = \frac{WV^2}{2 \times 32.2}$$

W = 10 tons = 20,000 lb (2000 lb = 1 ton)
V^2 = 58.895 $\times$ 58.895 = 3468.621

$$E = \frac{20,000 \times 3468.621}{64.4} = 1,077,211\ ft \cdot lb$$

550 ft $\cdot$ lb/sec = 1 hp

$$\frac{1,077,211}{550} = 1958.5 \text{ hp} \qquad Ans.$$

Q A motor runs at 1750 r/min and has an 8-in. pulley which is belted to a 20-in. countershaft pulley. At what speed does the countershaft turn?
A Solve by the inverse-proportion method.

$$\frac{20}{8} = \frac{1750}{\text{unknown } (x)} \qquad \text{(cross-multiply)}$$

$20x = 14,000$
$x = 700$ r/min   *Ans.*

Q Suppose that the countershaft speed in the previous problem is 300 r/min with the same motor and pulley. What size pulley is on the counter-shaft?
A Use the same mathematical process but substitute in the formula.

$$\frac{x\text{-in. diameter}}{8\text{-in. diameter}} = \frac{1750}{300}$$

$300x = 14,000$
$x = 46.6$ in.   *Ans.*

MECHANICAL ADVANTAGE

Q What are mechanical advantage problems?
A These problems involve the work done by (1) levers—ball and lever, (2) gears, (3) pulleys, (4) hydraulic cylinders, (5) inclined planes, and (6) screws. You will have to know various forms of these problems, which are fully covered in *Standard Basic Math and Applied Plant Calculations*.

Q Calculate the mechanical advantage of a lever.
A RULE: To calculate any form of a lever, multiply the distance from the fulcrum to the weight. To find the force, sum up the upward forces against the downward forces.

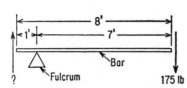

FIG. 7-1. Here, 175 lb on long end will balance 1225 lb on short end.

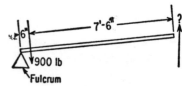

FIG. 7-2. Here, 56¼ lb lifts 900 lb.

Q A bar is 8 ft long. A man weighing 175 lb puts his full weight at one end of the bar. If the fulcrum is 1 ft from the other end, how much can the man lift? See Fig. 7-1.

A RULE: The sum of the downward forces is equal to the sum of the upward forces.

Down force	Up force
$7 \times 175 = 1225$	$1 \times X$

$$1225 \text{ lb} = X$$

Suppose that the same 8-ft bar is used again, but this time the weight to be lifted is 900 lb and is 6 in. from the end of the bar. How much force is needed at the other end of the bar? See Fig. 7-2.

RULE: The sum of the downward forces is equal to the sum of the upward forces.

Down: $0.5 \text{ ft} \times 900 = 450 \text{ ft·lb}$

Up: $8 \times X = 8X \text{ ft·lb}$

$$\frac{450}{8} = 56.25 \text{ lb} \qquad Ans.$$

Q Calculate a ball-and-lever safety valve based on:

Boiler pressure $= 75$ psi
Diameter of valve $= 2$ in.
Distance of valve to fulcrum $= 4$ in.
Weight of ball $= 50$ lb

Find the length of the lever needed to balance the ball.

NOTE: Ball-and-lever safety valves are prohibited by ASME and jurisdictional codes.

A See Fig. 7-3. Again, the basic rule: The sum of the downward forces is equal to the sum of the upward forces.

Area of valve $= D^2 \times 0.7854 = 2 \times 2 \times 0.7854 = 3.1416 \text{ in.}^2$
$3.1416 \text{ in.}^2 \times 75 \text{ psi} = 235.62$
$4 \text{ in.} \times 235.62 = 942.48$ upward force

RULE: Sum of up force = sum of down force; therefore,
$50 \text{ lb} \times X \text{ length of lever} = 942.48$

$$X = \frac{942.48}{50}$$

$$= 18.8496$$
$$= 18.85 \text{ in. length of lever} \qquad Ans.$$

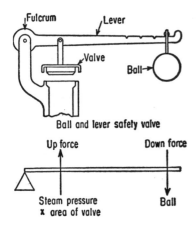

FIG. 7-3. Lever-type safety valves are obsolete, but you must know how to calculate for examinations.

Q Explain why a barrel can be rolled up an inclined plank by a person not strong enough to lift the barrel.

A A person can push the barrel up the inclined plane because, in doing so, he sacrifices distance for height but obtains a mechanical advantage.

Q A barrel weighs 450 lb. An inclined platform is 18 ft long and the high end is 3 ft above the low end. How much force is needed to roll the barrel up the platform?

A Theoretical advantage $= \dfrac{\text{length}}{\text{height}}$

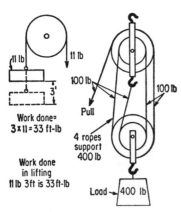

FIG. 7-4. Block and fall lifts heavy weights, depending on number of sheaves.

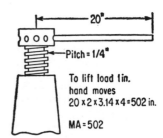

FIG. 7-5. Jack also trades distance moved to increase force.

$$TA = \frac{18}{3} = 6$$

$450 \div 6 = 75$ lb   *Ans.*

Q Explain how the block and fall works.
A A number of pulley wheels (sheaves) are in each of two blocks. A rope is run through them continuously. Again, the distance is sacrificed to gain force. An easy way to calculate these is to find the number of ropes led to lower block. This is the ratio of mechanical advantage. See Fig. 7-4.

Q Why can a person lift a heavy machine with a screw jack?
A See Fig. 7-5. A screw is an inclined plane bent to a spiral. Again, distance is sacrificed for height to gain the advantage.

Q A screw jack has four threads per inch pitch and a 12-in.-long handle. How much weight can be lifted with a steady pull of 80 lb on the end of the handle? Neglect friction.
A The distance that the end of the handle moves $= R \times 2 \times 3.1416 = 24 \times 3.1416 = 75.40$ in.

The height that the screw moves in one revolution is 0.25 in., using a four-thread-per-inch pitch.

$$TA = \frac{L}{H} = \frac{75.40}{0.25} = 301.60$$

$301.60 \times 80 = 24,128$ lb   *Ans.*

NOTE: There is a great deal of friction in a screw jack.

Q Gears and pulleys are not only used to transmit motion but are also designed to gain mechanical advantage. Typical problems are as follows:
The driving gear has 48 teeth and the driven gear has 576 teeth. What is the theoretical advantage?

A $TA = \frac{576}{48} = 12:1$ *Ans.*

Q How are the speeds of gears calculated if the revolutions per minute and number of teeth are known?
A By the inverse-proportion method.

EXAMPLE: a 120-tooth gear drives a 60-tooth gear. The speed of the larger gear is 780 r/min. Find the speed of the driver gear.

$$\frac{60}{120} = \frac{780}{x}$$

$60x = 93,600$
$x = 1560$ r/min   *Ans.*

Q What is meant by gear ratio?
A While the inverse-proportion system is the basis, a ratio system is also used. The driver is the first number; the driven is the second number. The gear ratio is figured as a fraction. An example of the 120- and 60-tooth gear problem is:

$$\frac{120}{60} = \frac{2}{1} \text{ or } 2 \colon 1 \text{ ratio}$$

r/min × ratio = speed

$$780 \times \frac{2}{1} = 1560 \text{ r/min}$$

Q Explain how a hydraulic jack works. Neglect the lever.
A Two cylinders are used in a hydraulic jack. In the smaller one pressure is acquired from a lever. This pressure is transmitted to a larger cylinder. The difference in areas is the theoretical advantage; pressure is equal in all parts of the hydraulic system.

Q A cylinder of a hydraulic jack has a ½-in. bore and the large cylinder has a 3-in. bore. What is the mechanical advantage?
A 0.5 × 0.5 × 0.7854 = 0.19635 in.²
    3 × 3 × 0.7854 = 7.0686
    7.0686 ÷ 0.19635 = 36
    The ratio is 36 : 1.   *Ans.*

NOTE: This principle is used to control throttle valves by the use of a hydraulic system in which the lube-oil pressure or governor hydraulic-oil pressure is led to an oil piston attached to the throttle valve. The control or pilot valve is a small cylinder and valve that requires little effort to move.

Q A key measures 3⅞ in. at the large end and 3¾ in. at the small end. The total length is 15 in. What is the taper per foot?
A 3⅞ in. =   3.875 in.
    3¾ in. = −3.750 in.
            0.125 in. difference in 15 in.

$$\frac{0.125}{15} = 0.008333 \text{ taper per inch}$$

12 × 0.00833 = 0.09996 in. taper per ft   *Ans.*

Q An 8-ft 6-in. shaft weights 240 lb. How much would a 12-ft length of the same size shaft weigh?

A   8-ft 6-in. = 8.5 ft
 $240 \div 8.5 = 28.235$ lb per ft
 $28.235 \times 12 = 338.82$ lb   *Ans.*

Here is an alternate method.

$$\frac{8.5}{12} = \frac{240}{X}$$

$8.5X = 2880$

$X = 338.82$ lb   *Ans.*

Q   A flywheel is 40 in. in diameter. How many degrees will the rim move if the wheel is moved 18 in?

A $40 \times 3.1416 = 125.664$ circumference

$$\frac{125.664}{360} = 0.349 \text{ in. per degree}$$

$$\frac{18 \text{ in.}}{0.349} = 51.57° \qquad Ans.$$

SUGGESTED READING

Elonka, Stephen M.: *Standard Basic Math and Applied Plant Calculations,* McGraw-Hill Book Company, New York, 1979 (has extensive conversion tables, explanations of mechanical advantage problems).

8

ELECTRICITY AND ELECTRONICS

Electricity is the most readily available form of energy for many purposes and provides more than light and power alone. Here the basic methods of electrical power generation and distribution are explained. Not only are the examiners' questions covered but more is given to help solve the many problems that arise in plant operation.

Electronics as a field has progressed rapidly, going from vacuum tubes to the semiconductors that make our transistorized, computerized way of life one electronic wonder after another. Here we present electronics in an easy set of progressive explanations that show you both the how and the why of these devices. This chapter will help you remove much of the mystery from those "little black boxes."

FUNDAMENTALS

Q What is direct current?
A Direct current (dc) is the flow of electrons in a circuit in which one wire is considered positive and the other negative when completing the current flow arrangement. Direct current is considered unidirectional; alternating current follows a sine-wave shape.

Q What is alternating current?
A Alternating current (ac) is the flow of electrons in a circuit which is

generally in a sine-wave form from a neutral axis; the waves travel in repetitive reversals about this axis, at generated cycles or frequencies per second (or hertz, abbreviated Hz).

Q What is meant by line voltage drop?
A Supply lines have resistance since there are no commercial forms of perfect conductors. Resistance is given as circular mil foot for each conductor. This is 1 mil in diameter and 1 ft in length.

Q What are the advantages of direct current? What are some of its uses?
A Since the polarity of direct current never changes, it is used for some welding procedures, electroplating, and other processes requiring fixed polarity. It is also used for excitation. Dc motors have better speed regulation, making direct current the choice for variable-speed drives. However, the developments in electronic solid-state devices have narrowed this choice.

Q What are the advantages of alternating current?
A Alternating current can be transmitted with less loss and less copper at high voltage; then the voltage can be simply reduced by transformers. It is extremely versatile in use in 3- and 4-wire multiphase use, and permits the use of cheaper motors of rugged construction.

Q What is a short circuit?
A A short circuit is any connection, usually accidental, that provides a short path for current flow without completing a circuit through the load elements of the circuit.

Q What is a ground on an electrical system?
A When part of the circuit is led by either design or accident to the earth or to the major structure containing the generator, the system is grounded.

MOTORS AND GENERATORS

Q What is the difference between a dc motor and a dc generator?
A Essentially, there is no difference. For many uses they are easily interchanged.

Q What is a dynamo? What current does it produce?
A A dynamo, most commonly, is a dc generator. Technically, a dynamo can be either a generator, if driven, or a motor, if sufficient direct current is supplied.

Q What is residual magnetism? Describe the need of residual magnetism in dc generators.

A Residual magnetism is the permanent magnetism in the iron poles of a generator. When a generator is started, the revolving wire windings of the armature cut magnetic lines of force and generate electricity. The flow of current builds up the field magnetism to the proper value. If it were not for residual magnetism, the machine would not build up electricity, and outside excitation would be needed.

Q What is the function of the commutator?

A The commutator is a device for reversing the induced alternating currents in an armature to direct currents and conducting these direct currents to the external circuit. It is used to change the alternating current generated in the armature windings to direct current. Remember that the armature windings cut lines of force alternately—first the north pole, then the south pole. If this were in a closed circuit, alternating current would flow. The commutator corrects this by presenting a positive bar to the brush as positive current is generated. In a like manner, a negative bar is presented to a brush as negative current is generated. Even though alternating current is generated in the armature, the commutator presents the bars in such a way that the current flows in one direction. This is in a series of nearly smooth impulses that provide a steady dc flow.

Q Describe the windings of a compound generator.

A Each field pole has two windings; a shunt coil and a series coil. The shunt winding has many turns of fine wire as compared with the series field, which has only a few turns of heavy wire. The shunt field is parallel to the armature and little current flows through it.

The series field is in series with the armature and all the current output flows through it. On very large machines, the series field windings may be a rectangular or triangular cross section of copper conductors. Both field windings are insulated.

Q What is flat compounding?

A Flat compounding exists when the series field is proportioned to the shunt field in order to keep the voltage constant regardless of the load. The reason for this is that as load increases, the current in the shunt decreases, weakening the field. This tends to lower the voltage. It is counterbalanced by an increased current flow through the series field, which causes voltage to rise. One offsets the other and if the machine is properly designed, the voltage stays constant within the designed load range.

Q What is overcompounding?

A Overcompounding is the proportioning of the series field to give a rising voltage as the load increases.

Q Why do brushes spark during commutation? How is this overcome?

A The inductance of the coils discharges following the reversal of current.

If this occurs at the moment of commutation, a spark results. This is overcome by one of two ways: (1) neutral plane shift or (2) interpoles.

In neutral plane shift, the brush rigging is on a frame that can be swung about the commutator. By shifting the brushes slightly ahead of the neutral plane, current is induced opposite to that of the inductance and counteracts the spark effect. The point varies with the load and the brushes are set by trial and error until right.

Interpoles, sometimes called "commutating or auxiliary poles," are small auxiliary poles mounted between the main poles. Line current or a proportion of it passes through the interpole windings to produce a magnetic field of a little more than the armature produces. This counteracts the spark-producing armature reaction or induced current and minimizes the sparking. These poles require no adjustment as the manufacturer sets the brushes to the neutral plane of the machine. Interpoles have replaced the old neutral-plane-shift devices.

Q Why are armature cores, field pieces, and transformer cores made of laminated stock?

A By making these pieces of laminated metal and by insulating them with a compound from each other, no path of any length is furnished. This minimizes the eddy currents and the heat generated by them. If they were made solid, eddy currents would set up and cause heating.

Q What is meant by a generator being (1) series wound, (2) shunt wound, and (3) compound wound?

A The same answers that applied to dc motors apply here, since there is little or no difference between dc motors and dc generators. In fact, they are often used interchangeably in the same drive. See dc-motor types (Fig. 8-4).

Q What kind of current does an exciter furnish? Where are exciters used?

A Exciters furnish direct current. They are used on all types of machines that are not self-excited, whether alternating current or direct current. They are always used on synchronous motors and mostly on ac generators.

Q What additional pieces of equipment are needed on ac generators that dc generators don't require?

A Ac generators require (1) an excitation source, such as a small dc generator, (2) a rheostat to control the voltage of the exciter, and (3) synchronizing indicators, either synchroscope or lamps.

Q What is an alternator?

A A machine that produces alternating current. In an alternator, the rotor is the dc field, and the stator (stationary winding) becomes the armature. The dc excitation is fed to the poles which are mounted on the rotating shaft of an alternator. Magnetic flux sweeps past the fixed windings of the stator coils mounted on the frame. Voltage and current are induced when the shaft is turned as by an engine or other drive. Depending on the number of coils and their connections and the number of pairs of poles, alternating current having single or polyphase characteristics is produced.

Q How does generator speed affect the cycles of alternating current?
A Generator speed controls the cycles of alternating current. Each time the poles pass, the current rises and falls. So, the faster the rotor turns, the higher the cycle frequency.

AC MOTORS

Q What are the ac-motor types?
A Ac motors are classified as (1) universal, (2) single-phase, and (3) polyphase. Polyphase motors may be squirrel-cage, wound-rotor, or synchronous types.

Q What is a universal motor?
A A universal motor is a small, series-wound motor used on either alternating current or direct current. The iron core and field pieces must be laminated to break up eddy currents. (Eddy currents waste power and cause motor heating.)

Q What is a split-phase motor?
A A split-phase motor is a single-phase unit consisting of a squirrel-cage rotor, two stator windings, a starting winding, and a running (main) winding. The windings are electrically 90° apart. At start-up, both windings are parallel across the line. The starting winding is designed with the current out of phase with the main winding to produce a magnetic field. It is not very powerful but it is strong enough to start the motor on a light load. When the rotor reaches 75 percent of rated speed, a centrifugal switch opens the starting-winding circuit and the machine runs as an induction motor.

Q Describe a repulsion-start motor.
A A repulsion-start motor is a single-phase induction machine with a commutator and wound rotor similar to a series motor. There is no electric connection between the stator winding and the rotor. The brushes are connected to each other. To start, the current is led to the stator winding which sets up a typical revolving field. Field flux reacts on the rotor windings and causes it to turn with a strong torque. As the rotor comes up to speed, a centrifugal device presses a ring against the commutator, short-circuiting all the bars. The machine then runs as an induction motor. Some motors allow the brushes to ride the commutator; others incorporate

a brush, lifting linkage when running at induction speed. This motor has many starting characteristics similar to those of a dc-series machine and can be used for a loaded start.

Q What is a capacitor?

A A capacitor is another name for a condenser.

Q What is a capacitor-start motor?

A A capacitor-start motor is a single-phase motor using two stator windings, a squirrel-cage rotor, a centrifugal switch, and a capacitor. The capacitor is in series with the starting winding and causes it to be out of phase with the current in the running winding. This produces a small flux change and the revolving field starts the rotor spinning. At 80 percent speed, the centrifugal switch opens the starting circuit and the machine runs as a squirrel-cage induction motor.

Q What is a capacitor-run motor?

A It is similar to a capacitor-start motor except that no centrifugal switch is used. The capacitor remains in the circuit at all speeds. The effect is that of a two-phase motor having smooth operation.

Q What is a squirrel-cage induction motor?

A See Fig. 8-1. A squirrel-cage induction motor has a series of copper

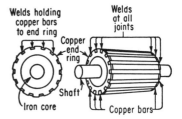

FIG. 8-1.   Squirrel-cage induction rotor.

(or aluminum) bars, running in slots through the length of the core. At each end each bar is welded to a copper end ring. These are called "short-circuiting rings." The bars form a cage that is like a squirrel cage.

Q How does the rotating magnetic field in a squirrel-cage motor get the cage rotor turning?

A See Fig. 8-2. In Fig. 8-2a the stator of a three-phase motor is shown as three coils. After the magnetic field is established, the peak of the field rotates in sequence from coil to coil. Rotor-cage metal bars and end rings are not connected to outside power. In b, current is induced in rotor windings as the magnetic field of each stator coil builds up and collapses. At standstill this induced current is at the same frequency as the power supply to the stator, much like that in a static-power transformer. In c, induced-rotor current produces its own magnetic field. This, in turn,

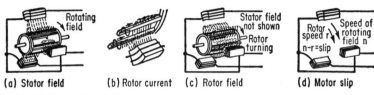

(a) Stator field   (b) Rotor current   (c) Rotor field   (d) Motor slip

FIG. 8-2.   Details of how the rotating magnetic field gets cage-rotor turning.

through the action of repulsion and attraction, twists the rotor in an attempt to catch up with the rotating stator field, but never quite makes it. In d, the squirrel-cage rotor runs slower than the rotating field since the latter must continually overtake and cut the rotor windings. This speed difference is called "motor slip" and is necessary for the induction of a torque-producing current.

Q   Why is the squirrel-cage popular?

A   The popularity of squirrel-cage motors is boosted by the fact that they are (1) inexpensive—windings are easily set in place; (2) safe—there is no danger of sparks since they have no brushes or commutators; (3) rugged—there are no contacts or slipping parts to get out of adjustment; and (4) can be designed to run under water as the armature is designed to be short-circuited.

Q   What is a wound-rotor induction motor?

A   A wound-rotor induction motor operates on the same principle as does a squirrel-cage motor, except that wire windings are used on the rotor. The ends of these windings are led out to slip rings (one per phase) where they are further connected to external banks of resistance through rheostat control. The external resistance permits cutting in and out resistance to the rotor for speed control and/or higher starting torque.

Q   What is the difference between an induction motor and a synchronous motor?

A   An induction motor has a revolving electric field in the stator coils. This is produced by the alternating current, which is usually of 60 Hz. The revolving field induces a magnetic reaction with the rotor windings (or bars) and causes the rotor to spin.

A synchronous motor has outside dc excitation to produce a magnetic field. Coils are mounted on a revolving spider frame, and excitation is led to them through brushes and slip rings mounted on the rotor shaft. The stator windings receive current from an ac source in phase with the generator. The magnetic reaction of the alternating current flowing in the stator with the direct current in the rotor causes the rotor to spin.

Q   How does the amortisseur winding start the rotor turning?

A   See Fig. 8-3. The amortisseur cage is a permanently short-circuited

FIG. 8-3. Amortisseur cage is a short-circuited winding used for starting the rotor.

winding having its bars uniformly distributed around the rotor's periphery. As in the squirrel-cage winding of an induction motor, all bars are joined to end rings. There are enough bars to start the motor as a squirrel-cage induction motor.

Q What is the difference in the stator windings of a synchronous motor, a squirrel-cage motor, and a wound-rotor induction motor?

A There is essentially no difference in the stator windings of these three motors. In each case, the rotating magnetic field goes around and the rotor follows it.

Q How is a three-phase motor reversed?

A You can reverse a three-phase motor by interchanging any two stator leads.

Q What are reverse-phase relays? Where are they compulsory?

A They are relays that will trip out if the phase leads are reversed ahead of the control board of a multiphase (three-phase) motor. They are compulsory on electric elevators, because the controls would act one way and the hoist motor would act in the other direction if the phase leads were accidentally changed.

DC MOTORS

Q What are the dc motor types?

A The dc motor types are (1) series, (2) shunt, (3) compound, and (4) universal (ac or dc types).

Q With the aid of a sketch, show the current path through a series motor.

A See Fig. 8-4a. The field is a heavy-wire conductor winding as all armature current flows through it. The armature is in series with the field. This motor has a heavy starting torque and will run away—up to bursting speed—if unloaded. At times, a small shunt-field winding is included to prevent a runaway.

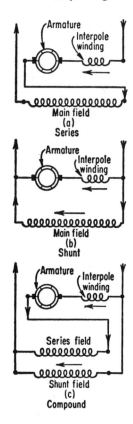

FIG. 8-4.   Windings of dc and universal moters.

Q Sketch and show the flow through a shunt motor.

A See Fig. 8-4b. This is a dc motor having very little change in speed between no load and full load. The field winding is parallel to the armature.

Q Sketch and describe a compound motor.

A See Fig. 8-4c. This is a dc motor with a series field and a shunt field. It has a high starting torque and will run at a nearly constant speed. Heavy windings make up the series field; lighter wire is the shunt field. The series field is in series with the armature and the shunt field is in parallel with the armature.

Q Why are interpole windings used on dc motors or generators?

A Interpole windings are small windings between the poles. They hold the neutral on the armature to minimize sparking on the brushes. The coils of these poles are in series with the armature.

Q What are compensating windings on dc motors or generators? When are they used?

A Compensating windings consist of low-resistance windings in series with the interpole windings. Slots are cut in the main pole pieces at the face to receive these windings. Windings further control the commutation to reduce arcing. These windings are used on high-voltage machines or in applications where the designed voltage difference between the commutator bars is great.

Q How are dc motors reversed?

A These motors can be reversed in two ways: (1) reverse the leads to the armature or (2) reverse the leads to the field coils. (Use either method, but not both at the same time.)

Q What is the basic method of speed control in dc motors?

A See Fig. 8-5. The speed of dc motors is controlled by changing the field strength. Weakening the field increases speed. Resistances are used to reduce the current to the field. A rheostat is commonly used for this purpose.

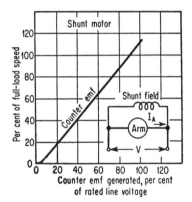

FIG. 8-5. Speed characteristics of a dc motor is important data for operators.

Q Discuss six ways of controlling motor speed.

A See Fig. 8-6a to f. (a) Here, an adjustable resistor for the series motor varies the armature and field current. Speed holds constant only under a steady load. (b) A shunting resistor is placed across the field winding in order to increase the speed of the series motor beyond its full-load value. (c) Shunt-motor speed can be cut below its normal full-load point by armature resistance, similar to the series motor. (d) Field control of motor speed is the most economical and satisfactory method. The rheostat is small since the current is only about 5 percent of the total. (e) A variable voltage control, using an individual dc generator, is an efficient way to

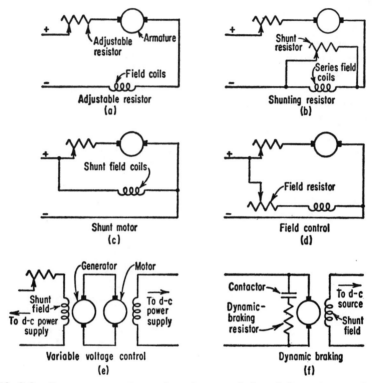

FIG. 8-6. Six ways a motor's speed can be controlled, each for a given service.

get speed from zero to maximum. (*f*) The dynamic braking setup uses a resistor across the armature to slow the motor. Field coils are kept energized.

Q Why are starters needed for dc motors?

A The current input of a dc armature is controlled by the counterelectromotive force developed as the armature turns. If a heavy inrush of current is led through a stationary armature, the current is apt to exceed the normal load and burn out the armature windings. Resistances are used to limit the starting current to safe values until the rotor turns fast enough to generate counterelectromotive force.

Q How does a series-motor starter work?

A A series of resistances are placed in series with the armature. Resistances are cut in to start and limit the inrushing current to safe limits until the motor comes to speed gradually. Resistances are cut off step by step as the motor speeds up, and all resistance is cut out at full speed.

Q What is the function of the starting box used on a shunt or compound motor?

A A starting box furnishes resistances for armature-circuit starting and incorporates a low-voltage protection device. Its handle works against a spring tension, which pulls the handle to the "off" position if the electromagnet has either a low or interrupted current. This stops the motor; it must be restarted by the operators.

Q Why are field connections located on the line side of the starter?

A To provide maximum starting torque, the field must be as strong as possible. Therefore, the field circuit is complete on the line side. If the resistance of a field-control rheostat for speed control is in the field circuit, the rheostat is adjusted to cut out all resistance when the motor is started.

Q How does a manual dc starting box operate during motor start-up?

A During motor start-up, the starting-box handle is moved slowly from point to point, allowing about 15 sec from the "off" to the full "on" position. Holding the handle on intermediate positions will overheat the starter resistance since they are not designed for running.

Q What happens if the voltage is low?

A Low voltage will cause the motor to overheat; torque is reduced in proportion to the square of the voltage. The motor may not start, or it may stall under a load. Current amperage will rise and overheat the motor. A 10 percent temperature change is the limit a motor can stand.

Q What happens if the supply voltage is high?

A High supply voltage increases core losses. Some part of the rotor probably will overheat because of the design change if the voltage is much above 10 percent.

MOTOR STARTERS

Q Name five hookups for starting electric motors.

A See Fig. 8-7a to e. (a) A part-winding setup allows full voltage to flow singularly to the various stator circuits until all the circuits are energized. The motor accelerates smoothly, since the line is not opened during start-up. (b) A full-voltage setup is preferred where the power source allows kVA inrush. Your utility may want reduced-voltage starting to limit the starting current to a fixed percentage of full load. (c) An autotransformer is used to reduce the voltage on starting. Transferring to full voltage at 75 percent synchronous speed interrupts the current. An autotransformer is generally used on hand-operated compensators. (d) A series resistance (or reactor) arrangement provides for closed transition from start to run, raising motor kVA and torque by steps when an uninterrupted starting

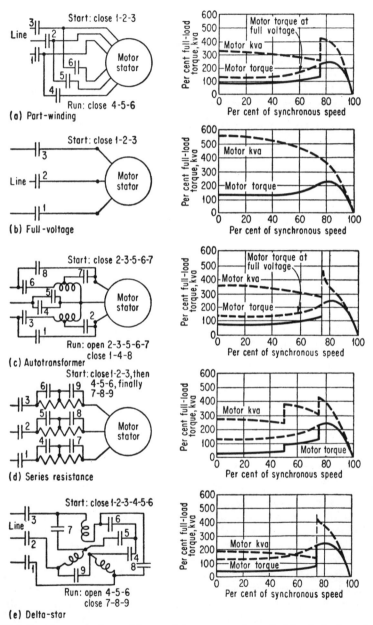

FIG. 8-7. Five methods used for starting motors, each applied for desired results.

current is desired. (e) A delta-star scheme is used widely in Europe but seldom in this country. Here, the motor starts star and runs delta. The results are equal to starting on autotransformers at 75 percent tap.

Q Explain the operation of squirrel-cage motor starters.
A Most squirrel-cage motors—up to 7.5 hp and some larger units—can be started with an across-the-line switch. The objection to this method is the large, low-power-factor current that disturbs the feed lines.

To reduce the starting current, a starting compensator is often used. Although two autotransformers are needed, three are used for a better balance. The starting lever is manually operated and has three positions— "stop" (or "off"), "start," and "run." In "start," the transformers reduce the line voltage and control the inrush of current until the motor comes up to speed. Then the operator throws the lever to "run," which cuts out the autotransformers. A magnetic low-voltage release holds the lever in the "run" position. If the line voltage drops, or if a fuse or overload relay opens, the lever falls to the "off" position. This gives protection to the motor. A "stop" button allows the operator to stop the machine by opening the release circuit.

REMEMBER: Overload relays are in two lines only!

Q Why are across-the-line starting switches made double-throw?
A The double-throw design allows high-rating fuses to start, since the current may be five times normal. When the motor is up to speed, the switch is thrown to low-rating fuses to protect the motor.

Q How are some wound-rotor motors started?
A Some wound-rotor motors are started by speed-control rheostats. The first position should add enough resistance to the motor to give it maximum torque, which is a good starting condition. Current is held to a little more than normal full load. As the motor comes up to speed, resistance is gradually cut out and there is little line disturbance. These controls are usually of a drum type with multiple contacts and several banks of resistors. A drawback to this type of starter is the difficulty involved in using an overload or no-voltage protective device in the circuit.

Q What is part-winding full-voltage starting?
A In this type of starting, the stator windings have at least two windings. One set is used to start at full-line voltage which, in effect, acts as a small motor. As the motor comes to speed, the second set of windings is parallel to the first and the motor accelerates smoothly since there is no open switching period to interrupt the current.

Q What is a delta-star starting switch?
A A delta-star starting switch uses six motor leads instead of three; both

ends of the phase windings are brought out. The starting side is connected in star and the running side is hooked up in delta. The effect of starting in star is to reduce the starting current, since the voltage is $E/3$. When the motor is brought up to speed, the switch is moved to the "run" position, giving a voltage of E per phase. It is assumed that the starting in-rush is five times full load and that the torque is 1½ times normal full-load torque when an across-the-line start is made. The delta-star method reduces starting current to 1.67 times full load and the starting torque is one-half normal.

Q What is a reverse-current relay? Name a common application.

A A relay that trips out when the current stops flowing is a no-voltage or reverse-current relay. A good example is the cutout relay on an automobile generator. It prevents the battery current from flowing back to the generator and attempting to motorize the generator when the engine stops.

Q What is the basic operating principle of automatic switches?

A Automatic switches employ a solenoid coil that is energized and an electromagnetic field that attracts an iron armature into the magnetic field. Electric contacts are attached to the iron. These are either made or broken, according to the use of the switch. There may be a number of contacts in a single relay switch; they may be both making and breaking contacts, operating at the same time.

Q What is the air gap of a generator or a motor?

A The air gap is the clearance space between the armature and field pieces of a motor (rotor and stator) clearance. It is measured to detect wear in the bearings.

Q How is voltage raised or lowered on a nonpulsating dc circuit?

A Small decreases in voltage are effected by resistances. Increasing or great voltage changes are best accomplished by motor generators.

BRUSHES AND COMMUTATORS

Q What materials are used to classify brushes?

A (1) Carbon, (2) electrographite, (3) graphite, (4) copper graphite and (5) metal.

Q What are electrographite brushes?

A Electrographite brushes have the same chemical base as carbon, but they have been processed in an electric-furnace crucible to increase the electric and thermal conductivity. They are softer but tougher than carbon brushes. Electrographite brushes run cooler and with less chattering, but they are not self-cleaning.

Q What are graphite brushes?
A Graphite brushes have a silver color when compared with black carbon. High-grade graphite is mined and then processed at low heat. All sorts of things are possible, such as adding a slightly abrasive substance or having an increasing resistance between heel and toe of the brush to stop arcing.

Q What are copper-graphite brushes?
A Powdered graphite and copper are pressed together and baked at lower temperatures than electrographite to form copper-graphite brushes. They are used primarily for high-current and low-voltage use. Abrasiveness is proportional to copper, but often a metal film forms on commutators.

Q What are metal brushes?
A Metal brushes are bronze or copper made into fingers or leaves, rolled gauze, or bronze blocks. They are used in very small motors or for special applications.

Q What is the limitation of using slipping contacts as brushes on either slip rings or commutators? How is this problem solved?
A About 1000 V (either ac or dc) causes severe arcing and cannot be controlled. Alternators can produce very high voltage for transmission at economical rates. Transformers efficiently reduce high voltage to usable power.

Q How and why is the mica that is used to separate commutator copper segments undercut?
A Mica is cut either with a special machine or very carefully with a hacksaw blade to the full width of the mica. The depth of the cut is regulated by the size of the machine; about $\frac{1}{16}$ in. is plenty for most medium-sized commutators. The reason for cutting mica is to save the soft brushes from rapid wear. If harder brushes were used, the copper segments would wear rapidly. Always finish the job with a stone or sandpaper to smooth the cylindrical surface. High mica will cause the brushes to spark. Dirty slots will cause flashover on the commutator.

Q Describe the construction of a commutator.
A A commutator consists of copper segments (bars) insulated from each other by mica strips and mounted parallel to the armature shaft. Two rings of insulating material with a wedge-shaped cross section are fitted around the shaft and about another insulating ring. Copper segments are rooted and wedged in these rings to hold the assembly together. Wires of the armature windings are soldered (brazed) to the bars. Each coil in the armature has one lead attached to a bar and the other attached to the adjacent bar from which a connection is made to the next coil and so on around. Each segment has two wires fastened to it.

Q What causes the rapid wear or grooving of a commutator? How is it repaired?

A Commutator wear or grooving is caused by (1) brushes that are not staggered to cover the entire commutator, (2) too much spring pressure, or (3) the wrong grade of brushes. The commutator must be cut as in a lathe or on its own bearings, using a stone or tool. The hard mica is undercut to prevent wear or grooving of the carbon brushes.

INSULATION

Q What does each of the following classes of motor-winding insulations mean: (1) Class H, (2) Class A Special, and (3) Tropical?

A (1) Class H includes silicones and is used for especially high temperatures. (2) Class A Special is resistant to moisture but is not waterproof, dustproof, or immune to chemical vapors. (3) Tropical is used to protect against fungus, insects, and vermin.

Q How does total temperature affect insulation life?

A Roughly, each 10°C rise in temperature above the maximum allowed for Class A and B cuts the effective life of the insulation in half.

Q How is a motor selected for temperature service? Can you tell?

A Class A (cotton, silk, paper, or other organics impregnated with insulating varnish) is considered standard for most normal applications. They allow 105°C total temperature, figured as:

    40°C ambient (room) temperature
    40°C rise, measured outside
    15°C hot-spot allowance above outside temperature
    10°C service factor

Class B (mica, fiberglass, and other inorganics) allows 130°C total temperature. The difference is 70°C rise measured outside, plus a 20°C hot-spot allowance above outside temperature.

CIRCUIT PROTECTION

Q What is a carbon-and-copper contact-overload circuit breaker?

A This type of circuit breaker has three sets of contacts, one mounted above the other. The main contact is a heavy, fixed block of copper facing a movable laminated-copper brush. This brush closes against the copper block with a wiping motion and with enough pressure to establish a perfect contact. The secondary contacts are above the main contacts. They consist of a fixed copper plate, faced by a movable round contact disk on a stem. A bronze spring around the stem presses the contact securely when closed. The third contact is made of two carbon blocks, one fixed and one moving. The purpose of the carbon is to absorb the arc at the moment of breaking.

The contacts are made or broken successively as they are mounted on a spring-loaded pivoted arm. This arm is latched into place to close the switch and to hold the contacts in place. A connection to a solenoid-operated plunger causes the plunger to strike a trigger that, in turn, releases the latch on the spring-loaded arm. The solenoid opens the latch when the current becomes excessive.

Q How do circuit breakers protect motors?

A Almost any size of motor can be protected by a circuit breaker. As with fuses, an overload of momentary duration that is not harmful to the motor will open the breaker. The motor stays out until it is manually reset and started.

Q Why are fuses used to protect motors?

A Fuses are used to protect motors because they are less expensive than circuit breakers. Small motors usually depend on fuses; any sustained overload on the motor melts the fuse. Lag fuses should be used so that starting current or a momentary overload won't blow the fuse.

Q What is a thermal relay?

A A thermal relay is a protective device that operates on the principle of the heat expansion of metals. A heating coil element is used to heat the relays. Since this is proportional to the current, an overload will actuate the relay. Time is involved, and an overload of short duration won't cause enough heat to actuate the relay. This is called the inverse time-limit effect.

Q Why is low-voltage protection given to motors?

A Low voltage can overheat a loaded motor and cause a burnout. Or, if the motor stalls, a "cookout" can occur with low voltage and high current. Low voltage is bad for ac motors but even worse for dc motors.

Q Why are oil dashpots used with some overload relays?

A Oil dashpots are used to give an inverse time-limit effect. Dashpots hold the relays in for a brief period to allow a momentary overload of a circuit to pass.

AC CONVERTERS

Q What three methods are used to convert alternating current to direct current?

A Disk-type rectifiers, mercury-arc-type rectifiers, and mechanical rectifiers (converters) are used to convert alternating current to direct current.

Q Explain the disk rectifier.

A Metallic-type disk rectifiers are composed of metal sandwiches. Two types are shown in Fig. 8-8. In practice, the current will meet high resistance in one direction and low resistance in the other. The rectifier acts in a way similar to a water check valve and allows flow in one direction only. It can be used to give pulsating direct current. Depending on the hookup used, it will provide either half- or full-wave rectification.

NOTE: See circuit used with the moving-coil meter.

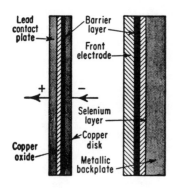

FIG. 8-8. Metallic-type disk rectifier allows only one-way flow.

Q How does a mercury-arc rectifier operate?

A After reading about the diode and the triode in this chapter, see Fig. 8-9. A mercury-arc rectifier consists of a carbon or iron anode and a mercury-pool cathode sealed in a vacuum tank. When ac voltage is applied, the current flows on every other half cycle. Bias voltage on the grid controls the amount of the positive half cycle current. Instead of a vacuum, a mercury vapor is used to carry the electrons. Vapor is generated by igniting an arc on each cycle or by having a continuous arc to provide the vapor cathode spot.

Two types, shown in Fig. 8-9, are the single-anode and multitank units called "ignitrons" because they have an ignitor that starts the cathode spot every cycle. Single tanks are grouped together in installations. The multianode single-tank rectifier has an anode head consisting of several anodes, one or more for each phase. Once started, the arc is maintained by the excitation anode.

Q What is a mechanical rectifier?

A See Fig. 8-10. A mechanical rectifier, also called a "contact converter," produces direct current from alternating current by making a metallic

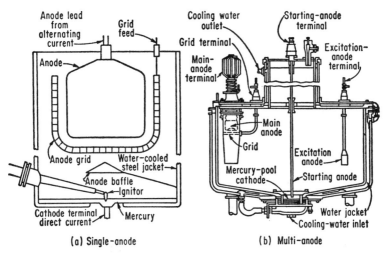

FIG. 8-9.   Mercury-arc rectifers are of the (a) single-anode and (b) multianode types.

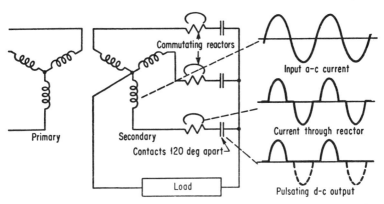

FIG. 8-10.   Mechanical rectifier, also known as a contact converter, direct to alternating current.

contact between the ac system and the dc system for each phase when each phase voltage is on the positive half cycle. The contact is broken as the negative half cycle is approached. Reactors are used to choke off current flow, and contacts open and close to permit flow in one direction. They open at the beginning of the negative half cycle and close at the start of the positive half cycle.

TRANSFORMERS

Q What is a transformer?

A A transformer is a device for changing voltage and current relations in ac circuits. This is done by mutual induction. Circulating alternating current from the primary causes a magnetic flux to circulate through the secondary, and electric current results. See Fig. 8-11.

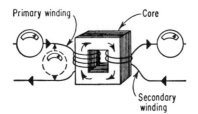

FIG. 8-11. Transformers have core of thin steel sheets with windings as indicated.

Q What are step-up and step-down transformers?

A Step-up transformers increase voltage; step-down transformers decrease voltage. Step-up transformers have more turns on the secondary windings than on the primary windings, while the opposite is true of step-down transformers.

Q Do transformers change power?

A Transformers do not change power; only the voltage and amperage relationship is changed. Aside from the losses, the total power remains the same.

Q What is a potential transformer?

A A potential transformer changes the voltage on an electric system to a higher or lower voltage.

Q What is a current transformer?

A The output voltage of a current transformer is proportional to its input voltage. It is used for measuring large currents on ac circuits, as it furnishes current at low, safe rates for operators and their instruments.

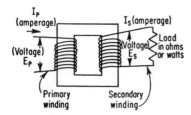

FIG. 8-12. Load placed on secondary of 110-V transformer with ampere flow.

Q Suppose that a 22-Ω load is placed on the secondary of a 110-V transformer. How many amperes would flow?
A See Fig. 8-12.

$$I_s = \frac{E_s}{R_s}$$

where I_s = amperage, secondary winding
E_s = voltage, secondary winding
R_s = resistance, secondary winding

$$I_s = \frac{110}{22} = 5 \text{ A} \qquad Ans.$$

Q How are transformer voltages calculated?
A Transformer voltages are calculated by the ratio of turns between the primary and secondary windings.

EXAMPLE: Suppose a primary winding of 1800 turns has 440 V and the secondary winding delivers 110 V. How many turns would be in the secondary winding? Use the formula

$$\frac{E_p}{E_s} = \frac{T_p}{T_s}$$

where E_p = voltage, primary winding
E_s = voltage, secondary winding
T_p = turns, primary coil
T_s = turns, secondary coil

$$\frac{440}{110} = \frac{1800}{T_s} \qquad T_s = \frac{1800 \times 110}{440} = 450 \text{ turns} \qquad Ans.$$

Q How is amperage calculated from the number of turns in the primary and secondary windings?
A This amperage is calculated by the formula $I_p T_p = I_s T_s$. Used inversely, the more turns, the less current.

EXAMPLE: A transformer has 1800 turns in the primary winding and 450 turns in the secondary winding. If the secondary has a current of 5 A, how many amperes are in the primary?

$$I_p T_p = I_s T_s$$
$$I_p = \frac{450 \times 5}{1800} = 1.25 \text{ A} \qquad Ans.$$

Q What is the volt-ampere output formula for a single-phase transformer?
A There is so little loss that it is usually neglected; so the formula for volt-ampere is $P_p = P_s$ or $I_p E_p = I_s E_s$.

EXAMPLE: A single-phase transformer has a primary voltage of 440 V and 1.25 A. What is its volt-ampere?

$E_pI_p = P_p$
$440 \times 1.25 = 550$ volt-ampere   *Ans.*

The secondary delivers 110 V and 5 A. What is its volt-ampere?

$E_sI_s = P_s$
$110 \times 5 = 550$ volt-ampere   *Ans.*

NOTE: The same transformer has been used for each proposition. Let us review the three propositions:

1. $\dfrac{E_p}{E_s} = \dfrac{T_p}{T_s}$
2. $\dfrac{I_p}{I_s} = \dfrac{T_s}{T_p}$
3. $I_pE_p = I_sE_s$

Q What controls the load on the primary windings?
A The load on the primary windings is controlled by the load on the secondary winding which is self-induction when unloaded.

Q What limits the current in the primary windings of a transformer?
A Although the transformer is connected across the line, current E_p is limited by self-induction in the primary coil. This current is E_{si} and is almost as strong but opposite to E_p. The small current that flows is called the "magnetizing current." The reason for the E_{si} current is the tight windings about the iron core. Every winding is cut by the magnetic flux that builds up and collapses and causes a counterelectromotive force.

Transformers are very efficient; for all practical purposes they are calculated as 100 percent efficient. Actually they may be 98 percent efficient or less.

Q Why do transformers use oil baths, radiators, air blowers, or other heat dissipators?
A Heat dissipators are used to reduce the heat of the windings. The reason for this is that the resistance of copper and other conductors increases as the heat is increased. This is a vicious cycle: the hotter the conductor, the hotter and less efficient it becomes.

Q Why are two secondary coils usually used in a plant distribution transformer?
A Two secondary coils are used to make two secondary voltages available from the transformer. By connecting the two coils in series you get 230 V, which can be used for motors. Connecting the two coils in parallel gives you 115 V for your lighting load.

Q What determines the wire gage of transformer windings?

A The amperage that a transformer will carry determines the wire gage of its windings.

Q What is an autotransformer?

A An autotransformer uses one winding, a portion of which is common to both the primary and secondary. The current flow of the primary and secondary is opposite; therefore, the common portion current is the difference between the supply current and the load current, neglecting exciting current.

An autotransformer is economical since one winding is eliminated. However, never use this type for house wiring or for motor-driven tools because a grounded primary would allow full-line voltage into the house circuit. If a high-voltage supply is used, the house wiring and all plumbing would have a deadly voltage.

Q Sketch and explain a three-phase ac circuit.

A A three-phase arrangement is the most common polyphase system. It has three distinct voltages out of step with one another. There are 120° between each voltage. In Fig. 8-13a note that at any instant the algebraic sum (measured up and down from the center line) for those three voltages is zero. When one voltage is zero, the other two are 86.6 percent of the maximum and have opposite signs.

The sine waves, shown in Fig. 8-13b, are an oscillograph trace taken at any point in a three-phase system. (Each voltage or current wave comes from a separate wire, but for comparison, they are shown on a common base.) The big benefit of a three-phase system comes from motor application. The advantages of a three-phase motor having three separate stator windings are similar to the advantages a three-cylinder engine has over a one-cylinder (single-phase) engine.

The three phases are generated by placing each phase coil in the generator 120° apart, mechanically. Rotating the dc field will cut each phase coil in turn, inducing voltage in each phase out of step with the other two phases.

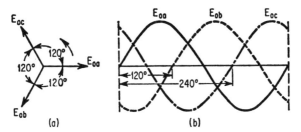

FIG. 8-13.   Sine waves of three-phase ac circuits; common polyphase system.

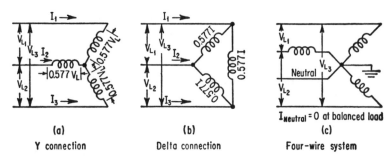

(a)
Y connection

(b)
Delta connection

(c)
Four-wire system

FIG. 8-14. Current values in Y, delta, and four-wire connection are as shown here.

Q Sketch and show the values of the current in a Y connection, delta connection, and four-wire system.

A See Fig. 8-14a to c. (a) You can consider the three windings of a Y connection as the primary of the transformer. The current in all windings is equal to the line current, but voltage across the windings equals 0.577 times the line voltage. (b) Delta connection shows that the winding voltages equal the line voltages, but currents split up so that 0.577 times the line voltage flows through the windings. These transformers operate at 5 percent capacity with one winding open. (c) A four-wire system is the most popular secondary distribution setup. The highest secondary voltage is usually 208 V, which feeds small power loads. Lighting loads at 120 V can be tapped from any line to neutral.

Q How is temperature controlled in transformers?

A Copper loss shows up as heat in transformer windings, and this heat must be dissipated. In liquid-filled units, the liquid absorbs heat from the windings and transfers it to the cooling surfaces. Air does a similar job in dry-type units. The final coil temperature depends on (1) the rate that the heat is generated, a function of copper loss; (2) the area of the coil surface that is exposed to the liquid or air; (3) the speed of the coolant circulation (a unit with high-viscosity oil runs hotter than one with low-viscosity oil); and (4) the condition of the heat-dissipating surfaces.

The operating limits of a transformer tie in closely with the age of the transformer insulation. A useful life depends on the time required for the insulation to lose its mechanical strength. Aging occurs at all temperatures, but the rate doubles (life is halved) for about each 10°C increase. If a transformer usually operates at light load and low temperature, it can work for short times at high load and high temperature and still have a good insulation life.

Q Would you use a transformer for voltages and frequencies other than those for which it is rated?

A Yes. You can increase supply frequency if the supply voltage is held constant. If the voltage rises sharply, the transformer may overheat; but normal current can be carried in this case, and there is no need to reduce the kVA rating. Supply frequency can be dropped if the voltage is lowered proportionately. This leaves the flux density at the same level. The lower frequency cuts iron loss and exciting current. It is generally safe to use a 60-Hz transformer on a 25-Hz circuit if voltage is dropped to about one-half normal rating. Naturally, kVA output will also be cut in half.

Input voltage can be decreased at normal frequency. With normal current, this will drop kVA output in proportion to the voltage drop. But don't up the voltage input at constant frequency; core and coil losses are too high.

Q What is transformer impedance?

A Transformer impedance is the combined effect of resistance and reactance. You can measure the percent of impedance by measuring the primary voltage needed to force a full-load current through the secondary winding with the secondary short-circuited. The result is expressed as a percentage of the rated primary voltage. If transformers are hooked in parallel, impedance (hence, voltage drop) must be about the same in the parallel units in order to obtain successful operation.

Q How do you measure transformer current?

A The function of all transformers is to change voltage. But some transformers also change current values for metering and relaying purposes. See Fig. 8-15. These are called "current transformers" (ct). The relationship between the primary and secondary voltages and the currents is the same as that in voltage transformers. The secondary winding of a current transformer is generally designed for 5 A with the primary winding carrying the full-load current.

Don't open a ct secondary circuit while the primary circuit is carrying full-load current. Close the short-circuiting switch on the ct itself. Otherwise, the open-circuit secondary voltage in some ct's may build up to a value dangerous to both you and the insulation. This happens because no bucking flux opposes the mutual flux linking the primary and secondary circuits. The secondary voltage depends on the core flux, a function of

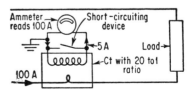

FIG. 8-15. Current transformer (ct) isolates high voltages, changes current value for relaying.

primary current. With no opposition from the secondary winding, the mutual flux will soar when any sizable primary current flows.

Q How can you determine transformer polarity?

A See Fig. 8-16. The polarity mark of a transformer refers to the direction of the induced voltage in the transformer leads, as brought outside the case to a terminal strip. Transformer-winding leads are marked to show polarity and to distinguish between the high- and low-voltage side. Primary and secondary windings are not identified as such because they depend on input and output connections. The high-voltage side is marked H; each lead and tap is designated as H_1, H_2, H_3, etc. The low-voltage side is tagged X; each lead and tap is marked X_1, X_2, X_3, etc.

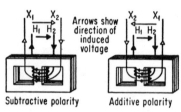

Subtractive polarity   Additive polarity

FIG. 8-16. Before connecting a transformer, be sure you know the correct polarity.

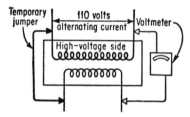

FIG. 8-17. Testing for transformer polarity.

Q How would you test a transformer for polarity?

A See Fig. 8-17. To test a transformer for polarity, use a temporary jumper and voltmeter as shown. If the voltmeter reads less than 110 V in this case, the polarity is subtractive; if it reads more than 110 V, it is additive.

Q How are transformers usually classed? What is the job of each group?

A 1. *Power transformers,* rated over 500 kVA, are used in generating plants to step up voltage, and in substations to step down voltage.

2. *Distribution transformers* step down voltage to 600 or 480 V for industry or to 240 or 120 V for residential and commercial use. These range in size from 1.5 to 500 kVA.

3. *Instrument transformers* (potential and current) serve low-voltage meters and relays.

4. *Specialty transformers* change voltages for specific uses, such as for signs, arc lamps, and bell ringing.

Q Show a Scott connection for phase transformation.

A See Fig. 8-18. Here a Scott connection changes two-phase to three-

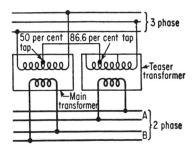

FIG. 8-18.   Scott connection is useful for changing two-phase to three-phase voltage.

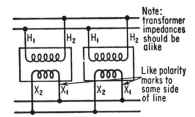

FIG. 8-19.   Two single-phase transformers connected as shown for parallel operation.

phase voltage. You need two transformers that have a 50 percent and 86.6 percent tap on the three-phase side.

Q   Sketch a hookup for two single-phase transformers operating in parallel.
A   See Fig. 8-19.

Q   Show a wiring diagram for single-phase transformation.
A   See Fig. 8.20. Here, the left side shows a secondary winding in parallel that splits the load between two sections. On the right, a three-wire system gives two voltage levels.

Q   Diagram an open-delta hookup for small power demands.
A   See Fig. 8-21. Here, one-half of the line-to-line voltage is available between the two line wires and the neutral.

Q   Diagram a delta-Y connection for a 208/120-V transformer.
A   See Fig. 8-22. Here, small three-phase power loads connect across the 208-V line.

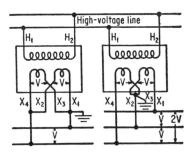

FIG. 8-20.   Single-phase transformation.

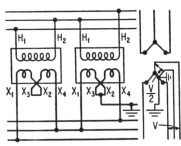

FIG. 8-21.   The open-delta hookup shown is ideal where power demands are small.

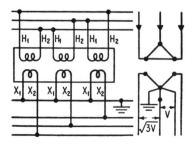

FIG. 8-22. Delta-Y connection for a 208/120-V small three-phase load.

ELECTRONIC DEVICES

Q What is thermionic emission?

A See Fig. 8-23. Thermionic emission is the basic process by which most vacuum tubes work. It is like a cloud of steam forming over boiling water; without heat, the steam is water. Heat makes the water more lively. When enough energy has been added to the water, kinetic energy causes drops of water to jump out of the liquid in the form of steam. When a steam droplet is cooled, it falls back as water. In a similar manner, a hot wire will cause electrons to boil over with heat.

When heat is applied to electrons, the electrons pick up speed in their orbits (kinetic energy). They whirl faster and faster around the nucleus until they fling themselves out of the wire and into the air around the wire. A cloud of electrons grows around the hot wire as long as heat is applied. Every electron in the wire cannot escape because each *emitted* electron leaves a positive charge in the wire. This positive charge is an attraction to all the remaining electrons and it also pulls back many of the emitted electrons. But enough electrons escape to do work and the hotter the wire, the greater the number of emitted electrons. A cloud of electrons forms a *negative* space charge. A space charge is similar to static

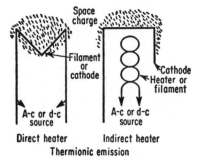

FIG. 8-23. Thermionic emission is similar to steam issuing from boiling water.

electricity, which can shock you or cause silk clothing to cling on a dry, cold day.

Figure 8-23 shows the negative space charge around the filament or cathode of a direct- and an indirect-type heater. The terms *filament* and *cathode* have the same meaning and are often used interchangeably.

Q Why are electronic tubes either vacuum- or gas-filled?

A When a filament (cathode) is used as a source of electrons, air molecules load up the space around the filament. This interferes with the action of the electrons, and smooth flow becomes impossible. Air is removed from the tubes to form a vacuum and to prevent interference. Some inert gases, such as argon, do the job as well as a vacuum. Inert gases don't interfere with the electrons as they boil out of the cathode. Some rectifiers use gas or vapor as they carry more current than a vacuum.

Q What is a diode?

A A diode is a vacuum tube containing two electrodes—a cathode and an anode. The cathode is the heater or filament and is surrounded by the space charge of negative electrons. The anode is a metal plate that connects to the external load. Diodes are used as rectifiers; they change alternating current to direct current.

Q Draw a sketch showing how a diode works.

A See Fig. 8-24. In the two circuits shown, the solid arrows depict the filament heating circuit using an A battery. The plate circuit is represented by the dotted arrows, and the current is furnished by a B battery.

NOTE: The arrows show the flow of electrons which is opposite to conventional current; that is, from minus to plus instead of from plus to minus.

The filament is heated to incandescence by the A battery. Thermionic emission causes a space charge to surround the cathode. The B battery makes the cathode negative, no matter how the filament is heated. The

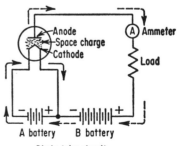

FIG. 8-24. Diode tube; two circuits.   Diode tube circuit

plate (anode) is connected to the positive side of the B battery and is maintained as a positive potential. The electrons of the cathode space charge are negative and are attracted to the positive plate. They drift to the plate and out through the circuit (dotted arrow), passing through the load and out through the battery, to the cathode. The heat of the cathode throws the electrons into space and the cycle is repeated. This continues as long as the cathode is heated and the plate is positively charged. An ammeter would show the flow in the circuit because the diode acts almost like a copper connection.

Q   What happens if the leads of the A battery are reversed? What happens if alternating current is used?

A   In either case, nothing happens, since the current to the filament is only a source of heat. Just be sure that voltage is at the proper value because it acts like a common incandescent lamp filament.

Q   What happens if the B battery is reversed to make the plate negatively charged?

A   If the B battery is reversed, negative electrons emitted from the cathode will be repelled and no current will flow through the plate circuit.

Q   How does a diode act as a rectifier?

A   Remember that a diode can act like a check valve in a water pipe. When the plate is positively charged, there is flow, but when it is negatively charged, there is no flow. If an ac source is used in place of the B battery, the polarity of the plate will be positively charged for one-half of the cycle. Only when the plate is positively charged is there flow. This would allow one-half of the ac wave and would produce a pulsating direct current. This is called half-wave rectifying.

NOTE: Although only alternating current is impressed, direct current flows.

Q   Sketch a simple diode used as a rectifier. Don't show transformers, etc.

A   See Fig. 8-25.

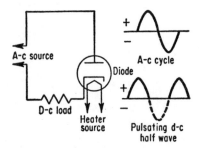

FIG. 8-25.   Simple diode used as rectifier.

Q Can full-wave rectification be achieved with diodes?
A You can achieve full-wave rectification by using two diode tubes or by using one tube with two plates hooked up properly.

Q Sketch a full-wave pulsating direct current.
A See Fig. 8-26.

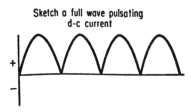

Sketch a full wave pulsating
d-c current

FIG. 8-26. Full-wave pulsating direct current.

Q What is a triode?
A A triode is a tube containing three elements. The plate and the cathode are similar to the diode but a third element, called the "grid," is between them. Although the interior arrangement and the shape of the parts may vary, one thing is certain: the grid is always between the cathode and the plate. This causes all electrons moving from the cathode to the plate to pass through the grid.

The main use of triodes is for amplifying. These tubes increase a feeble signal to a strong electrical force. Your radio is a good example. A feeble input from the antenna is amplified to sound at high volume. Triodes make all electronic control possible. They are used in oil-burner controls, smoke alarms, and intercom systems. In fact, triodes are common radio tubes, since they team up with the diodes in any amplifying system.

Q Why is the grid called the "control grid"?
A The grid is a perforated screen or cage through which the electrons pass from the cathode to the anode. As long as there is no charge on the grid, there is no interference with this flow. But if a negative charge is impressed on the grid, it will repel the stream of negative electrons. If the negative voltage is high enough, it will stop all flow.

The grid is like a water valve in a pipe. A person can easily open or close a valve that controls a great flow of water at high pressure. For this reason English people call their radio tubes "valves." The current flowing in a vacuum tube can be heavy, but a small negative charge in the grid can control it just as a person can close, open, or throttle a water valve.

If the grid were to become positively charged, it would try to become the plate (anode) by attracting the electrons. Control of the flow would be lost. For this reason the grid is normally negatively charged.

Q Sketch a triode used as an amplifier. Explain how it works.

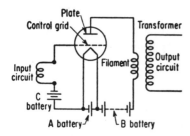

FIG. 8-27. Triode can be used as amplifier.

A See Fig. 8-27. Voltage received as a signal is too weak to operate control relays or a loudspeaker. So amplification is achieved with the triode and transformer circuit, as shown in the illustration.

A signal is fed into the grid current. In the grid, the signal is strong enough to control the plate current. The negative electrons surrounding the cathode (filament) flow through the grid to the plate. The potential of the grid controls this flow. As long as the grid is negative, it throttles the flow of electrons; the more negative the grid, the less the plate current. A great amount of flow is instantly responsive to the small signal to grid. A C battery must be used to keep the grid negative or the grid will become a plate and will lose control. Since the signal is alternating current and the C battery is direct current, the two voltages are impressed on the grid. When the alternating current of the signal is positive, the negative direct current from the C battery subtracts this positive signal and keeps the grid negative. When the ac signal is negative, it is added to C battery current to make the grid more negative. A C battery is called a "grid bias" because no matter what signal is received, the grid stays negative.

The plate current is a changing or pulsating direct current, instantly responsive to the tiny alternating current reflected from the signal. Plate current is fed to the primary windings of the transformer and the pulses are stepped up. The rising and falling shape of the signal is amplified and an ac voltage flows from the transformer. If this one stage of amplification isn't enough, the grid of a second triode is connected to the secondary windings of the transformer for a second stage, and so on. Study the circuit shown in Fig. 8-27, as this is the best-known way to amplify a feeble signal.

Q Sketch a grid leak and condenser and explain how the C battery is eliminated.
A See Fig. 8-28. To eliminate the C battery use a condenser and a resistor to bias the grid circuit. The condenser stores the electrons and keeps the grid negative. The function of the resistor is to leak electrons back off of the condenser in order to prevent it from getting too strong a negative charge.

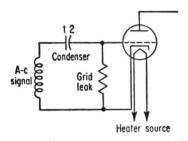

FIG. 8-28. This is how the grid leak eliminates the C battery.

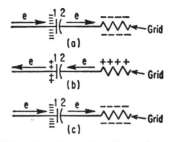

FIG. 8-29. How the grid condenser functions when it is used to bias the grid.

Q With the aid of a sketch, show how to bias the grid with a grid condenser.

A See Fig. 8-29a to c.

a. When the alternating current impressed on the grid is negative, the negative electrons pile up on plate 1, giving it a negative charge. This charge forces electrons out of plate 2 and into the grid. This is OK when alternating current is negative, since negative-impressed voltage produces a negative voltage.

b. When the alternating current impressed on condenser plate 1 is positive, it attracts electrons from the grid onto condenser plate 2. The grid loses electrons and acts like an anode; it attracts electrons from the cathode. These are stored on plate 2.

c. When the alternating current impressed on the grid changes to negative again, the grid has two negative charges, one from the condenser, the other from the grid since it was positive. As this continues, the grid collects more and more negative charges. Negative charges bias the grid as surely as the C battery did.

Q Why is the resistor or "grid leak" connected across the condenser?

A The "grid leak" is connected across the condenser because the process of piling up electrons is too efficient to be good. The grid becomes so negatively biased that all plate current is shut off. The grid leak is a high resistance of nichrome wire or carbon. It passes off some of the grid electrons around the condenser. When the impressed alternating current is positive, the electrons leak from the grid to condenser plate 1. This leak-off keeps the grid from acquiring too high a negative charge.

Q How is the B battery eliminated?

A If there is a source of the positive potential, such as a dc circuit, there is no problem in eliminating the B battery. A resistor is used to reduce voltage to about 45 V. All that the B battery does is provide a steady positive potential for the plate (anode). If alternating current is used, there are problems in converting the alternating current to steady direct current to feed to the plate. A diode tube will rectify alternating current to pulsating direct current, but steady direct current is needed. So, the ac voltage is reduced to about 45 V in a transformer. The 45-V alternating current is converted to 45-V pulsating direct current. Pulsating direct current is fed to a filter choke coil that smooths out the pulses to a steady flow of dc potential suitable for positive voltage to the anode of the triode.

Q Sketch and describe a filter choke coil.
A See Fig. 8-30. A filter choke coil is an induction coil connected with two condensers across the line. Electrons marked e come from the rectifier in the pulsating waves. Condenser A fills up and current starts to trickle through the coil. The self-induction principle of the coil holds the current back (flywheel effect of induction coils).

The trickle then acts as a self-induced voltage and holds the current back. As pulsation diminishes, condenser A begins to unload electrons and feeds them to the coil. As pulsation nears zero, the self-induced voltage of the decaying coil further draws electrons from condenser A and keeps the current moving. Condenser A and the self-induced voltage of the coil provides a nearly steady flow of current. The coil acts like a flywheel; as a surge comes, the coil resists it, and as the surge passes to zero, the coil provides power as would a flywheel in smoothing out piston strokes.

Condenser A acts as a reservoir tank. It fills up on strong pulses and empties on weak pulses, helping the coil. As stated, the flow is not entirely smooth. This is remedied by condenser B, which stores the strong humps of the pulse that surge through the coil. It then feeds these humps back when the hollows come through. The final current is a smooth uninterrupted flow of direct current, as shown in Fig. 8-31.

Q Sketch an amplifier, showing the rectifier, choke coil, grid leak, and grid condenser.
A See Fig. 8-32.

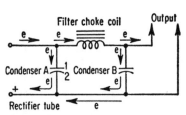

FIG. 8-30. Filter choke coil (induction coil) connected with two condensers.

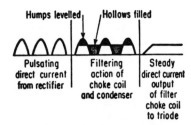

FIG. 8-31. Condenser acts as a reserve tank, producing smooth uninterrupted flow.

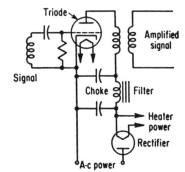

FIG. 8-32. Amplifier with rectifier, choke, coil, grid leak, and grid condenser.

ELECTRONIC BASICS

Q Why do we continue to discuss vacuum tubes when solid-state devices are rapidly replacing them?
A Vacuum-tube circuits are easier to comprehend and thus provide a foundation to build upon.

Q Do vacuum tubes have the same names and functions as do solid-state devices?
A Yes, in some instances, but solid-state technology is rapidly developing and there is a need for new names. Miniaturized solid-state devices now replace whole rooms full of vacuum tubes with a "chip" that is the size of a small coin.

Q Is the disk rectifier shown in Fig. 8-8 a form of solid-state technology?
A Yes; it is a very large diode designed for heat dissipation of larger loads at low frequencies such as 60 Hz (cycles per second). Miniature diodes use small voltages but can utilize high frequencies. They cannot dissipate heat because of their small size. Figure 8-36c is the diode symbol.

Q Is there a simple way to explain semiconductors much as beginners start learning electricity by the analogy of water pressure and flow?
A See Fig. 8-33. Imagine a mixture of steel balls and lead shot, both of equal diameters, which are to be separated. If the mixture is pushed to flow down a brass tube slightly larger than the spheres toward a junction of an upper magnet and a lower hole, separation will occur. The steel balls will be attracted to the upper magnet, blocking the hole until a lead shot pushes the steel ball along and opens the hole and traps out. The continuing flow will exchange the separation on a one in, one out basis. Once separated, there can be no reverse flow. The device will not do

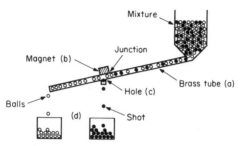

FIG. 8-33. Ball analogy illustrates solid-state electronic flow of current.

anything but block reverse flow. The hole is blocked by an undisplaced ball at the junction.

Keep these ideas in mind for visualizing semiconductors: in Fig. 8-33*a*, exchange flow on a one-in, one-out basis; in *b*, attraction; in *c*, hole trap; and in *d*, blocking reverse flow.

Q What are the two principal parts of an atomic structure?

A All atoms have a center (nucleus) of very heavy protons around which electrons orbit. Protons are positively charged, and electrons are negatively charged. Like charges repel, and unlike charges attract, much like magnets. Protons and electrons are equally charged.

Q Silicon is the most frequently used element for manufacturing semiconductors. Show its atomic structure.

A See Fig. 8-34. Silicon has a nucleus of 14 protons with 14 orbiting electrons. (See Fig. 19-1 for paths of the orbits—called "shells.") Silicon has three shells, and Fig. 8-34 depicts them as rings for simplicity. The two inner shells contain 10 electrons, the outer shell has 4, and all 14 are bound to the dense positive protons in the nucleus. The outer 4, however, are readily influenced by nearby forces. A pure silicon crystal would contain atoms in numbers almost beyond imagination, no matter how small the crystal.

Q Show the effects of neighboring atoms on the outer electrons of an atom and its neighbors.

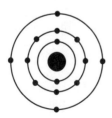

FIG. 8-34. Silicon atom is tiny solar system. (*Texas Instruments, Inc.*)

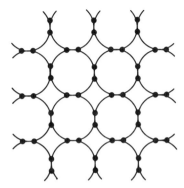

FIG. 8-35. Silicon atoms arranged with their neighboring electrons. (*Texas Instruments, Inc.*)

A See Fig. 8-35. Here only the outer electrons are shown in rings. Notice how the outer four electrons are trying to become eight electron orbits. The electrons are in balance with the protons, as there are an equal number of each. The mutual actions of the outer four electrons allow pushing in of electrons from a source other than a neighboring silicon atom. Silicon is a very stable element and is a nonconductor of electricity.

Q How do impure crystals of silicon act?

A When molten silicon is "doped" with either phosphorus or boron, the impure crystals become partially able to conduct electricity. Phosphorus atoms have one more proton and one more outer electron compared with silicon. Thus phosphorus has five, and silicon four outer electrons. The fifth electron seeks a place with the four electrons, but the protons balance their electrons until an outside source of flowing electrons disturbs this relationship.

It is now possible to pump in an electron and push out an electron of the silicon phosphorus crystal much as the magnet separated the steel ball from the lead shot. This is the N used for the negative portion. The greater the amount of phosphorus, the greater the ability to conduct electricity, which means the greater the number of free electrons. Because of the unchanged number of protons, the total number of electrons is constant, but the one-in, one-out idea is apparent. It is like adding water to a full pail. The excess overflows, but the same quantity remains in the pail.

Q How does boron affect silicon?

A Doping with boron, which has three electrons in the outer orbit, creates a "hole" because of its deficiency of one electron in the proximity of the four electrons of silicon. Think of the hole orbiting in the impure silicon-boron crystal. This hole will trap free electrons pumped in much as the lead shot passed through the hole in the tube.

The hole is a deficiency of 1 and therefore is a minus 1 (−1); but the trapped electron was taken by a minus quantity and upon being released is an additional quantity, or plus 1 (+1), even though the electron by its nature remains negative. Again, one electron pumped in pushes one electron out. The boron-doped crystal is the P for the positive portion, and together this is a PN diode. Properly, it is a PN junction diode.

Q How do PN diodes prevent reverse current flow?

A The "blocking" effect is the reason why alternating current is rectified to pulsating direct current. Compare Fig. 8-36*a* with *b*. They are both alike except that the electron flow is reversed in the ac cycle. The P crystal with moving holes acts like a pure silicon crystal which is nonconductive, there being no unsatisfied outer orbits and therefore no current flowing back to the N crystal. Remember how a steel ball clinging to the magnet blocked the hole?

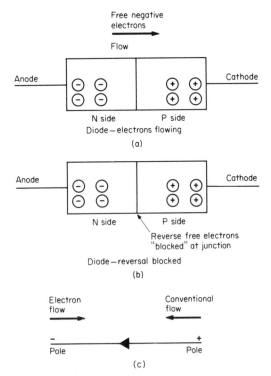

FIG. 8-36. Blocking effect rectifies the alternating current to pulsating direct current. (*Texas Instruments, Inc.*)

Q Show a diode symbol with direction of flow.
A See Fig. 8-36c.

Q What ideas must you keep in mind when dealing with transistors?
A 1. Current can flow only in the forward direction of the arrowhead symbol for a diode.
    2. Diodes act to block reverse flow.
    3. There is little voltage drop from anode to cathode.
    4. Direction is always the conventional flow direction of dc polarity, and the positive (+) pole flows toward the negative (−) pole. (Again, scientists have flow the other way, as some of the explanations show, but our daily practical work is always conventional current. *Follow the arrows!*)

Q What is a thyristor?
A Thyristors are electronic switches that act in microseconds by receiving a momentary signal pulse. Once "on," they remain "on" until the working current is interrupted, at which point they are switched to "off" until again pulsed. They are used for power controls in both ac and dc applications.

Q What is an SCR?
A A silicon controlled rectifier (SCR) is a solid-state device, a semiconductor which checks current flow from anode to cathode. A spurt of current into the gate will open the SCR, allowing full working current to flow continuously as if it were an "on" switch. If the working current is interrupted, the SCR stops the flow, as an "off" switch would. Pulsing the gate control current would again open the SCR. In the "off" period, little flow is permitted, which is a rectifier function. (A diode plus a control current is a triode whether in vacuum-tube or solid-state technology.)

Q What is SCR control? How is it shown in a circuit?
A See Fig. 8-37. As will be explained in a few examples to follow, SCR is applied to control power to small dc motors, lamp dimmers, and internal-combustion systems. The technical name for SCR is "reverse blocking

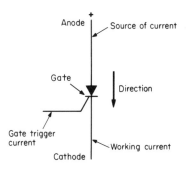

FIG. 8-37. SCR symbol with current flow indicated. (*Texas Instruments, Inc.*)

triode thyristor." The symbol resembles a diode symbol, but a third terminal is for gate-control current. A pulse of current will open the gate, and once open, it stays open until the working current is interrupted, whereupon it closes. In a rectifier, current can only flow forward, and reverse flow is blocked. Since the gate current controls flow, the SCR is a thyristor. The term SCR is simpler to say.

Q   What is happening in the SCR shown in Fig. 8-38?

A   Figure 8-38*a* and *b* shows a four-layer stack PNPN with three leads, which identifies it as a triode. This semiconductor has the anode, cathode (when these two are used alone, they form the familiar diode), and the third lead into the inner P. In Fig. 8-38*c* one can visualize the flow in the device. Although they are not really made this way, they work as if this sketch were true. The new symbol in *a* is a collector, and that in *c* an emitter.

Looking from the anode side, there is a PNP transistor, which is a collector. In the symbol, the internal arrow is inward. Looking from the cathode side, there is an NPN transistor, which is an emitter. The symbol shows the arrow outward.

Figure 8-38*d* is staggered, as the collector symbol is shown as being higher than the emitter symbol. The flow arrows show the electron paths. Now look at the triangular SCR symbol *(b)*. Current flow enters at the base (cathode). Visualize the first P. This is the PNP, which is a collector. The other half is NPN, which is an emitter. *Follow the arrows!*

Q   What kind of current does the SCR provide?

A   Pulsating direct current. See Fig. 8-25 and compare to Fig. 8-40.

Q   What kind of current do the interrupter points of an automobile distributor provide?

A   Pulsating direct current. This builds up and collapses the primary windings of the spark coil for inductance to provide high voltage to the spark plugs.

Q   What is SCR ignition in internal-combustion engines?

A   It is a solid-state device widely used in modern automobile engines. SCR has replaced full voltage flow across the breaker points. Figure 8-39 is a schematic system. Battery power is stored in a capacitor during the "off" period for the SCR. When the breaker points close, gate control triggers power flows to trigger the SCR. The trigger power is very small, but the capacitor has a full charge which spurts into the primary of the spark coil as the SCR is on.

The capacitor is almost instantly discharged and the SCR is off, which again starts the cycle of charge and discharge of the capacitor. The SCR relieves the points of heavy current switching, which gives them a very

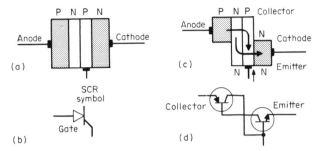

FIG. 8-38. *(a)* Stack representing SCR by PNPN layers. *(b)* SCR symbol. *(c)* Staggered PNP sketched to visualize flow to PNP collector and NPN emitter. *(d)* Collector and emitter symbols. *(Texas Instruments, Inc.)*

long life. Stronger spark due to higher voltage results in better ignition.

General Motors (GM) products have an improvement that eliminates breaker points. GM utilizes permanent magnets to form "teeth" on the rotor, and as these revolve, passing a fixed coil, the device acts as a small generator. The induced voltage is timed to signal the SCR when the pole is aligned with the coil and timed to the piston for ignition. This type of ignition is called: "breakerless," "transistorized," etc.

Q Discuss SCR control for lamp dimmers or small dc motors.

A See Fig. 8-40. The SCR is both a diode rectifier and a switch. A rectifier provides half-wave direct current (see Fig. 8-25). When the SCR is triggered to provide less than half a wave, less power is passed, which dims the lamp or slows the motor. Electric drills are an example. The SCR is

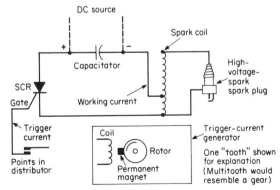

FIG. 8-39. Schematic SCR ignition system as used for ignition system of automobile engines. *(Texas Instruments, Inc.)*

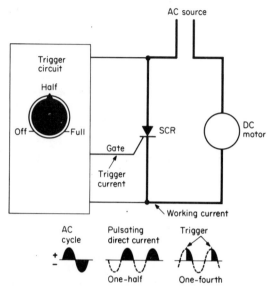

FIG. 8-40.   Schematic of SCR dc motor speed control. (*Texas Instruments, Inc.*)

used because it dissipates less energy to heat. The SCR utilizes portions of the ac wave only for work.

REMEMBER: No flow, no loss.

Q Can SCR devices control larger ac motors?
A See Fig. 8-41. Yes, the use of two SCR devices arranged head to foot forms what is called a "triac." At this point, you have some basic knowledge which should be further advanced by books or courses in elementary electronics.

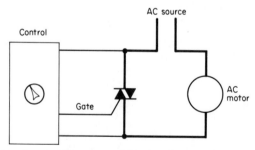

FIG. 8-41.   Triac is two SCRs arranged head to foot for ac motor control. (*Texas Instruments, Inc.*)

Q What does *interface* mean?

A Whatever gives you a display message such as a light-emitting diode (LED) or liquid crystal display (LCD) watches, electronic computer printouts, and television receivers.

Q What is a microprocessor?

A It is a chip containing an integrated circuit like that in a small handheld calculator with a memory as well as other stored information. Upon receiving signals from plant instruments, the microprocessor decides what to do and then acts to control plant process and equipment. These are the heart and brains in those "little black boxes."

OPERATION AND MAINTENANCE

Q How is a compound-wound dc generator started and paralleled?

A (1) Check the oil and bearings. (2) Cut in the full resistance on the field. (3) Bring the machine up to speed and on the governor. (4) Adjust the field rheostat and allow the voltage to be equal. (5) Close the overload switch. (6) Close the line switch.

NOTE: If three separate switches are used, close the equalizer switch first, the series coil switch second, and the single line switch last.

Q Why must operators be familiar with brushes and settings?

A The only way to determine the correct brushes and settings for a motor is by the fit-and-try scheme. What works well on one machine may not be satisfactory on another unit that is identical in make, model, and use.

Q What causes sparking on motor-generator sets?

A Sparking is caused by (1) overload, (2) a dirty commutator, (3) brushes that stick in holders or a spring that is not at the right tension, (4) brushes that aren't on neutral, (5) brushes that aren't fitted to the commutator, (6) brushes made of the wrong material, (7) commutator mica that is too high, (8) commutator bars that are high, flat, or rough, and (9) short circuits (check the field coils as well as the armature).

Q How is a second ac generator paralleled with a generator on the line?

A See Fig. 8-42. The two generators must be synchronized. (1) Voltages must be equal, (2) they must be in phase, and (3) the frequency must be the same. To parallel, do the following: (1) Bring the second machine up to speed with switches open. (2) Cut in full resistance on the field rheostat. (3) Adjust exciter voltage to the normal excitation voltage. (4) Close the field switch. (5) Adjust the generator field resistance until the voltage is the same as on bus bars from the other machines. (6) Synchronize

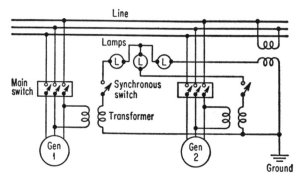

FIG. 8-42. Wiring diagram used for two three-wire high-voltage ac generators.

with the lamps or synchroscope. At the instant of synchronization, turn the main switch. (7) Adjust the rheostat until cross flow is at a minimum. (8) Adjust the governors of the engines so that load is equally divided.

Q If you use lamps to synchronize ac generators, should you cut in at "light" or "dark"? Explain.

A In the United States, "dark" is preferred because judging maximum brightness is difficult. Besides, the light period is much longer than the dark period. The danger of synchronizing "dark" is that the filament of the synchronous lamp may be broken at the moment of synchronization and may cause an accident. To prevent this, two synchronizing circuits or two lamps in paralleled circuits are used.

Q How is an ac generator cut out when it is in parallel with others?

A (1) Cut down on the governor until the no-load point is reached. (2) Adjust the resistance in the field circuit until the armature current is at its minimum. (3) Open the main switch.

> CAUTION: Don't open the field switch before the main switch. If the field is disconnected, a heavy current will flow between the two armatures.

(4) Small units may be disconnected by opening the main switch and allowing the other units to furnish the full load.

Q What is a synchroscope?

A See Fig. 8-43. A synchroscope instantaneously indicates phase differences and is used for synchronizing polyphase generators. A hand moves on a dial to indicate whether the phase is ahead or behind the bus-bar load. When the machine speed and phase are right, the synchroscope hand indicates the moment to cut in.

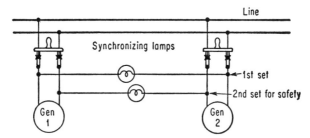

FIG. 8-43. Simple synchronizing hookup used for synchronizing polyphase generators.

Q What are the requirements for parallel operation of dc generators?
A The general requirements are (1) polarities of the generators must be alike, (2) voltage of the incoming machine must be the same as the running machines, (3) field rheostats must be used to adjust the load between the machines, and (4) the machines must have compatible operating characteristics that allow load changes to divide between the machines.

Q What is the purpose of the equalizer on parallel dc generators?
A See Fig. 8-44. Overcompounded generators have a rising voltage characteristic; that is, the heavier the load, the higher the voltage. This leads to difficulties in parallel operation since a division of load is difficult. The reason for this is that the machine with the heavy load has a higher voltage and therefore tries to "motor" the light-loaded machine with a lower voltage. As a result, it is probable that one machine will try to take all the load. To prevent this, an equalizer line connects the machines at the series fields in parallel with each other. A momentary load change will not change the voltage of one machine since the total series fields are equalized with the same total current in each. Both machines must share the load alike; neither should dominate.

Q Sketch and describe at least four methods of single-phase motor starting and running. Don't describe a universal type.
A See Fig. 8-45. *(a)* A capacitor that holds current at the start, winding out of phase with the running current. A centrifugal switch opens at about 80 percent speed. *(b)* A capacitor that always remains in the circuit. Since this is a form of a two-phase motor, it is quieter and vibrates less than a split-phase motor. *(c)* Like capacitor motors, this design has two windings in the stator. One is the running or main winding and the other is for starting. *(d)* In some designs, brushes are lifted automatically after the bars are short-circuited. Others let the brushes ride on the commutator.

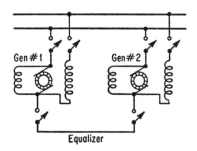

Equalizer

FIG. 8-44. Equalizer assures both dc generators of dividing the load evenly.

Q What happens if one phase is lost to an induction motor?

A If an induction motor loses one phase, it won't start. However, if it is running, it will continue to run, but as a single-phase induction motor. If it is loaded above 60 percent, it will overheat and may burn out. Wound-rotor motors are apt to vibrate heavily.

Q How is a synchronous motor started?

A See Fig. 8-46. A synchronous motor is not self-starting; its rotor is too heavy to fall into magnetic lock with the rotating field. Two methods are used to start synchronous motors. (1) Amortisseur windings, which are squirrel cages and short-circuiting rings, are added to the pole faces outside the dc rotor windings. This induction winding brings the motor up to speed, close enough to pull into synchronism. Once in synchronism, the motor speed is constant so long as it is not overloaded beyond its pull-out torque. (2) Another motor may be used to start the induction motor and to get it up to speed. It is best to start a synchronous motor unloaded. If this isn't practical, the amortisseur windings must be designed to start and carry the load to speed.

Q What does a 40°C rise indicate?

A A 40°C rise means that the motor cores and windings will maintain full-load conditions without rising more than 40°C above the ambient temperature of the enclosing space. Ambient temperature is usually assumed to be 40°C.

Q What causes armature windings to overheat?

A Overheating of armature windings is caused by short circuits due to poor insulation resulting from moisture, oil, or abrasion; overloading; low voltage; poor ventilation; and poor commutation.

Q What simple methods are used to test for grounds, shorts, or opens in armature windings?

A To test armature windings, wire a low-voltage battery and light in series to one lead. Remove the brushes and attach one lead to the armature-

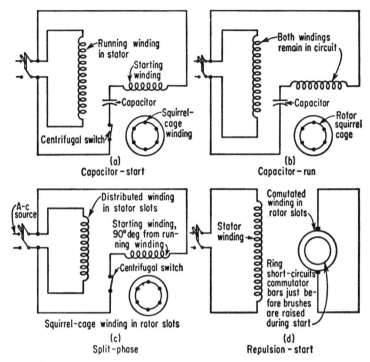

FIG. 8-45.   Single-phase motors are started by these four methods.

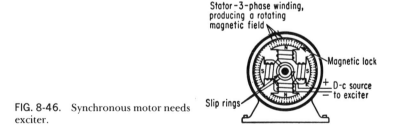

FIG. 8-46.   Synchronous motor needs exciter.

shaft metal. Try each segment in turn with the other lead; any grounded coil will light the lamp. To find a short or open coil, place the ends of the test wires on each pair of adjacent segments. The lamp will light dimly on normal coils; grounded coils will cause a bright light, and open coils will give no light.

Q In an emergency, how can you temporarily repair an internally damaged armature coil?

A Solder a jumper across the ends of the commutator bar on the damaged coil. Then, cut the coil open at the back of the armature. This shorts out the coil and gives you an emergency repair.

Q What causes a motor to overheat?

A Overloading; low voltage, grounds, short circuits; open phase, wrong motor type for service; poor ventilation, dirty motors; too high ambient; defective brushes or commutations; loose connections; field excitation; friction of rubbing parts; belt slipping, defective bearings; bent or misaligned parts, improper windings, or repairs causing eddy currents.

Q What would you do if upon starting a dc generator you found the polarity reversed in relation to the other generators?

A To correct this situation, lift all the brushes and slip a piece of bakelite fiber or some other thin insulating material between the brushes and the commutator. Close the circuit breaker on the board connected to the other running generators of correct polarity. Next, close and open the main switch to the troubled generator a few times. (This restores the residual magnetism in the field poles.) Finally, restore the brushes and start the generator. Polarity should be right.

If this doesn't work for a compound machine, it is because the series field has current flow opposite to normal flow. This will strengthen the reversed polarity. In this case, short-circuit the series-field winding before going through the above process.

Q How is moisture kept out of motor or generator windings during shutdown?

A If you have condensation trouble, it is due to metal parts getting cooler than the atmosphere (below dew point). To correct this condition use heaters or blow warm air through the idle machine to keep it warm.

Q What would you do if inspection revealed a generator with moisture grounds?

A Since the machine must be thoroughly dried out before using, heat and air flow are the answers to this problem. Electric heaters are good for this job, and hot air from a heating system is also OK. You can dry the machine by short-circuiting the terminals beyond the ammeter and by running the machine with full resistance cut in on the shunt-field rheostat. Be careful not to overheat the windings, as insulation can be destroyed. A megger test will show when the generator is dried out.

CALCULATIONS: RESISTANCE

Q What is the best way to solve resistance or network calculations?
A To solve resistance or network calculations, always make a diagrammatic sketch, insert the values, and solve by use of the correct formula.

Q What are the four basic rules for series circuits? (Remember how conductors wired end to end on some miniature Christmas lights act; when one is out, all are out.)

FIG. 8-47. Series circuit with conductors.

A See Fig. 8-47. The four basic rules for series circuits are: (1) Voltage differs in different parts of the circuit, while amperes are the same throughout the circuit. (2) The sum of the resistances is equal to the total resistance: $R_t = R_1 + R_2 + R_3$, etc. (3) Ohm's law: $V = AR$, $A = V/R$, $R = V/A$. (4) Power rule for dc circuits or single-phase, unity power factor: $W = AV$; $A = W/V$; $V = W/A$.

Q Resistances of 5, 6, and 7 Ω in a series on a 110-V dc line can be made into typical series-circuit problems. (1) Calculate the total resistance in the circuit. (2) Calculate the amperage in the circuit. (3) What is the power in the line?

A

1. $R_t = R_1 + R_2 + R_3$

    $= 5 + 6 + 7$
    $= 18\ \Omega$ *Ans.*

2. $A = \dfrac{V}{R} = \dfrac{110}{18} = 6.111$ A   *Ans.*

3. $W = AV = 6.111 \times 110 = 672.21$ *Ans.*

Q What are the four basic rules for parallel circuits? (Conductors are across the line as on new style Christmas lights. Each one is a 100-V lamp; when one goes out, the others remain lit.)
A See Fig. 8-48, which shows a dc circuit. (1) Voltage is the same throughout the circuit, while amperage differs in different parts of the circuit. (2) Total resistance is the reciprocal of the sum of the reciprocals:

$1/R_t = 1/R_1 + 1/R_2 + 1/R_3$, etc. (3) Ohm's law: $V = AR$, $A = V/R$, $R = V/A$. (4) Power rule: $W = AV$, $A = W/V$, $V = W/A$.

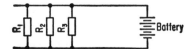

Battery   FIG. 8-48.   Parallel circuit with conductors.

Q In the parallel-circuit problems for a dc circuit, resistances of 5, 6, and 7 Ω are placed in parallel on a 110-V line. (1) Calculate the total resistance. (2) Calculate the total amperage. (3) Calculate the voltage through each resistance. (4) What is the power in the line?

A

1. $\dfrac{1}{R_t} = \dfrac{1}{R_1} + \dfrac{1}{R_2} + \dfrac{1}{R_3}$

   $= \dfrac{1}{5} + \dfrac{1}{6} + \dfrac{1}{7}$

   Lowest common denominator $= 210$

   $\dfrac{1}{R_t} = \dfrac{42 + 35 + 30}{210}$

   $\dfrac{1}{R_t} = \dfrac{107}{210}$

   The whole equation is inverted in this next step:

   $\dfrac{R_t}{1} = \dfrac{210}{107} = 1.962$ *Ans.*

   $Rt = 1.962$ Ω total resistance (Compare this with the series-circuit problem that used the same resistance.)

2. $A = \dfrac{V}{R}$

   $= \dfrac{110}{1.962}$

   $= 56.06$ A (Compare this with the series circuit.)   *Ans.*

3. Voltage $= 110$ V (as it is constant across the line)   *Ans.*

4. $W = AV$
          $= 56.06 \times 110$
          $= 6166.60$ W
   1 kW $= 1000$ W

$$W = \frac{6166.60}{1000} = 6.166 \text{ kW} \qquad \textit{Ans.}$$

Q Four resistances, each of 50 Ω, are in parallel across a 110-V line. Find (1) the total current in the circuit and (2) the current in each resistor.

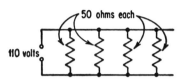

FIG. 8-49. Four resistances in parallel.

A See Fig. 8-49.

1. $\dfrac{1}{R_t} = \dfrac{1}{R_1} + \dfrac{1}{R_2} + \dfrac{1}{R_3} + \dfrac{1}{R_4}$

$\qquad = \dfrac{1}{50} + \dfrac{1}{50} + \dfrac{1}{50} + \dfrac{1}{50}$

$\qquad = \dfrac{4}{50}$

Invert

$\qquad R_t = \dfrac{50}{4} = 12.5 \ \Omega$

$\qquad I_t = \dfrac{E_t}{R_t} = \dfrac{110}{12.5} = 8.8 \text{ A total} \qquad \textit{Ans.}$

2. $I = \dfrac{E}{R} = \dfrac{110}{50} = 2.20 \text{ A} \qquad \textit{Ans.}$

NOTE: Since all four resistances are alike, the answer is 2.2 A each.

Q State the power equation, which is based on Ohm's laws (for dc or single-phase circuits, unity power factor).
A Power = volts × amperes $(P = EI)$

$\qquad \text{Volts} = \dfrac{\text{power}}{\text{amperes}} \ \left(V = \dfrac{P}{A} \right)$

$\qquad \text{Amperes} = \dfrac{\text{power}}{\text{volts}} \ \left(A = \dfrac{P}{V} \right)$

Q How much current is there in a 100-W lamp on a 110-V circuit?

A $A = \dfrac{P}{V} = \dfrac{100}{110} = 0.909 \text{ A}$ *Ans.*

Q Determine the potential drop in a circuit that consumes 800 W, carrying 15 A.

A $E = \dfrac{P}{I} = \dfrac{800}{15} = 53.33 \text{ V}$ *Ans.*

Q If 7 A of current will flow through a conductor of 19 Ω resistance, how many amperes will flow through a conductor of 13 Ω resistance?

A The current varies as the resistance; so using the formula for new amperes, we get

$$A^1 = \dfrac{RA}{R^1}$$

where A^1 = new amperes
R = old resistance
A = old amperes
R^1 = new resistance

$$A^1 = \dfrac{7 \times 19}{13} = \dfrac{133}{13} = 10.2 \text{ A}$$ *Ans.*

Q If 15 A flow through a conductor of 30-Ω resistance, how many amperes will flow through a 20-Ω resistance?

A $A^1 = \dfrac{RA}{R^1}$

where A^1 = new amperes
R = old resistance
A = old amperes
R^1 = new resistance

$$A^1 = \dfrac{30 \times 15}{20} = 22.5 \text{ A}$$ *Ans.*

Q Three 1000-W heaters are in series on a 240-V line; 12.5 A are flowing in the circuit. Find (1) the total resistance, (2) the resistance of each heater, and (3) the total power.

A See Fig. 8-50.
1. Solve for the total resistance:

$$R_t = \dfrac{E_t}{I_t} = \dfrac{240}{12.5} = 19.2 \text{ Ω}$$ *Ans.*

2. Solve for the resistance of each heater:

$$R_1 = \frac{P_1}{I^2} = \frac{1000}{12.5 \times 12.5} = \frac{1000}{156.25} = 6.4 \ \Omega$$

NOTE: Since all are equal, each is 6.4 Ω   *Ans.*

3. Solve for the total power:

$P_t = P_1 + P_2 + P_3$
$1000 + 1000 + 1000 = 3000$ W   *Ans.*

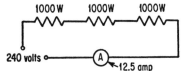

FIG. 8-50. Three heaters are in series.

Q What is the minimum fuse to be used in a 110-V circuit carrying eight 100-W bulbs?
A $8 \times 100 = 800$-W load

$$\frac{800}{110} = 7.27 \ A$$

Therefore, use a 10-A fuse, the nearest commercial size.   *Ans.*

Q A 220-V circuit has two lamps in series: a 192-Ω lamp and a 288-Ω lamp. Find (1) total amperage, (2) total power, (3) amperage in each lamp, and (4) watts of each lamp (nearest commercial size).
A The best way is to make the diagram shown in Fig. 8-51:
$R_t = R_1 + R_2$
$\quad = 192 + 288 = 480 \ \Omega$ total
1. To solve for the total amperes in circuit,

$$A_t = \frac{V_t}{R_t} = \frac{220}{480} = 0.458 \ A \qquad Ans.$$

FIG. 8-51. Diagram of lamps in series.

2. To solve for the total power (watts):

$$P_t = V_t \times A_t = 220 \times 0.458 = 100.76 \text{ W} \qquad Ans.$$

3. The answer here is 0.458 A, because the amperage is the same in all parts of a series circuit.   *Ans.*

4. Solve for the power of lamps by determining voltage drop across each lamp as the first step:

$$V_1 = A_1 \times R_1 = 0.458 \times 192 = 87.93 \text{ V}$$
$$V_2 = A_2 \times R_2 = 0.458 \times 288 = 131.90 \text{ V}$$

NOTE: Check at this point by adding these two voltages: 87.93 + 131.90 = 219.83. The small error is due to decimal errors; the total number of volts should be 220. Split the difference and use voltages of 88 and 132; then,

$$P = V_1 \times A_1 = 88 \times 0.458 = 40.304 \text{ W}$$
$$P = V_2 \times A_2 = 132 \times 0.458 = 60.456 \text{ W}$$

NOTE: It is probably that a 40- and a 60-W lamp were wired in series but that our decimal work changed the value.

In the last question, the power was found in two steps. First, the voltage drop was found across each lamp; second, the power rule of $P = AV$ was used. Since I is A and V is E, the power rule is also $P = IE$. Except for different letters, nothing is changed. Now for the I^2R method. In the equation $P = IE$, substitute for E the value of IR thus:

$$P = I \times IR \qquad \text{or} \qquad P = I^2R \qquad \text{(for dc and single-phase circuits, unity power factor)}$$

To apply this to the last problem, for solving for power in a one-step method, we get

$$P = I^2R$$
$$I = 0.458 \text{ A}$$
$$R = 142 \ \Omega$$
$$P = 0.458 \times 0.458 \times 192 = 40.27 \text{ W}$$
$$P = 0.458 \times 0.458 \times 288 = 60.12 \text{ W}$$

Compare this answer with the previous example and note how decimal errors creep into the calculations.

CURRENT CAPACITY

Q What is used to determine the allowable current capacity of insulated copper conductors for interior wiring?
A The regulations and requirements given in the tables of the National Board of Fire Underwriters limit the current to give safe installations for each size and type of conductor.

REMEMBER: Overloading causes overheating, and insulation breaks down or even burns out.

Q What is the designation system of numbers to gage copper conductors?
A The American wire gage in which 40 is the least size and 0000 the largest.

Q What is the approximate ratio between gage numbers?
A The diameters double for each three gage numbers. This means that size 4 is twice as large as size 7; size 7 is twice as large as size 10; etc.

Q Explain the circular-mil system of calculating conductors.
A A circular mil is the diameter (cross section) of a round conductor squared. Measurement is reduced to thousandths of an inch, called mils. Thus a ⅛-in.-diameter conductor would measure 0.125 in. To calculate circular mils is easy:

0.125 in. = 125 mils

125 × 125 = 15,625 circular mils

The problem of flat bars of rectangular or other shapes is not as simple. To convert square mils to circular mils, multiply by 1.273. For example, a bus bar is ⅛ in. thick and 1½ in. wide. Find (1) square mils and (2) circular mils.

1. Solving for square mils,

⅛ in. = 0.125 in. = 125 mils
1½ in. = 1.500 in. = 1500 mils
125 × 1500 = 187,500 sq mils
2. Solving for circular mils,
187,500 × 1.273 = 238,677 circular mils

Q What is the rule of thumb used to calculate the circular mils of a copper conductor per ampere?
A Bus bars and large feeder circuits allow *one thousand circular mils* per ampere, or 0.001 A per circular mil.

MOTORS AND GENERATORS

Q Determine the power consumed by a 110-V motor if it uses 15 A.
A $P = EI = 110 \times 15 = 1650$ W

What is the horsepower?

1 hp = 746 W

$$hp = \frac{1650}{746} = 2.21 \text{ hp} \qquad \textit{Ans.}$$

Q Two 100-kW generators are running in parallel. Calculate (1) minimum power, (2) maximum voltage, and (3) maximum amperage. Neglect all losses. The machines are 440-V units.
A 1. Maximum power is the sum of the two machines = 100 + 100 = 200 kW. *Ans.*

2. Maximum voltage is 440 as voltage is constant in parallel circuits. *Ans.*

3. Use the power rule 200 kW = 200 × 1000 = 200,000 W:

$$A = \frac{W}{V} = \frac{200,000}{440} = 454.5 \text{ A} \qquad \textit{Ans.}$$

Q A dc motor draws a current of 5 A at 100 V unloaded. Armature resistance is 0.03 Ω; field resistance is 60 Ω. What is the output of the motor if it takes 75 A at 110 V? What is the efficiency?
A The formula for calculating watts of motor for operation is

$$W^1 = AV - M + E$$

where W^1 = watts for operation (net)
$\quad A$ = amperes for motor
$\quad V$ = voltage for motor
$\quad M$ = mechanical losses, W
$\quad E$ = electrical losses, W

Efficiency of motor $= \dfrac{W'}{W} \times 100$

W^1 = watts for net power of motor
W = watts furnished to motor
$110 \times 5 = 550$ W, running unloaded
Power $= I^2 R$
$(75 \times 75) \times 0.03 = 168.75$ W for armature loss

$$\frac{V}{R} = A$$

$\dfrac{110}{60} = 1.83$ A for field excitation

$VA = W$

$110 \times 1.83 = 201.30$ W for field

$550 + 168.75 + 201.30 = 920.05$ W totals = electrical and mechanical losses of motor $(M + E)$

$VA = W$

$110 \times 75 = 8250$ W input

$W^1 = W - (M + L)$
$= 8250 - 920.05$
$= 7329.95$

746 W = 1 hp

$7330 \div 746 = 9.8$ hp

Efficiency $= \dfrac{W'}{W} \times 100 = \dfrac{7330}{8250} \times 100 = 88.8$ percent   *Ans.*

Q How many amperes will a 5-hp motor draw on a 220-V line?
A The formula for calculating amperes of a motor is

$A = \dfrac{\text{hp} \times 746}{V}$ (for dc or single-phase circuits, unity power factor)

where A = amperes
746 W = 1 hp
V = line voltage

$A = \dfrac{5 \times 746}{220} = \dfrac{3730}{220} = 16.95$ A   *Ans.*

Q Three different types of generators are each capable of producing 350 A at 220 V. Each is 88 percent efficient. If each is separately driven, calculate the horsepower of the engine to drive (1) direct current, (2) ac single phase, and (3) three phase. Assume that the ac machines have a unit power factor.
A 1. Dc machine calculations are:

$\text{hp} = \dfrac{VA}{746} = \dfrac{220 \times 350}{746} = 103.21$ hp

$\text{Input} = \dfrac{\text{output}}{\text{efficiency}} = \dfrac{103.21}{0.88} = 117.28$ hp   *Ans.*

2. For ac machines, single phase at unity power factor is the same as for dc machines—117.28 hp.   *Ans.*

3. The formula for three phase is:

$$kVA = \frac{VAC}{1000}$$

$C = 1.73$ factor used with three phase

$$kVA = \frac{220 \times 350 \times 1.73}{1000} = 133.21 \text{ kVA}$$

kW = kVA (pf) = $133.21 \times 1 = 133.21$ kW (Note that pf is power factor and unity means 1.000.)

$$hp = \frac{kW}{0.746} = \frac{133.21}{0.746} = 178.56 \text{ hp}$$

$$\text{Input} = \frac{\text{output}}{\text{efficiency}} = \frac{178.56}{0.88} = 202.91 \text{ hp} \qquad \textit{Ans.}$$

Q A 20-hp dc motor of 220 V and 85 percent efficiency is located 1900 ft from the generator. If the generator voltage is constantly held at 240 V, what cross section of copper conductor is needed for full power of the motor?

A 20 hp $\times$ 746 W = 14,920 W

$$\frac{14,920}{0.85} = 17,553 \text{ W}$$

$$A = \frac{W}{V} = \frac{17,553}{220} = 79.78 \text{ A}$$

Line drop = $240 - 220 = 20$ V

Resistance of line: $R = \dfrac{V}{A} = \dfrac{20}{79.78} = 0.25 \ \Omega$

To calculate wire size, use formula $A = P \dfrac{L}{R}$

where A = area, circular mils

$\quad\quad\ P$ = resistance factor of material. Copper is 10.6 at 25°C (77°F)

$\quad\quad\ L$ = length of conductor, ft

$\quad\quad\ R$ = resistance, Ω

NOTE: Two conductors are used to complete the circuit. Therefore, $2 \times L$ is used in practical problems.

$$A = 10.6 \times \frac{1900 \times 2}{0.25} = 161,120 \text{ circular mils} \qquad \textit{Ans.}$$

NOTE: Upon consulting an electrical handbook or tables, choose the nearest size of commercial conductor, which is 000 AWG, and which has a diameter of 0.470 in. and an area of 168,000 circular mils.

There is an alternate method for conservatively estimating conductors.
1. For direct current, single phase, and for two phase use the following formula:

$$\text{Circular mils} = \frac{21.6 \times \text{amperes} \times \text{distance in feet}}{\text{volts line drop}}$$

Refer to the previous problem:

$$\text{Circular mils} = \frac{21.6 \times 79.78 \times 1900}{20} = 163,924 \qquad Ans.$$

2. If a three-phase circuit is to be calculated, use the same method and the following formula:

$$\text{Circular mils} = \frac{10.8 \times \text{current in amperes} \times \text{feet} \times 1.73}{\text{voltage drop}}$$

Q What is the formula for figuring kilovolt amperes?

A $kVA = \dfrac{\text{volts} \times \text{amperes} \times C}{1000}$

where C = square root of the number of phases
For single phase, $C = 1.00$
For two phase, $C = 1.414$
For three phase, $C = 1.732$

EXAMPLE: A three-phase motor draws 250 A, 220 V. What is the kW at unity power factor and at 80 percent?

$$kVA = \frac{V \times A \times C}{1000} = \frac{220 \times 250 \times 1.732}{1000} = 95.26 \text{ kVA}$$

$kW = kVA \times pf$
At unity, $95.26 \times 1 = 95.26$ kW
At 80 percent, $95.26 \times 0.80 = 76.20$ kW $\qquad Ans.$

Q What is the formula for calculating induction-motor speed?

A $R = \dfrac{F \times 120 \times P}{N}$

where R = r/min of motor
F = cycles of current
N = number of poles
P = slip correction factor = (100 percent − the percent slip)
P' = percent slip from synchronous speed

EXAMPLE: An eight-pole induction motor has a slip of 5 percent and operates with a 60-Hz current. What is the speed of this motor?

$$R = \frac{F \times 120 \times P}{N}$$

$$= \frac{60 \times 120 \times (1.00 - 0.05)}{8}$$

$$= \frac{7200 \times 0.95}{8}$$

$$= 855 \text{ r/min} \qquad Ans.$$

Q What is the formula for calculating the speed of a synchronous motor?

A $R = \dfrac{F \times 120}{N}$

where R = r/min of the motor
F = cycles of current, frequency per sec
N = number of poles

EXAMPLE: What would the speed of a synchronous motor be if it has four poles and a 60-Hz current?

$$R = \frac{F \times 120}{N}$$

$$= \frac{60 \times 120}{4} = \frac{7200}{4} = 1800 \text{ r/m} \qquad Ans.$$

POWER FACTOR

Q What is power factor? What is the formula for figuring power factor?
A Power factor is the ratio of true power to apparent power. It is figured as follows:

$$pf = \frac{kW}{kVA}$$

Kilowatts (kW) = true power developed or received
Kilovolt amperes (kVA) = apparent power that should be received according to voltage and amperage

EXAMPLE: A 2000-kVA generator has a power factor of 85 percent. What is the kW developed?

$$pf = \frac{kW}{kVA}$$

$$kW = kVA \times pf$$
$$= 2000 \times 0.85 = 1700 \text{ kW} \qquad Ans.$$

Q A plant has a power factor of 75 percent and a load of 350 kW. A new piece of equipment will require 75 additional horsepower to drive it. (1) What type of motor should be used to furnish the added load and to improve the power factor to 90 percent? (2) Will a greater total load pull on the generators because of the new motor?

A (1) A synchronous motor is indicated for this use. (2) Synchronous motors are rated in kVA. Here are the calculations needed:

$$\frac{75 \text{ hp} \times 746 \text{ W}}{1000} = 55.95 \text{ kW}$$

55.95 kW = mechanical load to be added to the original load
55.95 + 350 = 405.95-kW total load

$$kVA = \frac{kW}{pf}$$

Original case, $\dfrac{350}{0.75} = 466.66$

New case, $\dfrac{405}{0.90} = 450.00$

Wattless component $= \sqrt{kVA^2 - kW^2}$
Present WC $= \sqrt{(466.66)^2 - (350)^2}$
$ = \sqrt{95,271.55}$
$ = 308.67$
New WC $= \sqrt{(450)^2 - (405)^2}$
$ = \sqrt{38,475}$
$ = 196.15$

The difference between the two wattless components is the leading wattless component that must be supplied by the synchronous motor.

Original WC = 308.67 kVA
New WC = 196.15 kVA
308.67 − 196.15 = 112.52 kVA

The 112.52 kVA is in addition to the 55.95-kW load that the new motor must furnish. The total motor capacity is equal to the square root of the sum of the squares.

$$\sqrt{(112.42)^2 + (55.95)^2} = \sqrt{15768.659}$$
$$= 125.57 \text{ kVA, size of the motor}$$

The power factor of the motor is equal to

$$\frac{kW}{kVA} \text{ or } \frac{55.95}{125.56} = 0.44 \text{ leading pf}$$

Summary. Install a synchronous motor of 125.56 hp and operate it at a leading power factor of 44 percent in order to furnish a load of 75-hp mechanical work and to improve the power factor to 90 percent overall. The electrical load on the generators will be reduced 16 kVA despite the additional 75 hp (466.66 − 450.00 = 16.66 kVA).

ELECTRICAL TABLES AND CURVES

Q How do you figure three-phase power?
A The power in any balanced polyphase system (more than one phase) equals the line voltage times the line current times the power factor times the square root of the number of phases. For three phase, the P total = $\sqrt{3}\ V_L \times I_L \times$ pf or 1.73 $V_L \times I_L \times$ pf.

> EXAMPLE: If a balanced three-phase load is 10 A with line-to-line voltage of 208 V, pf 85 percent, the power is 1.73 × 208 × 10 × 0.85 = 3060 W.

The total volt amperes is the line voltage times the line current times the square root of the number of phases. For three phase, VA = $\sqrt{3}$ $V_L \times I_L$ or 1.73 $V_L \times I_L$ and pf = watts ÷ 3 $V_L\ I_L$ or 0.577 × watts = $(V_L\ I_L)$.

The power (P) in any one phase is the phase volts times the phase current times the power factor. The total power is the sum of all phase powers. For balanced three phase, the P total = 3 × $V_P \times I_P \times$ pf.

The power can be measured in any balanced or unbalanced polyphase system by using a number of single wattmeters (or elements on a single shaft) equal to one less than the number of wires. This means two wattmeters for three-phase three-wire and three for three-phase four-wire.

Q What is the two-wattmeter method of figuring three-phase power?
A See Fig. 8-52. To use the two-wattmeter method of figuring three-phase power, add the readings of the two wattmeters to get the total power (subtract the negative reading, if there is any). Use the chart for power factor.

> EXAMPLE: W_1 = 20, W_2 = 120. Total power equals 140 W. Multiply the scales by 10 to bring readings on scale. Connect as shown to read power factor of 0.63.

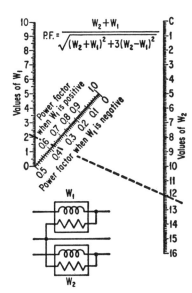

FIG. 8-52. Chart used for figuring two-wattmeter method for three-phase power.

SUGGESTED READING

Elonka, Stephen M., and Julian L. Bernstein: *Standard Electronics Questions and Answers*, Krieger Publishing Company, Inc., Melbourne, Fla., 1979.

Moore, Arthur H., and Stephen M. Elonka: *Electrical Systems and Equipment for Industry*, Krieger Publishing Company, Inc., Melbourne, Fla., 1978 (has over 200 calculations and formulas).

Elonka, Stephen M.: *Marmaduke Surfaceblow's Salty Technical Romances*, Krieger Publishing Company, Inc., Melbourne, Fla., 1979 (has 120 technical solutions in story form).

9

REFRIGERATION

Heat always passes downhill, from a warm body to a cooler one, until both bodies are at the same temperature. Maintaining perishables at their required temperatures is accomplished by refrigeration. Not only perishables but many human work spaces in offices and factory buildings are air-conditioned, and a refrigeration unit is the heart of the system.

While today's sophisticated refrigeration plants are highly automated, operators must know the basics of this vital system in order to operate units efficiently; they must know how to correct malfunctions immediately; otherwise costly spoilage, work stoppage, and human discomfort will result.

In this chapter we can only skim the surface of this interesting technology (see Chap. 11, "Air Conditioning"), but our answers will help you to obtain a refrigeration operator's certificate required in many areas.

FUNDAMENTALS

Q What is refrigeration?

A Refrigeration is the science of producing and maintaining temperatures below that of the surrounding atmosphere. This means the removing of the heat from a substance to be cooled. This is possible because a liquid can be vaporized at different temperatures by changing the pressure on it. For a change from a liquid state to a gaseous state to occur, enough heat must be present or be extracted from the surrounding atmosphere to provide the heat of vaporization for the liquid. Water, or any other liquid, can be used as a refrigerant, but liquids boiling at low temperatures are the most desirable medium for removing heat. Many liquids boil at

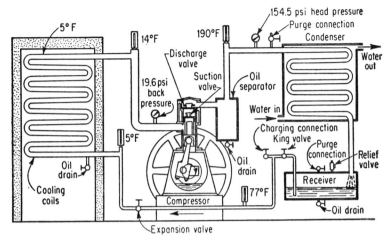

FIG. 9-1.   Basic compression refrigeration system with all the needed components.

temperatures below zero under atmospheric pressure. Methyl chloride boils at $-11°F$; Freon-12, at $-22°F$; ammonia, at $-28°F$; and carbon dioxide, at $-109°F$.

Q How is cooling produced by a compression refrigeration system?

A See Fig. 9-1. A compression refrigeration system produces cooling in various ways. The most common is by expanding a fluid to a gas so that it extracts heat from the space we wish to cool when changing states. In the sketch, ammonia in the receiver is at 77°F and under pressure of 154.5 psi from the compressor. By cracking the expansion valve, the liquid expands into a gas and leaves the evaporator at 5°F. Gas enters the compressor at 14°F at 19.6 psi backpressure. Here it is compressed to 154.5 psi, raising the temperature to 190°F. The condenser cools it down to 77°F, turning it into liquid again. Flowing to the receiver, it is ready to start the cycle over again.

Q Why is a compressor needed in this system?

A A compressor is needed to remove the gas from the cooled space so that evaporation can continue, and also to raise the pressure of the gas so that it can be condensed to a liquid by available condensing mediums, such as water or air, and the liquid diverted again to the expansion coils to repeat the process.

Q What is refrigerating effect?

A Refrigerating effect is the amount of heat absorbed in the evaporator, which is equal to the heat removed from the space cooled. It is measured by subtracting the enthalpy (heat content) of 1 lb of refrigerant entering the expansion valve from the enthalpy of the same pound of refrigerant leaving the evaporator.

Q What is latent heat of fusion?
A Latent heat of fusion is the heat needed to change a solid to a liquid. Ice at a constant 32°F requires 144 Btu/lb to melt. Conversely, 144 Btu/lb must be taken away from 32°F water to freeze it solid.

Q What is latent heat of vaporization?
A Latent heat of vaporization is the amount of heat used to convert a pound of liquid at boiling point into 1 lb of vapor at the same temperature. The temperature of the water boiling in open air remains at 212°F until all the water evaporates. The water absorbs a large quantity of heat while being converted into vapor, but the temperature does not change. Latent heat of steam at 212°F is 970.3. This means that it takes 970.3 Btu to convert 1 lb of water at 212°F to steam at the same temperature under atmospheric pressure.

Q What is sensible heat?
A It is heat that you can feel. The more sensible heat a substance has, the hotter it is; the more sensible heat that is taken away from a substance, the colder it is.

Q Name the three sources of heat.
A The three sources of heat are physical, chemical, and mechanical. The earth and the sun are physical sources of heat. Burning is a chemical source of heat because burning is a chemical action. If you rub two objects together (friction), or hammer an object until it becomes hot, you create a mechanical source of heat.

Q What is meant by superheat in a refrigeration system?
A Superheat is the temperature increase above the saturation temperature of a refrigerant or the temperature increase above the boiling point.

Q What is absolute temperature?
A All bodies are made up of a large number of small particles known as molecules. Molecules are in constant motion, vibrating to and fro. The faster they move, the hotter the body. On the Fahrenheit scale, 459.6°F below zero (−460°F) is known as absolute zero. At this point, there is absolutely no vibration of molecules; there is therefore no heat (−273°C).

Q What is meant by "work of compression"?
A "Work of compression" is the amount of heat added to a refrigerant in the compressor while raising a gas from a lower to a higher pressure. It is measured by subtracting the enthalpy of 1 lb of refrigerant at compressor suction from the enthalpy of the same pound of refrigerant at the compressor discharge.

Q What is the "coefficient of performance"?

A It is the ratio of the refrigerating effect to the work of compression. A high coefficient of performance results in a high efficiency of the refrigeration cycle.

Q What is meant by the term "horsepower per ton"?

A "Horsepower per ton" is the mechanical input in horsepower divided by the number of tons of refrigerating effect produced by the unit.

Q What affects the boiling point of a liquid?

A See Fig. 9-2. Pressure affects the boiling point of a liquid. Water remains as a liquid up to 212°F at atmospheric pressure. If we keep adding heat, it will keep turning to vapor at this same temperature and pressure. For every pound of water, we must add 1 Btu to raise the temperature 1°. Starting with water at 32°F, we need 180 Btu to raise 1 lb to 212°F. But to turn a pound of water into steam, we must add 970 Btu (latent heat of vaporization). If water is put into a closed container and the pressure is raised to 100 psi, the water will not boil until it reaches 328°F, as the sketch shows; but at a vacuum of 29 in. (in the condenser), it boils at only 79°F.

Q How does ammonia cool?

A Figure 9-3 shows a bottle of ammonia at 80°F in an insulated box. When the vent is opened, ammonia is allowed to escape to the atmosphere. It starts to boil because, at 80°F, it is 1° above the boiling point at atmo-

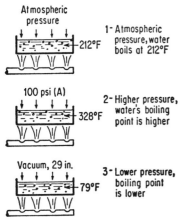

FIG. 9-2.   How atmospheric high and low pressure affects the boiling point of a liquid.

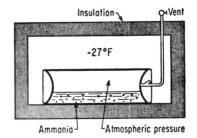

FIG. 9-3.   Ammonia boils at a low of 80°F.

spheric pressure. (Water boils at 212°F.) The temperature of the liquid ammonia is what makes it boil. As more ammonia boils, its temperature and pressure drop until both the tank and the liquid reach −27°F. At this point, the pressure becomes zero and the ammonia stops boiling. But, if the valve in the vent is closed and opened again later, the ammonia will again boil because of its latent heat content.

Q What does superheat mean? What causes ammonia to become super-heated in evaporator coils?
A There is a definite relationship between the pressure and the tempera-ture of saturated ammonia. For example, temperature corresponding to a pressure of 20 psi is 5.5°F. This should be the gas temperature as it leaves the evaporator coils, but the discharge temperature may show it to be 8 or 10°F. The difference is superheat. If the gas could be removed as soon as it forms, giving it no chance to remain in the coils and to pick up heat, there would be no superheat at this point. Superheat cannot be eliminated entirely. A poorly insulated suction line also superheats the gas.

Q What happens to ammonia passing through an expansion valve? Is its boiling point changed?
A The ammonia expands because it passes from a high to a lower pres-sure. As pressure drops, the boiling temperature falls and, depending on conditions, some or all of the ammonia changes from a liquid to a gas.

Q Explain the various ways that temperature can be lowered.
A (1) By melting a solid through heat transfer from warmer bodies, with no mechanical process needed. For example, ice used for cooling purposes. (2) By expanding a liquid into a gas by extracting heat from the surrounding bodies. The liquid used must have a low boiling point. This is a mechanical process. (3) By expanding gas so that heat in the gas is converted into work, thus lowering the temperature of the gas. For example, cold-air machines. (4) By evaporating a liquid, usually water, in a partial vacuum. This is known as the steam-jet vacuum process. It is used in air conditioning or for water cooling.

Q What is a ton of refrigeration?
A A ton of refrigeration is equivalent to melting 1 ton of ice in 24 hr. The latent heat of fusion (freezing) of the ice is 144 Btu/lb, i.e., the amount of heat that is removed from 32°F water to turn it into ice at 32°F. This takes place without any change in temperature. If 144 Btu must be taken out of every pound of water to freeze it into ice, ice will absorb 144 Btu when melting to water. Then 1 ton of ice must absorb 144 × 2000 (lb) or 288,000 Btu to melt. If it takes 24 hr to melt completely, then 288,000 ÷ 24 = 12,000 Btu/hr or 12,000 ÷ 60 = 200 Btu/min.

Q Is a 1-ton compressor large enough to handle a 288,000-Btu load if cooling is to be done in 10 hr?
A No. According to the rating, 1 ton will absorb 288,000 Btu in 24 hr. So when figuring capacity, keep in mind the amount of time it takes to do the job. There are other factors to consider, such as evaporator pressure and condensing pressure.

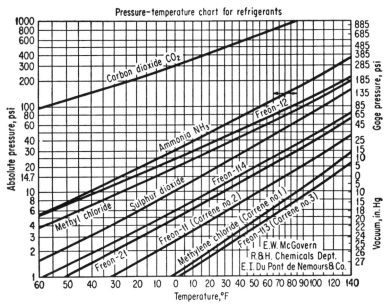

FIG. 9-4.   Use this handy chart for checking evaporator and condenser pressures.

Q What must we know about the boiling temperature of refrigerants?
A See Fig. 9-4. Each refrigerant has a given boiling temperature at a given pressure, as the chart shows. You can use either gage pressures, *right side of chart*, or absolute pressures, *left side*. If you know the temperature, the chart gives you the correct pressure. For example, take ammonia at 75°F; tracing the chart you find that its pressure should be about 135 psi. If the compressor is hooked directly to an insulated drum of ammonia and speeded up for a few minutes, the pressure will drop to, say, 65°F. You will hear the ammonia boiling violently in the receiver since part of the vapor is removed and the liquid tries to restore the balance. When the liquid stops boiling in the receiver, it will be a little cooler, for it gave up heat in order to boil.

REFRIGERANTS

Q What is a refrigerant?
A A refrigerant is the substance used for heat transfer in a refrigerating system. It picks up heat by evaporating at a low temperature and pressure, and then gives up this heat by condensing at a higher temperature and pressure.

Q Name two common refrigerants (see Fig. 9-4) in use today.
A (1) Ammonia (NH_3) is a compound gas composed of 1 part nitrogen to 3 parts hydrogen by volume, with a boiling point of $-28°F$. It is colorless, has a sharp pungent odor, and is very irritating. (2) Freon (F-12) is of the halocarbon family and is a colorless and practically odorless gas with a boiling point of $-21.7°F$. It is nontoxic, noncorrosive, nonirritating, and noninflammable.

Q Name two chemicals used in brine cooling (indirect) systems.
A (1) Sodium chloride is widely used for brine when the temperature need not be carried below 4 or $5°F$. (2) Calcium chloride is used for brines of moderately and extremely cold temperatures. Brine from this chemical can be made which will not freeze at $-50°F$.

BEWARE: Brine is often diluted with water from leaks, causing it to freeze and wreck piping and machinery.

NOTE: Glycol or antifreeze types of solutions are also used for some low-temperature applications.

Q Why must moisture be kept from mixing with refrigerants?
A Anhydrous ammonia has no effect on metals, but the addition of small quantities of water causes ammonia to attack copper and its alloys. Moisture in ammonia systems can also cause sludging of lubricating oils.

In systems using halocarbon refrigerants, water is much more critical. Very small quantities of water are enough to cause ice to form at the expansion valve and plug the system.

A more serious effect is that water in contact with these refrigerants will create acids that attack all metal parts of the system. Great care should be taken to keep moisture out of the system, and adequate driers should be kept in the system to remove any moisture that may get in.

REFRIGERATION SYSTEMS

Q What is an absorption system?
A See Fig. 9-5. In an absorption system, heat rather than a compressor is used to raise the pressure of the refrigerant. Ammonia, for example,

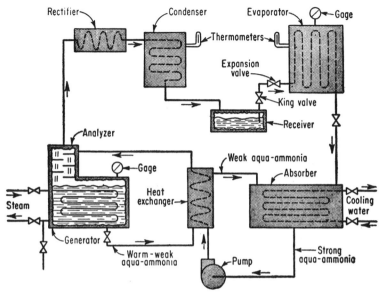

FIG. 9-5.   Absorption system needs no compressor, uses heat to raise pressure.

is absorbed by water, forming aqua ammonia. The colder the water is, the more ammonia gas it absorbs. At 50°F, under atmospheric pressure, water absorbs about 900 times its volume of gas. At 100°F, it absorbs only 460 times its volume. This gas can be driven from the water by heat. Then, when most of the ammonia is driven off, water is allowed to again absorb the ammonia, starting the cycle all over.

Q Describe a steam-jet refrigeration system.

A See Fig. 9-6. A steam-jet refrigeration system is also a compression type. Here, water is the refrigerant, and a steam ejector instead of a compressor is used to lower the pressure and to reduce the boiling point of water. Water to be chilled is sprayed into the vessel through a series of nozzles. The steam-jet ejector draws air and vapor out of the vessel, compresses it in a converging-diverging nozzle, and sends it to the condenser at a high velocity. A vacuum of about 29 in. Hg is thus formed in the vessel so that the pressure inside the vessel is only 0.4 psia. If water enters the vessel at 80°F, the boiling point of water at 0.4 psi is only 73°F, not 212°F. The heat needed to cause this evaporation is taken from the water in the vessel. Thus, its temperature is chilled to 42°F under these conditions. Secondary ejectors remove the last traces of air from the evaporator. The secondary condenser has two separate sections, upper and lower, with a jet ejector for each part. Water can be cooled to the freezing point

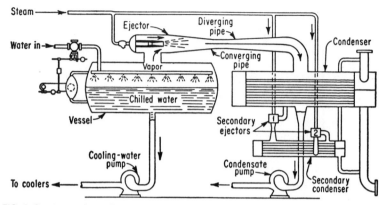

FIG. 9-6.   Steam-jet refrigeration system uses a steam ejector to raise the pressure.

with this system, instead of to 42°F as here. But the cost of the high-pressure steam needed is not economical. Water as a refrigerant is very safe and widely used in air-conditioning systems.

Q What is the difference between direct and indirect refrigeration systems?

A A direct system is shown in Fig. 9-1. Here, the refrigerant is expanded directly into the cooling coils of the storage box to be cooled. In an indirect system, the refrigerant is evaporated into the coils of the evaporator. These coils are in a brine tank. The brine is then circulated to the coils of the cold storage box to do the cooling instead of the coils with the refrigerant inside. While the indirect system is more complicated, brine is safer to use because coil leaks will not contaminate costly cold storage material as will ammonia.

Q Explain the booster cycle. Why is it used?

A A booster cycle is an efficient way to reduce temperatures down to subzero, which is needed for quick-freezing foods, etc. One pound of ammonia at zero psi has a volume of 18 ft³. But, if the same pound is pumped down to 10 in. Hg, it swells to 50 ft³. At 5 in. Hg the volume almost doubles to 98 ft³. As each pressure corresponds to a certain temperature, standard compressors can't handle loads from about −80 to +80°F because the volume of the gas is too large. Here is how the booster system solves the problem. Low-temperature suction gas at 10-in. vacuum, corresponding to the standard temperature of −42°F, is drawn into the suction of the booster compressor (Fig. 9-7). It discharges at 25 psi at 130°F to a water-cooled intercooler. Circulating water in the tubes of this shell removes some of the heat of compression, cooling the discharge

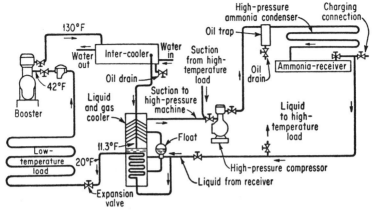

FIG. 9-7. Booster compressor helps system produce a lower temperature than is possible in a basic system.

gas to a temperature dependent on coldness and quantity of water. Gas discharges into the liquid-and-gas precooler, bubbling through the liquid that is held at a constant height in the precooler by a float control. This bubbling process cools the gas to saturation temperature, corresponding to 25 psi at 11.3°F. The liquid-and-gas precooler also cools liquid ammonia coming from the receiver (which is warm) to, perhaps, 20°F before passing it to the low-pressure evaporator. The high-pressure compressor handles (1) gas discharged from the booster compressor, (2) gas that cools the liquid ammonia, (3) gas that cools the discharge gas from the booster, and (4) high-temperature loads such as icemaking.

Q Can any refrigerant be used with a booster system?
A Yes, but ammonia is the best for temperatures down to −75°F. For −100 to −110°F, Freon-22 is better, as it works with a higher suction pressure. Below −80°F, you need three stages with Freon.

Q How can you tell if your plant needs a booster system?
A Your plant needs a booster system if the gas is compressed to more than eight times its original pressure. Use absolute, not gage, pressures when figuring compression ratio. A plant using suction pressure of less than 5 psig usually saves money with a booster system.

Q Is more power needed for a booster system?
A No. A booster system takes less horsepower per ton of refrigeration than does a single-stage compressor. At 0-psig suction, a single-stage unit takes 2.8 hp/ton, but with a booster it takes only 2.2 hp/ton.

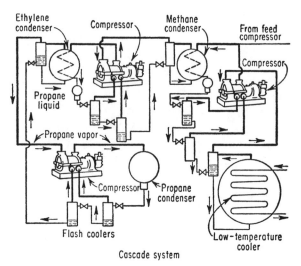

FIG. 9-8. Cascade system uses several refrigerants for very low temperatures.

Q How are extremely low temperatures obtained?
A Extremely low temperatures can be obtained in several ways. One method is the cascade system (Fig. 9-8). Here, a series of refrigerants having progressively lower boiling points are used. One refrigerant serves as the coolant to condense the refrigerant gas of the next lower boiling temperature. Cascading is usual for below −135°F.

Q What is meant by compounding?
A See Fig. 9-7. Compounding is just the same as adding a booster system.

Q Sketch and explain a flooded-coil refrigerating system.

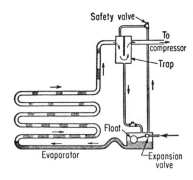

FIG. 9-9. Flooded-coil refrigerating system is popular for quick-freezing foods.

A See Fig. 9-9. Here, the lower coils in the evaporator are partly filled with liquid ammonia. The liquid level is kept constant by a ball float which actuates the expansion valve. A trap, placed between the evaporator and the compressor, catches any liquid that passes over and drains it back to the bottom of the evaporator. When the evaporator coils are filled with dry gas, the only heat that can be absorbed by the gas is superheat. The reason for this is that its latent heat capacity was used up as soon as it passed through the expansion valve and evaporated. At this point, liquid ammonia still retains its latent heat capacity. So coils that are partly filled with liquid ammonia will have a much higher heat-absorbing capacity than those filled with dry gas. This type of system is used for low temperatures and quick freezing.

COMPRESSORS

Q Name four types or classifications of compressors (refer to Fig. 9-10 on the following page).

A Four broad classifications of mechanical compressors are (1) reciprocating, (2) centrifugal, (3) rotary sliding-vane, and (4) rotary screw compressor (rsc), which is the newest type of compressor. Each classification may have several types of arrangement.

Q Describe reciprocating compressors.

A Early reciprocating compressors were large horizontal or vertical slow-speed machines of 50 r/min. Today, most reciprocating compressors are motor-driven at speeds up to 3600 r/min. Water or air cools the cylinders, making the entire unit simpler and more rugged. Complete or semiautomatic controls are used today. The machines are either single- or double-acting. In single-acting machines, the refrigerant is compressed in only one end of the cylinder. Double-acting compressors take the refrigerant in both ends and compress two charges per revolution. The crankcase of modern machines is enclosed and partly filled with oil. Oil, splashed about by the rotating cranks, lubricates the crankshaft bearings. Some bearings are pressure-lubricated by a central oiling system.

Q Describe a centrifugal refrigeration compressor.

A See Chap. 13, "Compressed Air." Centrifugal refrigerating compressors, usually of large capacity, are used for extremely low temperatures. They are mostly high-speed units, direct-driven by a motor, turbine, or internal-combustion engine. Today's top speed is about 8000 r/min. They are usually built as complete units with the compressor, condenser, cooler, drive, and auxiliaries mounted on a single base. See Fig. 9-11. The com-

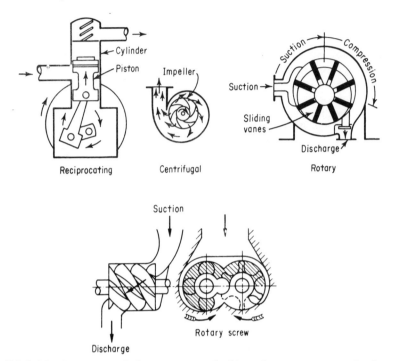

FIG. 9-10. Rotary screw is the newest type of refrigeration compressor used today.

pressor raises the pressure of the refrigerant in steps through each stage of blades. A divided water box and multiple-pass shell-and-tube condensers are used. The machines chill the water or brine that has circulated to areas where cooling is needed. To reduce the power input to the compressor, an interstage flash chamber is placed between the condenser and the cooler. Here is how the system works: A refrigerant cycle starts at the evaporator. Brine flowing through the tubes is warmer than the refrigerant in the shell which surrounds the tubes. So heat is transferred from the brine to the refrigerant. This heat evaporates the refrigerant at a temperature corresponding to the pressure in the evaporator.

The refrigerant evaporated is drawn into the suction of the compressor. The suction gas is partially compressed by the first-stage impeller and joins the stream of gas coming from the economizer before it enters the second-stage impeller. Compression of the mixture of the suction and the economizer streams is completed by the following stages, and the compressed gas is discharged into the condenser. The refrigerant dis-

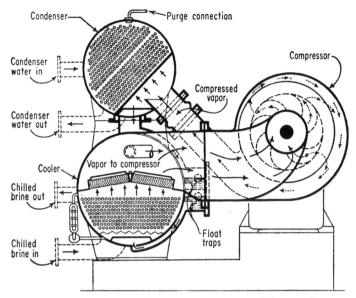

FIG. 9-11. Centrifugal refrigeration compressors are used for very low temperatures.

charged by the compressor condenses in the condenser. Since the condensing temperature is higher than that of the water in the tubes, the heat of condensation is transferred to the condenser water. Liquefied refrigerant drains into the condenser float chamber, at the end of the cooler.

The rising refrigerant level opens the float valve and allows liquid to pass into the economizer chamber. The pressure in the economizer chamber is halfway between the condensing and evaporating pressures. So enough warm liquid evaporates to cool the remainder to the lower temperature of the economizer chamber. This evaporation takes place by rapid flashing into the gas as the liquid passes through the float valve and conduit leading into the economizer chamber. The evaporated portion passes through eliminators to the compressor, with gas coming from the cooler which has been compressed by the first-stage impeller. The mixture enters the second-stage impeller. Then, the cooled liquid flows into the economizer float chamber below the condenser float chamber. The rising level in the economizer float chamber opens the float valve and allows this liquid to flash again into the bottom of the cooler. As the pressure in the cooler is lower than the pressure in the economizer, some liquid is evaporated to cool the remainder to the lower temperature. This gas passes up through the liquid to the compressor suction, while the remaining liquid serves as makeup for the refrigerant continually being evaporated by the brine. This completes the cycle.

Q   What is a dual- or multiple-effect reciprocating compressor?
A   See Fig. 9-12. A dual-effect compressor handles suction gas at two

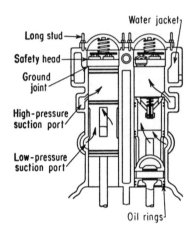

Long stud
Safety head
Ground joint
High-pressure suction port
Low-pressure suction port
Water jacket
Oil rings

FIG. 9-12.   Dual-effect single-acting cylinder handles suction gas at two pressures.

different pressures in the same cylinder. The lower-pressure gas is drawn in during the normal suction stroke and is compressed. Near the end of the stroke the piston uncovers a port through which the higher-pressure gas is admitted. The piston completes its stroke, compressing all gas in the cylinder and discharging it to the condenser.

Q   Is a multiple-effect system the same as compounding?
A   No. There is no chance for intercooling with a multiple-effect system. Instead, multiple-effect compression is similar to a system having two separate compressors, each operating at different suction pressures but discharging to a single condenser. Some designs of dual-effect compressors have clearance pockets to provide for capacity control. The main advantage of multiple-effect compression is a reduction in power cost. Used widely for ice making, it also allows the operation of two evaporators at different temperatures.

Q   Describe the helical rotary screw compressor in Fig. 9-10.
A   Compressor designers have long dreamed of a machine combining the best characteristics of the positive-displacement reciprocating unit and the continuous-flow rotary centrifugal machine, without the shortcomings

of either. The helical rotary screw (hrs) compressor, also known as the Lysholm type (see Fig. 13-5), comes pretty close to fulfilling those wants. Today it is challenging the other designs.

The male rotor has four lobes, the female six. Thus the male rotor revolves 50 percent faster. The female serves mainly as a rotating sealing member as the gas moves through the machine in an axial direction. Normally, the inlet is at the top at one end, and the discharge outlet is at the bottom at the other end. At the inlet end, as the male lobe pulls out of the female lobe, the void draws inlet gas in through the inlet opening and a port in the inlet plate.

By the time the full length of the groove has drawn in a charge of inlet gas, the inlet port is cut off. This is about one-third of one revolution. A little later, a male lobe starts rolling down the female gully, starting at the inlet end. The opposite end of the gully is sealed at the discharge end by an end plate. As the male lobe squeezes the trapped gas within the gully, compression occurs.

The trapped gas at design pressure is forced through a port in the discharge plate as it is uncovered by a lobe. This same action occurs within subsequent female gullies. (For more details, see *Standard Refrigeration and Air Conditioning Questions and Answers.*)

COMPONENTS

Q Explain how an ammonia compressor with a valve-in-piston-head piston works.

A See Fig. 9-13. This valve is well balanced and opens as soon as the

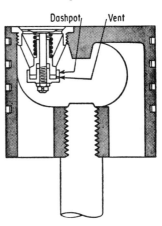

FIG. 9-13. Details of valve-in-piston-head piston for ammonia compressor.

pressure is equal on both sides of the piston; it closes as soon as the compression pressure is slightly above suction pressure. These pistons are used in single-acting machines. Pistons have one or more valves, depending on size. To keep the valve from slamming, a dashpot is placed under the valve to dampen shock. Make sure these work properly.

Q What is a safety head?
A See Fig. 9-14. Some reciprocating compressor cylinders have a safety

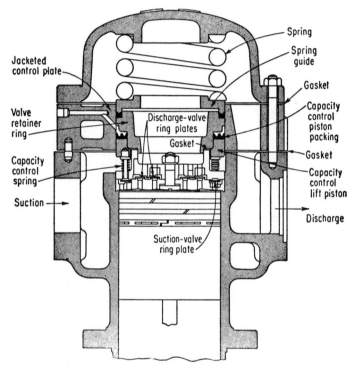

FIG. 9-14.   Safety head protects the cylinder of a reciprocating compressor.

head. These use a spring to hold the discharge valve deck against the end of the cylinders. Then, if a slug of liquid refrigerant reaches the cylinder, the valve deck lifts and no harm is done to the cylinder.

Q Describe the purpose and construction of an expansion valve.
A See Fig. 9-15. An expansion valve meters the refrigerant to the evaporator or cooling coils. Some are hand-controlled needle valves; the unit shown is thermostatically controlled. Here, the bulb and diaphragm are

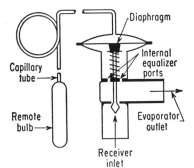

FIG. 9-15. Expansion valve with remote bulb is thermostatically controlled.

connected with a capillary tube and charged with a volatile fluid. If the bulb is heated, the fluid inside evaporates, increasing the pressure that is transmitted through the capillary tube to the diaphragm. As the pressure is increased, the diaphragm is forced downward, opening the valve. Then, if the bulb is cooled, the condensing fluid lowers the pressure, the diaphragm recedes, and the spring closes the valve. This automatic system does away with manual adjustments to the expansion valve; it can be set for any desired temperature.

Q How does a thermostatic valve cause cooling automatically?
A See Fig. 9-16. A remote bulb is attached to the suction line near the

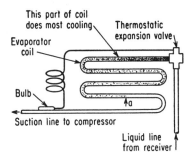

FIG. 9-16. Thermostatic expansion valve holds set temperature automatically.

outlet of the coil. The valve passes the liquid refrigerant, which evaporates in the coil. The resulting gas leaves the coil through a suction line. If the valve is set for 10°F superheat, for example, the gas passing the remote bulb must be 10°F warmer than the temperature of the evaporating refrigerant. So, the part of the coil immediately ahead of the suction header must be used to heat the completely evaporated refrigerant from a temperature corresponding to the suction pressure to a temperature 10°F higher.

The coil contains a mixture of liquid and gas from the liquid header to point *a* in the sketch. At *a* the liquid is completely evaporated. From there to the bulb, the coil surface is used only to raise the temperature of the gas to the superheat setting of the valve. If the load decreases, the super-heating section of the coil between *a* and the bulb absorbs less heat. The temperature of the superheated gas then warms the gas to the superheat setting of the valve.

Q Describe a sequence capacity control device used in refrigeration systems.
A One such capacity control device is the pneumatic-step type. It gives on-off operation of steps in sequence and positive prevention against starting more than one compressor at a time after night shutdown or current failure. It also has manual or automatic changing of the operating sequence to equalize wear on the compressors.

Q List the important parts of a simple refrigeration system.
A (1) Compressor, (2) discharge valve, (3) oil trap, (4) condenser, (5) safety valves, (6) receiver, (7) expansion valve, (8) evaporating coils, (9) scale trap, and (10) suction valve.

Q Why is a shutoff valve placed in the discharge line from a compressor?
A A shutoff valve is used in the discharge line to isolate the compressor from the system so that it can be worked on without interference from the refrigerant in the system.

Q What should you know about the location and use of safety valves?
A Safety valves are placed in high-pressure areas, as at the condenser and the receiver. They relieve the system from excessively high pressure and thus prevent injury if pressure exceeds a safe level. Safety valves are set to blow at a given pressure. The setting adjustment is sealed to prevent tampering. The valves blow back into the low side of the system or to the atmosphere outside the plant. Consult local codes.

Q Explain why the receiver is placed after the condenser.
A The receiver is placed after the condenser to prevent the condensed refrigerant from building up in the condenser and reducing the effect of the cooling water. The receiver must be large enough to hold the entire refrigerant charge. This ensures a drained condenser and provides a place to store the refrigerant when the system is pumped down for repairs.

Q On what part of the system must the charge connection be?
A The charge connection is always on the high-pressure side of the system. This prevents damage to the compressor by keeping out slugs of liquid. The connection is close to the receiver where the refrigerant may be stored.

OPERATION AND MAINTENANCE

Q List the sequence of actions in starting an ammonia compressor.
A (1) Turn on the cooling water to the condenser. (2) Open the discharge valve on the compressor. (3) Start the compressor's motor. (4) Open the suction valve gradually until it is wide open and the compressor is running smoothly. (5) Set the ammonia expansion valve to provide the desired suction pressure.

Q List the sequence of actions in stopping the ammonia compressor.
A (1) Close the king valve (see Fig. 9-1). (2) Pump the coils down slightly, so that most of the ammonia is removed (except in a flooded system). (3) If the expansion valve is closed each time the machine is stopped, you must readjust this valve, causing extra work. Also, there is a chance that excessive pressures will build up between the two valves in the liquid line and cause leaks under certain conditions. (The best practice is to close the king valve instead of the expansion valve.) (4) On systems that have automatic float-valve liquid-level control, or thermoexpansion valves, you must pump down the system each time the compressor is shut off. (5) Close the suction and discharge valves and all oil cups and water valves.

Q List the sequence of actions in pumping out the compressor.
A (1) Close the suction-stop valve. (2) Allow the compressor to run (not for long) until the ammonia in the lubricating oil in the compressor sump has had time to evaporate. (3) Close the discharge valve on the compressor and any safety bypass valves that might cause a leak into the compressor.

Q How would you charge a new Freon-12 refrigeration system?
A See Fig. 9-17. First, attach a compound gage to the suction gage con-

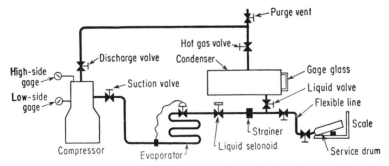

FIG. 9-17. Proper hookup for service drum when charging Freon refrigeration system.

nection. This gage shows pressure above the atmosphere and inches of vacuum. Next, attach a pressure gage to the discharge connection. Place a Freon-12 service drum on the scale and connect it to the charging valve on the liquid line. Use flexible copper tubing or a flexible metallic hose to make this connection; solid piping puts a strain on the connections as the scale lowers, causing leaks or breaks. Then open the drum valve slightly to test the charging connections for leaks. Open the compressor discharge and suction valves, the condenser hot-gas and liquid valves, and the liquid solenoid valve. Then open the charging valve and crack drum valve enough to raise 40 psi in the entire system. Test every joint in the system with the exploring tube of a halide torch. If the system is for air conditioning, turn on the air-conditioning fan to put a load on the evaporator. Close the condenser liquid valve and note the weight of the service drum. Then, circulate water through the condenser and run the compressor intermittently until the system is charged. Freon should show in the bottom of the condenser gage glass. Close the charging valve and open the condenser liquid valve. For an air-conditioning system, keep the suction pressures at 30 to 45 psi and the head pressures at 115 to 140 psi.

Q   How would you charge a large ammonia system?
A   See Fig. 9-18. Most large plants take ammonia charge to the connection

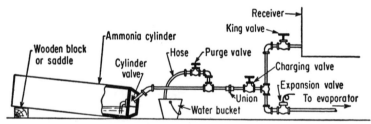

FIG. 9-18.   Proper charging hookup used for an ammonia refrigeration system.

between the king valve and the expansion valve. First, raise the bottom end of the cylinder about ¾ in.; be sure that the dipper pipe points down. If the charging line and connections are tight, close the king valve and open the cylinder valve and charging valve. After the king valve is closed, pressure between it and the expansion valve will drop to suction pressure, allowing liquid ammonia to flow into the system. To be sure that the cylinder is discharging into the system, put it on the scale and watch the change in the weight. The ammonia may be taken from the cylinder at the rate of 1½ to 2 lb/hr; heating the cylinder with warm water will speed up the flow, but this is not recommended. Always check to make sure that the gas flows out of the cylinder and doesn't condense into it.

Q How much ammonia should a system contain?
A For the first charge or a complete recharge, the best answer should come from the plant designer. If the figure isn't handy, you can calculate the amount needed from the data given in refrigerating handbooks. In a running plant, the gage glass on the receiver tells the story: the receiver should be about one-half full. Without a gage glass, you have to rely on watching the operation. If only the lower coils frost when the expansion valve is wide open and when the plant is not overloaded, the system needs ammonia. A clicking sound in the expansion valve also indicates a lack of ammonia.

Q What is a halide torch?
A A halide torch is a sensitive probe for detecting Freon leaks as small as 0.01 percent by volume. It is a better and faster method of detection than using soap and water around suspected parts. The torch has a replaceable copper reaction plate, surrounded by a metal shield that has a window through which you can watch the flame. The body of the torch has a gas passage and intake to admit air for burning. A soft-rubber detector tube is attached to the air intake. The free end of the detector tube is passed over suspected joints. The torch is fed from a small portable tank of acetylene gas. When the torch burns properly, a draft of 3 ft/sec is induced through the rubber tube. If the open end is passed over leaking Freon, fumes are drawn in and the color of the flame changes. Normally, the flame is colorless and somewhat pear-shaped. A very slight Freon leak fringes the colorless flame with green. As the leak gets stronger, the entire flame turns first to a bright green and finally to a bright green fringed with red. Serious leaks snuff out the torch flame by cutting off its air supply. But a halide torch is not reliable if the air in the space is contaminated.

Q How are leaks found in an ammonia system with a sulfur (taper) candle?
A Leaks can be found by burning a sulfur candle to produce sulfur dioxide. Explore all suspected places; leaks will be revealed, since the candle smokes when in contact with escaping ammonia. But, if the leak is large enough to pollute the nearby air, its exact location may be hard to find.

Q What precaution would you take when starting a reciprocating compressor?
A When a plant has been closed down for some hours, suction pressures may increase to 45 to 50 psi in some ammonia systems. Liquid may accumulate at the low points in the suction line. Therefore, you must open the suction valves on the compressor slowly until the line is pumped down to normal working pressures.

Q What effect does frost have on cooling coils?

A Frost acts as an insulation; it wastes power and causes needless wear in machinery. For example, you have a cold-storage room piped with 1000 ft² of 2-in. direct-expansion coils. Assume that it is figured on a heat-transfer coefficient from still air to evaporating surface of 2 Btu/(ft²)(hr)(°F). The room is 30°F and the refrigerant is 5°F. The refrigerating capacity under these conditions would be 1000 × 2 × 25 ÷ 12,000 = 4.16 tons. If the coil is covered with 2 in. of fine, dry frost, the coefficient might be as low as 0.9 Btu/hr. So, the capacity of your coil is reduced about 50 or 60 percent.

Q How would you defrost a simple ammonia coil on a direct-expansion system?

A To defrost an ammonia coil, reverse the compressor discharge by changing the crossover valves so that hot gas flows back into the suction line. The expansion valve must be closed and hot gas must be fed from the ammonia condensing system by cracking the hot-gas valve. When defrosting, feed the hot gas slowly. A fully opened gas valve may set up heavy expansion stresses where the coils are frozen solid to the pipe supports. After the coils reach 40 to 50°F, it is easy to knock or scrape off the remaining frost or ice formations.

Q How would you test safety valves in an ammonia refrigeration system?

A The simplest way to test safety valves is during shutdown. First, replace the safety valves. Then, hook up used valves to the fittings, as shown in Fig. 9-19. Use fittings of extra-heavy steel of 500 psi. Connect a common test gage, graduated up to 600 psi. With this arrangement, either a pressure gage or a relief valve may be tested separately. Fill a high-pressure grease gun with a medium-heavy-grade lubricating oil. Pump the pressure up with the grease gun and check the gage. After testing the pressure gage, close the gage valve and test the relief valve. Drain the overflow from

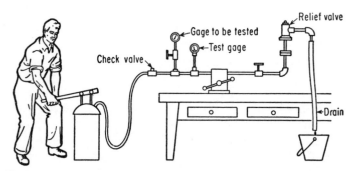

FIG. 9-19.   Test both safety valve and gage with test gage and hand pump.

the valve into a can. Check all the relief valves in your refrigeration system periodically. It is the only way to be sure that they work. If the discharge line from the relief valve is piped outside of the building instead of back to the suction line, check the relief piping to make sure it is clear.

Q Why is moisture harmful in a Freon system?
A Water vapor in a Freon system freezes the automatic regulating valves. Moisture also causes oil breakdown and sludging, gummed-up bearings, copper plating, and similar troubles.

Q Name some of the more common driers.
A Activated alumina is a granular aluminum oxide and removes moisture by absorption. Silica gel is a glasslike silicon dioxide which also removes moisture by adsorption. Drierite is an anhydrous calcium sulfate, prepared as a granular white solid. It removes moisture by chemical action. Calcium oxide and calcium chloride remove water and acid by chemical action.

Q How are driers used?
A Arrange pipelines so that the drier can be connected temporarily into the system and Freon circulated through it for about 12 hr. An alumina drying material usually does the job in that time. If left in the system, a fine white powder, representing dry material that has slaked out, will go through the system and cause trouble. The powder passes through liquid strainers and collects into putty-like masses at the expansion valves.

Q What effect does air have in a refrigeration system?
A Air or other noncondensable gases cause excessive condensing pressure in a refrigeration system. To remove air, close the return valve to the condenser receiver. Then, run the compressor until you are sure that most of the Freon charge has been pumped into the condenser receiver. But watch the high-pressure gage to be sure discharge pressure doesn't rise too high. With the compressor shut down, let the water flow through the condenser and note the outlet-water temperature. After an hour, when the cooling water should be balanced, observe the condenser pressure. Compare this pressure with the data on a chart that shows condenser-water temperature and corresponding condenser pressure for Freon. (All plants should have such a chart.) If the pressure is higher than it should be, purge the system by slowly opening the valve at the top of the condenser. Watch the pressure gage and also note the odor of the gas from the condenser to avoid loss of Freon. Be sure to cool the condenser until the gage pressure is as low as possible before purging. The larger systems have automatic purgers.

Q Is oil in a refrigeration system dangerous?
A Oil has a bad effect on a system—this is why an oil separator is used.

The separator should be blown down regularly so that entrained oil is drained out. Always lead the drain from the oil separator to a tank or covered vessel containing water. Operators have been badly burned by ammonia flowing from an open oil-separator drain. A sudden spurt of oil and ammonia splashes into water, causing serious burns.

Q Would you use oxygen to test a refrigeration system for leaks?
A No. Oxygen mixing with oil is very explosive. It may ignite without a spark.

Q How would you remove a cylinder head from a compressor?
A If the cylinder head has some long studs, first remove the nuts from the short studs, then back off the nuts on the long studs a few turns. See if the springs that hold the safety head begin to lift the cylinder head. Never remove all the nuts from the long studs until the joint is broken. If all the nuts are removed while the cylinder head sticks to the gasket, there is enough spring tension on large units to throw the head off when the joint is suddenly released. This has caused serious injuries. *Beware* of refrigerant pressure.

Q Is it dangerous to smoke while drawing oil from an oil trap?
A Yes. Oil vapor and ammonia gas explode from an open light. In one plant a gasket blew out of a compressor head. The operator pulled the switch because the plant was filled with ammonia fumes. The switch arced, and an explosion wrecked the plant. Freon decomposes in a fire to form extremely toxic gases.

Q Should you test your system from time to time?
A City codes specify various test pressures for the low and high side with various refrigerants. A common practice is to test the ammonia high-pressure side at 250 to 300 psi and low-pressure side at 15 psi.

Q Are refrigerants toxic?
A In a strict sense, all refrigerants except air can cause suffocation by oxygen deficiency. The term "toxic" is usually applied to refrigerants which are actually injurious to human beings. Some cause death or serious injury even though mixed in small doses with air. In these cases, enough oxygen cannot be obtained from the air-refrigerant vapor mixture. A mixture of toxic vapors and air may attack the membranes of the lungs, nose, eyes, or even skin; or they may be absorbed into the blood and carried to other parts of the body. So, know your refrigerants and what to do in case of an accident.

Q What happens when a cylinder is hooked up for charging, causing a reversed flow that sends more ammonia to the cylinder?
A At times, a mistake in hooking up the equipment, or some other error,

may cause a reversed flow (from system to cylinder). As a result, the cylinder is overfilled with ammonia. If an overfilled cylinder is exposed to even slight overheating, it may cause a dangerous explosion. So be careful when charging.

CORRECTING FAULTY OPERATIONS

Q What are some causes of high head pressures in a refrigerating system?
A (1) Not enough condenser water, (2) noncondensable gas or air in the system, (3) a fouled condenser, (4) too much refrigerant, (5) a faulty evaporative condenser, and (6) an evaporative condenser that is too small.

Q What are some causes of low head pressures in a refrigerating system?
A (1) Too much condenser water, (2) condenser water that is too cold, (3) not enough refrigerant, (4) leaky compressor valves, and (5) a leaky oil-return valve or trap.

Q What are some causes of low suction pressures in a refrigerating system?
A (1) An evaporator load that is too light (compressor short cycles), (2) a clogged strainer, (3) a low-pressure switch that is set too low, (4) an oversized compressor, (5) an evaporator pressure drop that is too large, and (6) not enough refrigeration.

Q What are some causes of high suction pressures in a refrigerating system?
A (1) Too much load on the evaporator, (2) faulty-compressor suction valves, (3) an expansion valve that is stuck open, (4) an oversized evaporator, (5) a low-pressure switch that is set too high, (6) an oversized expansion valve, and (7) air or noncondensable gases.

Q What causes a refrigerating system to have low capacity?
A (1) An evaporator pressure drop that is too large, (2) a wrong superheat adjustment, (3) a clogged strainer, valve, or pipe, or (4) a dirty or frosted cooling coil.

Q What might cause a low oil level in a compressor?
A (1) A dirty strainer, tubing, or valves, (2) liquid slugs in suction, (3) not enough charge, (4) a refrigerant suction line that traps the oil, (5) a faulty oil separator, or (6) leaks.

Q Why do compressors sometimes fail to start?
A Compressors may fail to start because of (1) a power failure, (2) an open disconnect switch, (3) a blown fuse, (4) low voltage, (5) a burned-

out motor, (6) an inoperative motor starter, (7) an open control circuit, (8) a broken or sheared coupling, (9) a frozen compressor due to a locked or damaged mechanism, (10) suction pressure that is below the cut-in setting of the low-pressure cutout switch, (11) discharge pressure that is above the cut-in setting of the high-pressure cutout switch, or (12) the cutout of the oil pressure-failure-control switch.

Q What causes a compressor to short cycle?

A (1) Intermittent contact in the electric control circuit, (2) a low-pressure controller differential that is set too close, (3) a high-pressure controller differential that is set too close, (4) a leaky solenoid valve in the liquid line, (5) a dirty or iced evaporator, (6) a faulty condenser, (7) an overcharge of refrigerant or noncondensable gas, (8) lack of refrigerant, (9) a water-regulating valve that is inoperative or restricted by dirt, (10) water temperature that is too high, (11) restricted water piping, (12) supply water pressure that is too low, (13) a restricted strainer in the liquid line, (14) a faulty motor, (15) a fouled shell-and-tube condenser, or (16) faulty operation of the evaporative condenser.

Q What causes a compressor to run continuously?

A (1) An excessive load, (2) thermostat controlling at too low a temperature, (3) "welded" contacts on the electrical control in the motor-starter circuit, (4) lack of refrigerant, (5) an overcharge of refrigerant, (6) a leaky valve in the compressor, or (7) a solenoid stop valve that is stuck open or held open by a manual lift stem.

Q What causes noise in reciprocating compressors?

A (1) A loose compressor-drive coupling, (2) lack of oil, (3) a dry or scored seal, (4) broken or worn internal parts, (5) liquid floodback, (6) a dirty water-regulating valve, (7) water pressure that is too high or intermittent, (8) an expansion valve that is stuck in the open position, or (9) a compressor or motor that has worked loose from the base.

Q How would you prevent slugs of ammonia from returning to the compressor in a large, overworked system?

A See Fig. 9-20. The common practice is to overfeed liquid ammonia to the evaporator coils. This creates the danger of liquid-ammonia slugs coming back to the compressor. In some cases, the compressor head blows off, often killing or maiming someone. Also, ammonia that isn't vaporized does no cooling and is wasted. The sketch shows a hookup that not only overcomes the danger of slugs in plants working at peak loads but also gets full value from the ammonia.

This is a common heat exchanger installed on the low side of the line. All return lines from the expansion coils enter into a common header or accumulator. Instead of the suction line from the compressor being

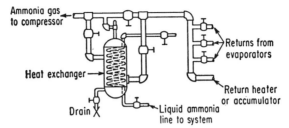

FIG. 9-20. Hookup prevents slugs of ammonia from returning to the compressor.

hooked directly to the accumulator, it has bypass valves and is hooked to the heat exchanger. The pipeline from the accumulator is also tied in to the heat exchanger. The liquid-ammonia line is piped through the heating coil in the heat exchanger. Any liquid ammonia carrying over from the evaporator picks up enough heat from the liquid-ammonia coil to vaporize before passing out of the exchanger through the suction line to the compressor. This also prechills the liquid ammonia that is fed into the system and adds to the overall efficiency of an overloaded system. It allows the operator to overfeed the system slightly without endangering the equipment. The heat exchanger and piping should be insulated.

SUGGESTED READING

Elonka, Stephen M., and Quaid W. Minich: *Standard Refrigeration and Air Conditioning Questions and Answers,* 2d ed., McGraw-Hill Book Company, New York, 1973 (has troubleshooting charts, 40 calculations).

INDEX

This is a combined index for Volumes I and II. Volume I contains pages 1 to 319; Volume II contains pages 321 to 622.

THE AUTHORS

Stephen M. Elonka is a contributing editor to *Power* magazine (he was senior associate editor before retiring) and is the creator of the famous Marmaduke stories (technical fiction) published monthly in *Power* since 1948. He is a Licensed Chief Marine Engineer, Oceans, Unlimited Horsepower. He has worked as a machinist building diesel and airplane engines and has sailed aboard 21 merchant ships (both steam and diesel) and two U.S. Navy vessels during World War II.

A licensed regular instructor of vocational high school, New York State, as the United States entered World War II in 1942, he was assigned to the U.S. Merchant Marine Academy at King's Point, N.Y. After a year as assistant training officer, he completed the famous steam Sea Project (study assignment for cadet midshipmen at sea) and requested sea duty "because that's where the action is." An engineering officer (Lieutenant Commander, U.S. Naval Reserve) aboard the *USS Wheatland*, at war's end, he was commissioned as Lieutenant Commander, U.S. Maritime Service, by Rear Admiral Telfair Knight, and was assigned as national engineering training officer based in Washington, D.C., for organizing the peace-time training program.

Steve Elonka has written hundreds of engineering articles and is the author and coauthor of thirteen books by ten publishers around the world, some translated into foreign languages.

Joseph F. Robinson holds a B.P.S. degree from Pace University. He saw active service in the Navy during World War II (shipboard engineering duty), and was Lieutenant Commander (Engineering Duties), U.S. Naval Reserve (retired). He was the Instructor in Charge of the officers in the Naval Boiler School in Philadelphia, and has sailed with the Merchant Marine. He is a Licensed Chief Marine Engineer, Oceans, Unlimited Horsepower, Stationary Engineer, New York City, and Commissioned Inspector of Boiler and Pressure Vessels, National Board (New York, Pennsylvania, Maryland, and Washington, D.C.). Mr. Robinson has authored technical and training manuals and curricula for shipboard engineering, and has a High School/Trade School license for the teaching of stationary engineering in the New York City school system (evening trade schools). For twenty-five years, he was with the Bureau of Plant Operation and Maintenance, Board of Education, City of New York, retiring as Borough Supervisor.